W9-CTX-477

Horizons

Mathematics 6

Teacher's Guide

Authors:

Cindi Mitchell & Lori Fowler

Editor:

Alan Christopherson

Graphic Design:

Chris Burkholder   *JoAnn Cumming*   *Lauren Durain*

Laura Miller   *Brian Ring*

Alpha Omega Publications, Inc.
Rock Rapids, IA

Scripture taken from the HOLY BIBLE, NEW INTERNATIONAL VERSION,
Copyright © 1973, 1978, 1984 by International Bible Society.
Used by permission of Zondervan Publishing House.

Horizons Mathematics 6 Teacher's Guide
Published by Alpha Omega Publications, Inc.
804 N. 2nd Ave. E., Rock Rapids, IA 51246-1759

Printed in the United States of America
ISBN 978-0-7403-0012-7

Contents

Section One
Introduction

Page

Before You Start.. 5
Readiness Evaluation 6
Preparing a Lesson 13
Scope & Sequence 17
Where to Use Mathematics Worksheets........................... 20
Appearance of Concepts 22

Section Two
Teacher's Lessons 37

Section Three
Answer Keys (Lessons 1–160) 213
Test Keys (Tests 1–16) 289

Section Four
Worksheets (1–80) 301
Worksheet Answer Keys 381

Section Five
Unit Tests 401
Unit Test Keys 431

Introduction

Before You Start ...

THE CHALLENGE

Today's average high school graduate will need to know more math than their counterpart of ten, fifteen, or twenty years ago. Basic math skills must be strong if this country is to continue to be a leader in shaping the technology of the future. The general trend of modern education is to better prepare students for what lies ahead.

THE GOAL

The goal of this curriculum is to provide the parent and teacher with a tool that will help them effectively teach math skills and raise the level of student performance. Research of the content and methods of other existing curriculums, the concepts evaluated by achievement tests, and typical courses of study resulted in selection of the *Scope and Sequence* starting on page 17. This curriculum was not planned around any particular group of students. Rather, it was determined that the material in this curriculum constituted a reasonable level of performance for sixth grade students. The curriculum is designed so that the teacher can adapt its use to student(s) of widely varying ability. In other words, the curriculum is a tool that is capable of performing well over a broad range of student ability to help them achieve a higher minimum level of proficiency. The two major components of the curriculum are the student text (in two volumes) and the *Teacher's Guide*. These are the absolute minimum components for accomplishing the objective of teaching the concepts in the *Scope and Sequence*. Since this handbook was designed as an integral part of the curriculum, it is absolutely necessary to use the handbook. The handbook contains activities not found in the student texts that are essential to the accomplishment of the curriculum objectives. As you will see in the following sections, this *Teacher's Guide* contains a significant number of suggestions and helps for the teacher.

THE DESIGN

Take a moment to look at the sample chart entitled, *Appearance of Concepts*, on page 22. Take note of how the curriculum concepts are developed. The first presentation is usually a brief familiarization. Then the basic teaching is accomplished as part of three to five lessons. The thoroughness of a presentation depends on how new and how important the concept is to the student's academic development.

THE DEVELOPMENT

Each concept will be reviewed for three to five lessons after the complete presentation. For the next two months the concept will be presented every two weeks as a part of two or three lessons. After a break in presentation of a few weeks, the concept will be thoroughly reviewed as part of the lesson for three to five days. This will be followed by a period where the concept will be reviewed every two weeks as part of two or three lessons. This progression continues until the student(s) have had the opportunity to thoroughly master the concept.

AN EXAMPLE

Some mathematics curriculums might teach *division* for two months and not go back to it again. In this curriculum it will be introduced and practiced for two weeks. For the next two months, *division* will be presented every two weeks as a part of two or three lessons to give the student(s) continual practice to develop mastery of the concept. The third month will be considered a break from presenting the concept. In the fourth month, *division* will first be thoroughly reviewed and again practiced every two weeks as a part of two or three lessons. By having a series of practices every two weeks, the student(s) will retain what they have learned to a greater degree. Short periods of exposure repeated many times is much more effective than long periods with fewer exposures. Review the chart on page 22 to see how the concepts are developed.

Readiness Evaluation

WHY EVALUATE READINESS?

Teaching could be defined as the process of starting with what a student knows and guiding him to added knowledge with new material. While this may not be a dictionary definition of teaching, it is descriptive of the processes involved. Determining a student's readiness for sixth grade mathematics is the first step to successful teaching.

TYPES OF READINESS

True readiness has little to do with chronological age. Emotional maturity and mental preparation are the main components of academic readiness. The teacher who is dealing directly with the student is best able to determine a child's emotional maturity. All emotionally immature students may need special student training in their problem areas. A child's mental *preparation* can be more easily discerned with a simple diagnostic evaluation. Observing the child's attitude of confidence or insecurity while taking the evaluation may help determine emotional readiness.

DETERMINING READINESS

The sixth grade *Readiness Evaluation* on pages 8–12 helps the teacher to determine if student(s) are ready to begin studying math at the sixth grade level. Complete this evaluation the first or second day of school.

The evaluation should take 45-60 minutes. It would be helpful to evaluate all of the students to determine what each student knows. However, you may want to evaluate only those student(s) who have not had a thorough fifth grade program. It is especially important to evaluate any student who is using this curriculum for the first time. The student(s) should be able to complete the test on their own with the teacher making sure they understand the directions for each individual activity.

The answer key is on page 8. Count each individual answer as a separate point. The total for the test is 83 points. The student(s) should achieve a score of 59 or more points to be ready to begin sixth grade. Be sure to note the areas of weakness of each student, even those who have scored over 59 points. If the student(s) scored under 59 points, they may need to repeat fifth grade math or do some refresher work in their areas of weakness. For possible review of the identified areas of weakness, refer to the chart *Appearance of Concepts* on page 22 of the *Horizons Math 5 Teacher's Guide*. It will locate lessons where the concepts were taught.

Count each individual answer as a separate point. The total for the test is 83 points. The student should achieve a score of 59 or more points to be ready to begin sixth grade. Be sure to note the areas of weakness even for those who score over 59 points.

1.
   1. Rhombus –
   2. Square –
   3. Equilateral Triangle –
   4. Scalene –
   5. Isosceles –
   6. Pentagon –
   7. Hexagon –
   8. Chord –
   9. Octagon –
   10. Prism –

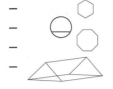

2.
   1. 18 cm²
   2. 12 cm²
   3. Front $\underline{18\ cm^2}$ x 2 $\underline{36\ cm^2}$
      Top $\underline{24\ cm^2}$ x 2 $\underline{48\ cm^2}$
      Side $\underline{12\ cm^2}$ x 2 $\underline{24\ cm^2}$
      Total   108 cm²

3. $\frac{15}{16}$ $2\frac{5}{8}$ $6\frac{8}{9}$ $14\frac{17}{24}$

   $20\frac{26}{21} = 21\frac{5}{21}$ $17\frac{10}{8} = 18\frac{2}{8} = 18\frac{1}{4}$

   $102\frac{67}{40} = 103\frac{27}{40}$

   $128\frac{12}{9} = 129\frac{3}{9} = 129\frac{1}{3}$

4. 21   9   20   36

5. $\frac{12}{35}$ $\frac{25}{96}$

   $\frac{28}{27} = 1\frac{1}{27}$ $\frac{55}{8} = 6\frac{7}{8}$

   $\frac{7}{12}$ $\frac{6}{5} = 1\frac{1}{5}$

   $\frac{18}{2} = 9$ $\frac{4}{45}$

6.
   1. $\overline{XY}$
   2. $\overline{AB}$
   3. $\overline{TX}$ or $\overline{TY}$
   4. 3 cm

7.

Name of Figure	Triangular prism	Hexagonal pyramid	cube
Faces	5	7	6
Edges	9	12	12
Vertices	6	7	8

8.

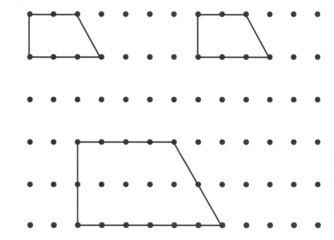

9.   53.4   2.43   0.66   54.18   30.66

10.   29.13   116.11   31.56   24.475

11.

Fraction	Decimal	Percent
$\frac{14}{100}$	0.14	14%
$\frac{62}{100}$	0.62	62%
$\frac{8}{100}$	0.08	8%
$\frac{19}{100}$	0.19	19%
$\frac{80}{100}$	0.80	80%
$\frac{75}{100}$	0.75	75%

12.   20   9   7   15

13.   range = 73
       mean = 35
       mode = 11

1. **Match the most common definition with each picture.**

1. Rhombus   a.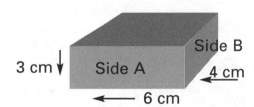

2. Square   b. ⬡

3. Equilateral Triangle   c. ▢

4. Scalene Triangle   d. ⬠

5. Isosceles Triangle   e. ▱

6. Pentagon   f. ⊖

7. Hexagon   g. ⯃

8. Chord   h. △

9. Octagon   i. ◿

10. Prism   j. ◺

2. **Find the surface area of the figure.**

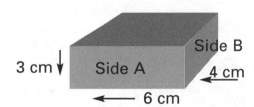

3 cm↓   Side A   Side B   4 cm
← 6 cm

Use the picture above to answer the following questions.

1. Find the area of Side A.

2. Find the area of Side B.

3. Find the surface area of the box.

Front _____ x 2 _____

Top _____ x 2 _____

Side _____ x 2 _____

Total _____

3. Write the sum or difference.

$$3 \frac{1}{4}$$
$$- \ 2 \frac{5}{16}$$

$$7 \frac{3}{8}$$
$$- \ 4 \frac{3}{4}$$

$$16 \frac{2}{3}$$
$$- \ 9 \frac{7}{9}$$

$$27 \frac{1}{3}$$
$$- \ 12 \frac{5}{8}$$

$$8 \frac{4}{7}$$
$$+ \ 12 \frac{2}{3}$$

$$13 \frac{6}{8}$$
$$+ \ 4 \frac{1}{2}$$

$$55 \frac{4}{5}$$
$$+ \ 47 \frac{7}{8}$$

$$29 \frac{6}{9}$$
$$+ \ 99 \frac{2}{3}$$

4. Find the fraction of each number

$\frac{3}{4}$ of 28

$\frac{1}{7}$ of 63

$\frac{5}{8}$ of 32

$\frac{4}{9}$ of 81

5. Multiply or divide. Write the answers in simplest terms.

$\frac{2}{5} \times \frac{6}{7}$

$\frac{5}{8} \times \frac{5}{12}$

$1\frac{5}{9} \times \frac{2}{3}$

$2\frac{3}{4} \times 2\frac{1}{2}$

$\frac{1}{3} \div \frac{4}{7}$

$\frac{2}{5} \div \frac{1}{3}$

$6 \div \frac{2}{3}$

$\frac{4}{9} \div 5$

6. **Use the circle to answer the following questions.**

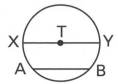

1. Name the diameter.

2. Name a chord other than the diameter.

3. Name a radius.

4. If the diameter is 6 cm, what is the radius?

7. **Define the figure and tell the number of faces, edges, and vertices. You may choose from the following names: rectangular pyramid, triangular pyramid, hexagonal pyramid, triangular prism, or cube.**

Name of Figure			
Faces			
Edges			
Vertices			

8. **Draw a figure that is congruent to Figure A. Draw a figure that is similar to Figure A.**

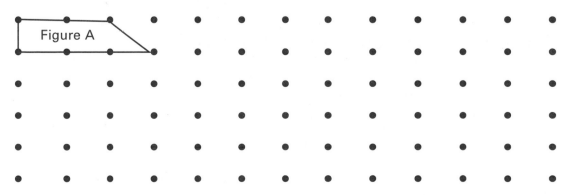

9. **Write each product.**

8.9	0.81	1.32	12.9	21.9
x 6	x 3	x 0.5	x 4.2	x 1.4

10. **Write each quotient. Write an extra dividend in the quotient when needed.**

$9\overline{)262.17}$ $4\overline{)464.44}$ $5\overline{)157.8}$ $2\overline{)48.95}$

11. **Complete the table.**

Fraction	Decimal	Percent
$\frac{14}{100}$	0.14	14%
$\frac{62}{100}$		
		8%
	0.19	
$\frac{80}{100}$		
	0.75	

12. **Find the percent of each number.**

20% of 100   15% of 60   10% of 70   25% of 60

13. **Find the range, mean, and mode for the set of numbers.**

13, 18, 61, 11, 47, 11, 84

range _____   mean _____   mode _____

Preparing a Lesson

GENERAL INFORMATION

There is some room on the teacher lessons for you to write your own notes. The more you personalize your teacher's guide in this way, the more useful it will be to you.

You will notice that there are 160 student lessons in the curriculum. This allows for the inevitable interruptions to the school year like holidays, test days, inclement weather days, and those unexpected interruptions. It also allows the teacher the opportunity to spend more time teaching any concept that the student(s) may have difficulty with. Or, you might wish to spend a day doing some of the fun activities mentioned in the Teaching Tips. If you find that the student(s) need extra drill, use the worksheets.

STUDENT'S LESSONS
ORGANIZATION

The lessons are designed to be completed in forty-five to sixty minutes a day. If extra manipulatives or worksheets are utilized, you will need to allow more time for teaching. Each lesson consists of a major concept and practice of previously taught concepts. If the student(s) find the presence of four or five different activities in one lesson a little overwhelming at the beginning, start guiding the student(s) through each activity. By the end of two weeks, they should be able to work more independently as they adjust to the format. Mastery of a new concept is not necessary the first time it is presented. Complete understanding of a new concept will come as the concept is approached from different views using different methods at different intervals. Directions to the student(s) are given and examples or explanations are presented.

Tests

Starting with Lesson 10, tests are included in every tenth lesson. They should require approximately forty minutes to administer. If your daily schedule time is a major factor, the student lesson may be completed the following day. This will require efficient scheduling of the lessons throughout the year to complete the program by the end of the school year. The 16 tests, 4 quarter tests, 1 final exam and 160 lessons each administered or taught on separate days would bring the scheduled curriculum days to a total of 181.

Do not make the test a special lesson. Allow the student(s) to perceive the test as a regular lesson with no undue pressure. The purpose of testing is not just to measure student progress, although that is an important consideration. A test is also an important teaching tool. It should be returned to the student and any missed items discussed so that it is a true learning experience. For this reason, it is important to grade and return the tests as soon as possible while the material is fresh in the student's mind.

The test structure is such that the student(s) will have had sufficient practice with a concept to have learned it before being tested. Therefore, no concept is tested until the initial presentation has been completed. For example, Test 2 in Lesson 20 covers concepts completed in Lessons 6–15. Lessons 16–19 may include the introduction of some new material which will not be covered in Test 2. Test 8 in Lesson 80 will cover Lessons 66–75. The new material from Lessons 76–79 will not be covered in Test 8.

TEACHER'S LESSONS
ORGANIZATION
Each lesson is organized into the following sections: **Concepts**; **Objectives**; **Teaching Tips**; **Materials**, **Supplies**, and **Equipment; Activities**; and a maxim or proverb. Each of the sections have a distinct symbol to help you locate them on the page of the teacher's lesson. To be a master teacher you will need to prepare each lesson well in advance.

Concepts
Concepts are listed at the beginning of each lesson. New concepts are listed first followed by concepts that are practiced from previous lessons. Sixth grade math has twenty-one major concepts. These are developed in a progression that is designed to give the student(s) a solid foundation in the basic math skills while providing enough variety to hold the student's interest.

Objectives
The Objectives list criteria for the student's performance. They state what the student should be able to do at the completion of the lesson. You will find objectives helpful in determining the student's progress, the need for remedial work, and readiness for more advanced information. Objectives are stated in terms of measurable student performance. The teacher then has a fixed level of performance to be attained before the student(s) are ready to progress to the next level.

Teaching Tips
Each tip is related to one of the Activities in the lesson. Some Teaching Tips require the teacher to make a manipulative needed to complete the activity. Teaching Tips are activities that the teacher can do to enhance the teaching process. You will find them useful for helping the student who needs additional practice to master the concepts or for the student who needs to be challenged by extra work.

Materials, Supplies, and Equipment
Materials, Supplies, and Equipment lists the things you'll need to find before you teach each lesson. Sometimes you will also find instructions on how to make your own materials, supplies, and equipment. This section also lists the worksheets. There is approximately one worksheet for every two lessons. If worksheets are suggested in a particular lesson you will find them listed. Each worksheet has a worksheet number. The chart on pages 20-21 gives the number of the lesson with which it is associated. The *Teacher's Guide* identifies where these resource worksheets are essential to the lessons. The worksheets will be handy for many purposes. You might use them for extra work for student(s) who demonstrate extra aptitude or ability or as remedial work for the student(s) who demonstrate a lack of aptitude or ability. You may also make your own worksheets and note where you would use them in the materials section on the teacher's lesson. Some of the worksheets become manipulative aids for specific concepts.

Activities
The teacher's greatest concentration should be on the **Activities** section. Here the teacher will find directions for teaching each lesson. All activities are designed to be teacher directed both in the student lesson and in the teacher's guide. You will need to use your own judgement concerning how much time is necessary to carry out the activities. Each activity is important to the over all scope of the lesson and must be

completed. Please do not put off looking at the activities in the lesson until you are actually teaching. Taking time to preview what you will be teaching is essential. Choose the manipulatives that fit your program best.

Each lesson starts with an **Explanation** section that discusses the new material being introduced in the lesson. Sample problems are often included in this section. Some students will be able to read and comprehend the information on their own. Other students need to be guided through this section for complete understanding. Following the **Explanation** of each lesson are the numbered **Practice** problems for the lesson. Number 1 of the **Practice** section always applies the skills learned in the **Explanation** box. Exercises from 2 on, review previously taught concepts.

Maxims
You will find a short maxim or proverb at the bottom of each lesson. These maxims provide a collection of various wise and pithy sayings that deal with character. They are intended for the teacher to share and discuss with the student(s). Ask the student(s) to suggest ways that they could apply the maxim to their day-to-day activities of life. Have them think of a time when their friends may have put the maxim into practice. Tell them to watch for opportunities to practice the maxim in the next week and report the incident to you. You may use or not use them as you wish.

ANSWER KEYS
The answer keys section of the *Teacher's Guide* provides answers to the student lessons. It is suggested that you give the student(s) a grade for tests only. Daily work is to be a learning experience for the student, so do not put unnecessary pressure on them. You should correct every paper, but you should not grade every paper. This means that each lesson should be marked for correct and incorrect answers, but it is not necessary to record a letter or percentage grade on every lesson. The lessons should then be returned to the student(s) so that they have the opportunity to learn from their mistakes.

WORKSHEETS
The next section contains the worksheets. They are reproducible and can be copied freely. These worksheets have been developed for reinforcement and drill. You will find a complete listing of worksheets and where they might best be used on pages 20 and 21. Separate packets of all the necessary worksheets for an individual student are also available. Answer keys to the worksheets are provided in the same manner as for the student lessons.

UNIT TESTS
Quarter, Semester, and Final Exam tests are provided to evaluate overall student progress. They can be administered after Lesson 40, Lesson 80, Lesson 120, and Lesson 160. Answer keys are provided for these tests.

Horizons Sixth Grade Mathematics SCOPE & SEQUENCE

1. PLACE VALUE & NUMBER THEORY

*word numbers through hundred trillion
billion (do not cycle)
Roman numerals (do not cycle)
divisibility
prime and composite
prime factorization
factor trees – start with a number other
  than the smallest factor
exponents
*scientific notation
*base 2 – teach from a place value chart
*order of operations
*square roots

2. NUMBER ORDER & INTEGERS

rounding to tenth, hundredth, and thousandth
>, <, =
*integers on a number line
*opposite integers
*comparing integers
*adding integers
*subtracting integers
*multiplying integers
*dividing integers

3. ADDITION & SUBTRACTION

*addition properties, terms, facts
*subtraction properties, terms, facts
*addition w/ 2, 3, 4, 5, & 6 digits
*subtraction w/ 2, 3, 4, 5, & 6 digits
add/subtract equations
missing addends
estimating
adding and subtracting money
counting change

* New concepts

4. MULTIPLICATION

properties, terms, facts
common multiples
triple digit times single digit
two digit times two digit
three digit times three digit
money by two-digit number
missing factors
estimating products
exponents
*four digit by four digit
*five digit by five digit

5. DIVISION

properties, terms, facts
one, two, and three-digit divisors
dividing money
estimating quotients
averaging with remainders
*four-digit divisor

6. GEOMETRY

perimeter and area
*area of a parallelogram
*area of a triangle
*area of a circle
volume of a cube
*volume of a cylinder
surface area
shapes and solids
symmetry
congruent figures
similar figures
line, line segment, ray, endpoint
parallel, intersecting, perpendicular
angles - rays, vertex, acute, obtuse, right
circles - diameter, radius, chord, central angle
types of triangles
polygons - sides, vertices, diagonals

* New concepts

7. GEOMETRIC CONSTRUCTIONS

protractors
compass
measuring and constructing angles
*construct a perpendicular bisector
*bisect an angle
*construct a regular hexagon
*construct an equilateral triangle
*construct a right triangle
*construct a square
*construct a parallelogram

8. FRACTIONS

equivalent fractions
greatest common factor
reducing fractions
compare and order fractions
add and subtract fractions with common
  denominators
mixed numbers
improper fractions
least common multiple
add and subtract fractions with unlike
  denominators
add and subtract mixed numbers without
  regrouping
rename mixed numbers
add mixed numbers with renaming fractions
more renaming
subtracting mixed numbers with common
  denominators - borrow from the whole
  numbers
subtracting mixed numbers with unlike
  denominators - borrow from the whole
  numbers
multiply fractions and a whole number
multiply two fractions
multiply mixed numbers
*simplify before you multiply
reciprocals
*divide a whole number by a fraction
*round and estimate with fractions
*divide a fraction by a whole number
*divide by a mixed number

9. DECIMALS

fractions to decimals
*word numbers to hundred thousandths
compare & order decimals
add decimals (horizontal and vertical)
subtract decimals
estimate decimals
multiply a decimal by a whole number
multiply two decimals
divide decimal by a whole number
*extend quotient to tenths, hundredths,
thousandths
*interpret the remainder
*divide by a decimal
*divide and multiply by 10, 100, 1,000
*repeating decimals

10. RATIO

write simple ratios
multiply to find equal ratios
divide to find equal ratios
cross products
*use cross products to solve for n
*ratio as a percent

11. MEASUREMENT

standard and metric linear equivalent
standard and metric liquid equivalent
standard and metric weight equivalent
temperature reading and understanding
fahrenheit and celsius
millimeter, centimeter, decimeter, meter
decameter, hectometer, kilometer

12. GRAPHS

bar
line
pictographs
circle
coordinate graphs
comparing graphs
*mean, mode, median
*graphing in all four quadrants

* New concepts

* New concepts

© MCMXCIX, Alpha Omega Publications, Inc.

13. EQUATIONS

addition
subtraction
multiplication
division
*writing equations for word problems
*equal ratios

 14. PERCENT

understand the concept
finding a percent of a number
percent and decimals
percent and fraction
discount and sales tax

 **15. APPLICATIONS**

writing checks
*budgeting
*banking
*savings
*understanding interest
computing interest
comparison buying
installment buying
using charts and tables

 16. PROBLEM SOLVING

choosing an operation
reasonable or unreasonable answers
too much information/ too little information
multiple step problems
understanding remainders
make an organized list
draw a picture
find a pattern
*use a chart, table, menu, schedule

© MCMXCIX, Alpha Omega Publications, Inc.

* New concepts

Where To Use
Mathematics Worksheets

*In this handbook you will find eighty worksheets to be used as **Duplication Masters.***

This chart shows where worksheets may be used for *Horizons Math 6*.
You will need to **duplicate** any worksheet that you plan to use more than once.

No.	Concept	Lessons Where Worksheets Are Used
1	Numeration to the trillions	1
2	Numeration-decimal side (hundred thousandths)	2
3	Rounding whole numbers	3
4	Comparing whole numbers	4
5	Six-digit addition and subtraction	8 & 9
6	Equations	11
7	Order of Operations	12
8	Multiplication three-digit x three-digit	15
9	Two-digit divisors	18
10	Averaging with remainders	20
11	Four-digit x four-digit	21
12	Five-digit x five-digit	22
13	Divide by a four-digit divisor	25
14	Angles – classification and measuring	32
15	Polygons – sides, vertices, and diagonals	33
16	Quadrilaterals - identification	34
17	Congruence and Symmetry	35
18	Types of triangles	36
19	Circles	38
20	Solid Figures - Identification	39
21	Factor trees	42
22	Prime and Composite	43
23	Exponents	44
24	Square roots	45
25	Scientific Notation	48
26	Base 2	49
27	Add and subtract decimals	53
28	Mean, Mode, Median, Range	57
29	Add and subtract fractions with common denominators	62
30	Equivalent fractions	63
31	Compare fractions	65
32	Add and subtract fractions with different denominators	66
33	Improper to mixed fractions - mixed fractions to improper	67
34	Add mixed numbers with different denominators	68
35	Subtract mixed numbers and borrow from the whole number	69
36	Multiply 2 decimals	72
37	Divide a decimal by a whole number	73
38	Change fractions to decimals	75

© MCMXCIX, Alpha Omega Publications, Inc.

Where To Use Mathematics Worksheets, continued:

No.	Concept	Lessons Where Worksheets Are Used
39	Round the quotient	76
40	Divide by a decimal	77
41	Interpret remainders	79
42	Coordinate graphs	80
43	Multiply fractions	81
44	Multiply mixed numbers	83
45	Multiplication of fractions (simplify by crossing out factors)	84
46	Divide a fraction by a fraction	87
47	Divide two mixed numbers	90
48	Standard measure to 1/16th	91
49	Standard Weight	92
50	Standard liquid measure	93
51	Metric linear measure	95
52	Metric weight	96
53	Metric liquid measure	97
54	Perimeter and area	101
55	Area of a parallelogram	102
56	Area of a triangle	103
57	Area of a circle	104
58	Volume of a cylinder	106
59	Surface area	107
60	World Time Zones	109
61	Measuring angles in a circle	112
62	Constructing bisectors of angles	115
63	Constructing a hexagon in a circle	116
64	Constructing an equilateral triangle	117
65	Constructing a square	119
66	Multiply to find common ratios	122 & 123
67	Use cross products to solve for N	125
68	Probability	127
69	Finding the percent of a number	132
70	Changing percents to decimals	133
71	Changing percents to fractions	134
72	Finding a percentage	136 & 137
73	Computing sales tax	138
74	Computing discounts	139
75	Add integers	144
76	Subtract integers	147
77	Four quadrant graphing	148
78	Multiply integers	149
79	Divide integers	150
80	Banking	152

Appearance of Concepts

Lesson 1
numeration-trillions
two-digit addition
two-digit subtraction
angles
identifying fractions
column addition
mystery number

Lesson 2
numeration-hundred thousandths
 trillions
two-digit addition
two-digit subtraction
identifying fractions
column addition with
 two-digit numbers
addition with missing integers

Lesson 3
rounding whole numbers
numeration-hundred thousandths
numeration-trillions
three-digit addition, subtraction
geometry-triangle, quadrilateral
pentagon, hexagon,
octagon, nonagon
equivalent fractions

Lesson 4
compare and order whole numbers
rounding whole numbers
numeration-hundred thousandths
 trillions
three-digit addition, subtraction
equivalent fractions

Lesson 5
addition and subtraction equations
compare and order whole numbers
rounding whole numbers
numeration-hundred thousandths
four-digit addition, subtraction
lowest term fractions

Lesson 6
order of operations
addition and subtraction equations
compare and order whole numbers
rounding whole numbers
four-digit addition subtraction
lowest term fractions

Lesson 7
addition and subtraction
 properties,
order of operations
addition and subtraction equations
compare and order whole numbers
five-digit addition subtraction
compare and order fractions

Lesson 8
vertical and horizontal addition
 with up to 6-digits
addition and subtraction properties
addition and subtraction equations
multiplication facts, triangles
compare and order fractions

Lesson 9
vertical and horizontal subtraction,
 addition with up to 6-digits
addition and subtraction
properties, order of operations
multiplication facts
space figures
addition of fractions with common
denominators

Lesson 10
estimating sums/differences using
 charts, tables, & maps
vertical and horizontal subtraction,
 addition with up to 6-digits
addition and subtraction
properties, division facts
identification of quadrilaterals
addition of fractions with common
denominators

Lesson 11
multiplication and division of
 equations
six-digit subtraction, addition
measurement to the 1/8 of an inch
subtract fractions
writing a check

Lesson 12
order of operations
multiplication and division of
 equations
six-digit subtraction, addition
measurement to the 1/8 inch
subtract fractions
word problems

Lesson 13
properties of multiplication and
 division
order of operations
multiplication and division of
 equations
three-digit addition
liquid conversions
change improper fractions to
 mixed fractions

Lesson 14
multiplication
order of operations
multiplication and division of
 equations
liquid conversions
change improper fractions to mixed
fractions
estimation and multiplication
who am I?

Lesson 15
two-digit multiplication
three-digit multiplication
compare and order fractions
linear conversions
multiplication
mixed fractions to improper
 fractions
order of operations
diameter and radius

Appearance of Concepts

Lesson 16
estimate products
missing numbers
linear conversions
change improper fractions to
   mixed fractions
geometric terms
logical reasoning
missing operation signs

Lesson 17
division
estimate products
two and three-digit multiplication
weight conversions
who am I?
two-step equations
magic square

Lesson 18
division
division and fractions
estimate products
multiplication and logical
   reasoning
weight conversions
who am I?
two-step equations

Lesson 19
estimation and division
division and fractions
estimate products
read a thermometer
find the missing numerator
logical reasoning
equations

Lesson 20
averaging with remainders
averaging with calculators
division
more division
read a thermometer
understanding Celsius
equations

Lesson 21
four-digit multiplication
place value
averaging
division
pattern sequencing
estimation of money

Lesson 22
five-digit multiplication
four-digit multiplication
place value
estimation of money
two-digit column addition
division

Lesson 23
estimation of larger numbers
four-digit multiplication
place value
rounding whole numbers
two-digit column addition
mystery number.

Lesson 24
three-digit division
estimation of multiplication
five-digit multiplication
four-digit multiplication
averaging
rounding of whole numbers

Lesson 25
three and four-digit division
estimation of multiplication
compare & order whole
   numbers
five-digit multiplication
averaging
simple equations
reasoning

Lesson 26
division
estimating division
compare & order whole numbers
rounding
simple equations
addition logic

Lesson 27
estimation of division
division
four-digit division
three-digit division
addition & subtraction equations
perimeter
word problems

Lesson 28
problem solving with division
estimation of division
division
four-digit division
addition & subtraction equations
perimeter

Lesson 29
giving change
problem solving with division
division
order of operations
addition of fractions with common
   denominators
area
estimating with division

Lesson 30
ordering from a menu
order of operations
sequencing patterns
rays, lines, line segments, planes
time conversions
addition of fractions with common
   denominators
area

Appearance of Concepts

Lesson 31
geometric terms
addition
word problems
multiplication and division
  equations
even and odd numbers
multiplication

Lesson 32
define and classify angles
measure angles
geometric terms
order of operations
decimal place value
word problems
finding sums and differences

Lesson 33
identify polygons
angles
geometric terms
subtraction
column addition
change

Lesson 34
quadrilaterals
angles
geometric terms
polygons
subtraction
column addition

Lesson 35
congruence & symmetry
polygons
geometric shapes
protractor
word problems
equations

Lesson 36
triangles
polygons
geometric shapes
sides, vertices, and diagonals
equations
word problems

Lesson 37
angles
geometric terms
polygons
equations
rounding
time definitions

Lesson 38
circles
diameter and radius
triangles
types of triangles
quadrilaterals
regular polygons
equations
century

Lesson 39
solids - face, vertices and edges
space figures
circles
triangles
angles
equations
mystery numbers.

Lesson 40
circle graphs
space figures
circles
equations
triangles
number patterns

Lesson 41
multiples
circle graphs
solids, circles, diameter, radius
  chord, central angle
addition and subtraction properties
order of operations
giving change

Lesson 42
prime and composite numbers
circle graphs
multiples
six-digit addition
four-digit by four-digit
  multiplication
solve for n

Lesson 43
factor trees
multiples
solids
order of operations
giving change
addition and subtraction properties

Lesson 44
exponents
prime and composite numbers
factor trees
multiples
six-digit addition
four-digit by four-digit
  multiplication
reading a table

Lesson 45
square roots
exponents
prime and composite numbers
factor trees
six-digit subtraction
logic problems
five-digit by five-digit
  multiplication

Appearance of Concepts

Lesson 46
greatest common factor (GCF)
square roots
exponents
prime and composite
six-digit subtraction
five-digit by five-digit
multiplication

Lesson 47
least common multiple (LCM)
GCF
square roots
exponents
division with a three-digit divisor
three-digit estimation
two-digit column addition

Lesson 48
scientific notation
LCM
GCF
square roots
division with three-digit divisors
three-digit estimation
two-digit column addition

Lesson 49
base 2
scientific notation
LCM
GCF
division with four-digit divisors
renaming fractions

Lesson 50
pictographs
base 2
scientific Notation
LCM
division with a four-digit divisor
four-digit estimation
renaming fractions

Lesson 51
place value with decimals
pictographs
base 2
scientific Notation
quadrilaterals
three-digit estimation
giving change

Lesson 52
comparing decimals
pictographs
base 2
quadrilaterals
three-digit estimation

Lesson 53
adding decimals
comparing decimals
measuring angles
four-digit estimation
logic problem

Lesson 54
subtracting decimals
comparing decimals
measuring angles
four-digit estimation
logic problems

Lesson 55
rounding decimals
subtracting decimals
adding decimals
comparing decimals
renaming fractions
simple multiplication
mathematical terms

Lesson 56
column addition with decimals
rounding decimals
adding decimals
subtracting decimals
renaming fractions
simple division
mathematical terms

Lesson 57
Roman numerals
column addition with decimals
rounding decimals
subtracting decimals
word problems with decimals
congruent figures/shapes
Logic problem - magic square

Lesson 58
range & mean
mode & median
column addition with decimals
rounding decimals
word problem with decimals
logic problem - magic number
congruent figures/shapes

Lesson 59
mode
median
column addition with decimals
rounding decimals
missing number addition
symmetry
equivalent fractions
logic problem

Lesson 60
problem solving - too much/too
  little information
mean
mode & median
column addition with decimals
rounding decimals
missing number subtraction
similar figures
equivalent fractions

Appearance of Concepts

Lesson 61
simplify fractions
decimal column addition
symmetry
division equations
mean
median, and mode
rounding

Lesson 62
add and subtract fractions
simplify fractions
mean
mode, and median
four-digit multiplication
order whole numbers
three step number sentence
round decimals

Lesson 63
LCD
add and subtract fractions with
    common denominators
simplify fractions
mean
mode, and median
four-digit multiplication
mystery number

Lesson 64
compare fractions
LCD
add and subtract fractions with
    common denominators
five-digit multiplication
rounding
define: decade, millennium, and
    century

Lesson 65
add & subtract fractions with
    different denominators
compare fractions
LCD
add or subtract fractions with
    common denominators
place value

Lesson 66
mixed number to improper fraction
add and subtract fractions with
    different denominators
compare fraction
LCD
place value

Lesson 67
improper to mixed number
mixed to improper
add and subtract fractions with
    different denominators
compare fractions
divide large numbers

Lesson 68
add and subtract mixed numbers
    with different denominators
mixed to improper
add and subtract fractions with
    different denominators
compare fractions
decimal place value

Lesson 69
add mixed numbers and rename
    sums
add and subtract mixed numbers
    with different denominators
mixed fractions
divide large numbers
place value
word problems

Lesson 70
subtract mixed numbers renaming
    whole numbers
add mixed numbers and renaming
    sums
mixed fraction
add larger numbers
decimal place value
decimal column addition

Lesson 71
multiply decimals by a whole
    number
subtract mixed numbers
add mixed numbers
add six-digit numbers
factor trees
word problems

Lesson 72
multiply decimals
subtract mixed numbers
add mixed numbers
subtract six-digit numbers
factor trees
word problems

Lesson 73
divide decimals by a whole
    number
multiply two decimals
multiply a decimal by a whole
    number
subtract two mixed fractions
subtract six-digit numbers
prime numbers
angles

Lesson 74
extending quotients
divide decimals
multiply two decimals
multiply a decimal by a whole
    number
divisibility
geometric shapes

Lesson 75
fractions to decimals
extend the quotient
divide decimals
multiply decimals
equivalent fractions
column addition

© MCMXCIX, Alpha Omega Publications, Inc.

Appearance of Concepts

Lesson 76
round the quotient
divide decimals
compare fractions and decimals
repeating decimals
divide a whole number by a
   decimal
exponents
multiple operations

Lesson 77
powers of ten
rounding decimals
repeating decimals
square roots
addition
place value

Lesson 78
divide decimals
equivalent division problems
powers of ten
compare fractions and decimals
square roots
subtraction
multiply decimals

Lesson 79
interpret remainders
divide decimals
powers of ten
rounding decimals
multiply

Lesson 80
coordinate graphing
interpret remainders
equivalent division problems
powers of ten
addition
multiplication

Lesson 81
multiplication of fractions
interpreting remainders
dividing by decimals
base 2
making change
time zones

Lesson 82
multiplication of fractions and
   whole numbers
multiplication of fractions
interpreting remainders
dividing by decimals
base 2
making change
rounding to the nearest tenth

Lesson 83
area
multiplication of mixed numbers
multiplication of fractions and
   whole numbers
multiplication of fractions
interpreting remainders
column addition with decimals
calculating discounts
comparing and ordering decimals

Lesson 84
simplifying fractions
multiplication of mixed numbers
multiplication of fractions and
   whole numbers
multiplying fractions
calculating discounts
comparing and ordering decimals

Lesson 85
reciprocals
simplifying fractions
multiplication of mixed numbers
multiplication of fractions and
   whole numbers
subtraction of decimals
addition problems
addition equations

Lesson 86
division of a whole number by a
   fraction
reciprocals
simplifying fractions
multiplication of mixed numbers
subtraction of decimals
subtraction problems
subtraction equations

Lesson 87
division of a fraction by a fraction
division of a whole number by a
   fraction
reciprocals
simplifying fractions
multiplication
intersecting
parallel and perpendicular lines
multiplication equations

Lesson 88
division of a fraction by a whole
   number
division of a fraction by a fraction
division of a whole number by a
   fraction
reciprocals
division
perimeter
division equations

Lesson 89
estimation of fractions
division of a fraction by a whole
   number
division of a fraction by a fraction
division of a whole number by a
   fraction
area
four-digit addition

Lesson 90
division by a mixed number
estimation of fractions
division of a fraction by whole
   number
division of a fraction by a fraction
volume
four-digit subtraction
bar graphs

Appearance of Concepts

Lesson 91
standard measure
dividing by mixed numbers
estimating fractions
division of fractions
numeration
quadrilaterals
factor trees

Lesson 92
standard weight
standard measurement
division of mixed numbers
estimation of fractions
numeration
quadrilaterals
prime and composite numbers

Lesson 93
standard liquid measure
standard weight
standard measure
division of mixed numbers
six-digit addition
angle measurement
exponents

Lesson 94
standard temperature
standard liquid measure
standard weight
standard measurement
six-digit subtraction
degrees in a triangle
exponents

Lesson 95
metric conversions
standard temperature
standard liquid measure
standard weight
six-digit subtraction
square roots
addition of mixed numbers with
  different denominators

Lesson 96
metric weight
standard temperature
standard liquid measure
six-digit subtraction
square roots
addition of mixed numbers with
  different denominators

Lesson 97
metric liquid measure
metric weight
metric measurement
standard temperature
scientific notation
subtraction of mixed numbers
10% discounts

Lesson 98
metric temperature
metric liquid measure
metric weight
metric measurement
scientific notation
subtraction of mixed numbers
10% discounts

Lesson 99
problem solving–drawing a picture
metric temperature
metric liquid measurement
metric weight
base 2
two step equations
multiplication

Lesson 100
bar graphs
metric temperature
metric liquid measure
base 2
two step equations
multiplication
logic problems

Lesson 101
perimeter
area
Fahrenheit
Celsius
multi-step word problems
multiply decimals
multiply fractions

Lesson 102
area of a parallelogram
perimeter
area of a rectangle and square
area of other polygons
multiplication
multiply fractions
add decimals
multiply decimals

Lesson 103
area of a triangle
area of a parallelogram
area of other polygons
multiplication
multiply fractions
add decimals
multiply decimals

Lesson 104
area of a circle
area of a triangle
area of a parallelogram
area of irregular figures
multiply fractions
logical reasoning

Lesson 105
volume of a cube
area of circle
area of a triangle and a
  parallelogram
division
divide decimals
rename fractions

Appearance of Concepts

Lesson 106
volume of a cylinder
volume of a cube
area of a circle
area of a triangle
mystery number
divide decimals
bar graphs

Lesson 107
surface area
volume of a cube
area of a circle
radius and diameter
divide decimals

Lesson 108
formulas
surface area
area of a circle
radius and diameter
volume of a cube
logical reasoning
divide fractions

Lesson 109
world time zones
area of triangles
area of rectangles
surface area
volume of a cylinder
multiply decimals
fractions to decimals

Lesson 110
two-step word problems
time zones
surface area
add improper fractions
divide decimals
divide mixed fractions
rename fractions

Lesson 111
measuring with a protractor
problem solving
area of triangles
time zones
LCM
dividing fractions
ordering decimals

Lesson 112
measuring angles in a circle
measuring angles
word problems
time zones
prime numbers
divide fractions

Lesson 113
drawing angles
angles in a circle
word problems
exponents
divide decimals
weight

Lesson 114
constructing perpendicular
  bisectors
draw angles
angles in a circle
measure angles
exponents
dividing decimals

Lesson 115
bisect angles
perpendicular bisectors
draw angles
angles in a circle
square roots
metric measure

Lesson 116
construct a hexagon
bisect angles
perpendicular bisectors
draw angles
square roots
metric measure

Lesson 117
construct an equilateral triangle
draw a hexagon
bisect angles
exponents
multiplication

Lesson 118
construct right triangles
draw a hexagon
bisect angles
exponents
multiplication

Lesson 119
construct a square
construct an equilateral triangle
multiplication
averaging
fluid measures

Lesson 120
construct a parallelogram
construct a square
construct a right triangle
construct an equilateral triangle
multiplication
measuring distance

Appearance of Concepts

Lesson 121
simple ratios
column addition with decimals
addition & subtraction of fractions
  with common denominators
area of a parallelogram
word problems
discounts
5-digit addition

Lesson 122
equal ratios
simple ratios
addition of decimals
addition & subtraction of fractions
  with common denominators
area of a parallelogram
word problems
discounts

Lesson 123
equal ratios
simple ratios
subtraction of decimals
equivalent fractions
area of a triangle

Lesson 124
cross products
equal ratios
simple ratios
equivalent fractions
area of a triangle

Lesson 125
cross products to solve for N
cross products
equal ratios
comparing fractions
area of a circle
metric temperature
logic problems

Lesson 126
ratio and percent
cross products to solve for N
cross products
equal ratios
comparing fractions
area of a triangle
metric temperature

Lesson 127
probability
ratio & percent
cross products to solve for N
cross products
addition & subtraction of fractions
  with different denominators
volume of a cylinder
bar graphs

Lesson 128
probability
ratio & percent
cross products
addition & subtraction of mixed
  numbers with different
  denominators
volume of a cylinder
line graphs

Lesson 129
word problems with ratios
probability
ratio & percent
converting mixed numbers to
  improper fractions
converting improper fractions to
  mixed numbers
measuring triangles
addition with missing data

Lesson 130
finding patterns
word problems with ratios
probability
converting mixed numbers to
  improper fractions
converting improper fractions to
  mixed numbers
measuring triangles
subtraction with missing data

Lesson 131
percents
quadrilaterals
factor trees
decimal multiplication
multiplication of fractions
using a protractor
using a compass to draw a circle

Lesson 132
percent of a number
percents
quadrilaterals
prime & composite
multiplication of decimals
multiplication of mixed numbers
using a protractor

Lesson 133
percents & decimals
percent of a number
percents
angle measurement
exponents
multiplication of decimals
cross out simplification

Lesson 134
percents & fractions
percents & decimals
percent of a number
percents
measuring angles
exponents
division of a whole number by a
  fraction

Lesson 135
conversion of fractions, decimals
  and percents
percents & fractions
percents & decimals
percents
square roots
division of decimals & whole
  numbers
division of fractions

Appearance of Concepts

Lesson 136
finding 1% of a number
conversion of fractions, decimals, and percents
percents & fractions
percents & decimals
numeration through trillions
square roots
division of decimals

Lesson 137
finding 10% of a number
finding 1% of a number
conversion of fractions, decimals, and percents
numeration through trillions
scientific notation
changing fractions to decimals

Lesson 138
sales tax
finding 10% of a number
finding 1% of a number
conversion of fractions, decimals and percents
numeration–decimals
scientific notation
changing fractions to decimals

Lesson 139
discounts
sales tax
finding 10% of a number
finding 1% of a number
comparing & ordering whole numbers
base 2
division of fractions by whole numbers

Lesson 140
problem solving–organized lists
discounts
sales tax
finding 10% of a number
six-digit addition
base 2
division of mixed numbers

Lesson 141
integers
fractions-decimals-percents
order of operations
perimeter and area
measuring with a protractor
equivalent fractions
coordinate graphs

Lesson 142
opposites
number lines
area and perimeter
equivalent fractions
fractions-decimals-percents
coordinate graphs

Lesson 143
compare integers
opposites
area and perimeter
5-digit multiplication
area of parallelograms
construct a square
adding decimals

Lesson 144
adding integers with like signs
compare integers
opposites
order integers
perimeter and area of parallelograms
construct a hexagon

Lesson 145
adding integers with like and unlike signs
compare integers
divide fractions
divide with 4-digit divisors
area of a triangle
construct a square

Lesson 146
subtracting integers on a number line
word problems with integers
adding integers with like and unlike signs
compare integers
area of a triangle
construct a square

Lesson 147
subtracting integers by adding the opposite
adding integers with like and unlike signs
compare integers
area of a circle
subtracting decimals

Lesson 148
graphing ordered pairs in four quadrants
subtracting integers by adding the opposite
adding integers with like and unlike signs
area of a circle
giving change

Lesson 149
multiplying integers
subtracting integers by adding the opposite
finding the volume of cylinders
graphing ordered pairs in four quadrants
bisecting angles
finding the perpendicular bisector of a line

Lesson 150
dividing integers
multiplying integers
multiplying fractions
graphing ordered pairs in four quadrants
finding the volume of cylinders
dividing fractions

Appearance of Concepts

Lesson 151
budgets
subtraction
prime numbers
multiply decimals
multiply fractions
area
ratio

Lesson 152
writing checks
budgets
subtraction
multiply decimals
multiply fractions
surface area
proportions

Lesson 153
savings accounts
banking services
writing checks
budgets
exponential form
add fractions
convert fractions to decimals
divide a whole number by a
   fraction

Lesson 154
simple interest
savings accounts
writing checks
checkbook ledger
budget finances
add and subtract fractions
change fractions to decimals
sales tax

Lesson 155
computing interest
savings accounts
savings withdrawal
checkbook
subtraction
compare fractions
reading circle graphs

Lesson 156
installment purchases
interest
compare interest rates
savings
binary
add or subtract fractions
divide mixed fractions

Lesson 157
compare products
installment buying
interest earned
missing numbers
geometric terms
exponential form
multiplying decimals

Lesson 158
average monthly expenses
compare products
installment buying
interest
mystery number
surface area
equivalent ratios

Lesson 159
type of operation
average monthly expenses
compare products
missing number
subtraction
add fractions
convert fractions to decimals

Lesson 160
traveler's checks, travel cards, gift
cards, and money orders
type of operation
average monthly expenses
prime numbers
divide decimals
convert pints to gallons
divide larger decimals

Lessons

Lesson 1

Concepts:

Numeration - trillions, two-digit addition, two-digit subtraction, angles, identifying fractions, column addition, mystery number.

Objectives:

1. The student will be able to identify place value through the trillions.
2. The student will be able to complete two-digit addition.
3. The student will be able to complete two-digit subtraction, using the regrouping process, if necessary.
4. The student will be able to identify, label, and draw acute, obtuse, and right angles.
5. The student will be able to complete column addition containing sets of one digit numbers.
6. The student will be able to identify a mystery number when given information about that number.
7. The student will be able to identify fractions.

Teaching Tips:

Place value should be a concept which all of the students have mastered.
The addition of the Trillions Period should not be a difficult concept for them.

Materials, Supplies, and Equipment:

1. Place Value Chart (Large Teacher Chart for demonstration)
2. *Worksheet 1*

Activities:

1. Read **Lesson 1 Explanation** together. Discuss the fact the God created things in an orderly fashion. Just as God uses order, so does mathematics. The place value chart is a perfect example of this. Every number has a specific value based on its location in a number.
2. Review the place value chart using a large display model for demonstration. Prior to the lesson, make a place value chart out of poster board. This chart should go through the Trillions' columns. Remind the students that there is also a decimal side to the place value chart. An easy student reminder is that the whole number side is like green money while the decimal side is like change. You can visually demonstrate this by using two separate sheets of poster board. Use a green sheet for the whole number side and another color for the decimal side. When the two sheets are joined together, have a large black line and a decimal point separating the two. This visually indicates the separation of the whole and decimal sides of the chart. The chart can be laminated for further use. Simply use overhead markers during lessons. This ink will wipe off when you are done.
3. Complete the sample problems together to insure basic understanding. Review the different ways to write a number (written form, expanded form, & standard form).
4. The student should be able to complete **Lesson 1-1** independently.
5. Combining this lesson with a study of the Solar System would be interesting. The students can research the distance between the earth and the other planets in our solar system. This will give them concrete experience dealing with large numbers.
6. For review of **Lesson 1-4** (angles) refer to Lesson 32.
7. For review of **Lesson 1-6** (prime numbers) refer to Lesson 42.

The prayer of a righteous man is powerful and effective.
James 5:16b

Lesson 2

Concepts:

Numeration- hundred thousandths, numeration-trillions, two-digit addition, two-digit subtraction, identifying fractions, column addition with two-digit numbers, addition with missing integers.

Objectives:

1. The student will be able to identify place value through the hundred thousandths place.
2. The student will be able to identify place value through the trillions place.
3. The student will be able to complete two-digit addition.
4. The student will be able to complete two-digit subtraction, using the regrouping process, if necessary.
5. The student will be able to complete column addition containing sets of two-digit numbers.
6. The student will be able to solve for missing integers within addition problems.
7. The student will be able to identify fractions.

Teaching Tips:

Materials, Supplies, and Equipment:

1. Large demonstration place value chart
2. Large Kit Kat Chocolate Bars
3. Large flash cards with decimal numbers written on them (through the hundred thousandths' place)
4. *Worksheet 2*

Activities:

1. Read **Lesson 2 Explanation** together. Remind the students of the three ways numbers may be written (standard form, written form, and expanded form). You may also need to practice pronouncing number names correctly. Remember that the word "AND" means decimal in mathematical terms.
2. Divide the class into two teams. Play "Read the Number" game. Each student reads a number off of the large flash cards. If the number is read correctly (including using the word "and" correctly) the team receives a point. If the student answers incorrectly, the opposing team has a chance to "steal" that point by reading the card correctly.

   Example:

143,978.089

   Correct student response: One hundred forty-three thousand, nine hundred seventy-eight AND eighty-nine thousandths

3. Review the value of decimals when compared with whole numbers. You may wish to use a large Kit Kat bar with this review. A large bar contains 10 individual bars that may be broken off and eaten one at the time. This is a fun way to illustrate the relationship between whole numbers and fractional (decimal) numbers. If one bar is broken off of the candy bar then 1/10 (one tenth or .10) of the candy bar has been eaten. If three bars are broken off and eaten, then 3/10 (three tenths or .30) of the candy bar has been eaten, etc...

© MCMXCIX, Alpha Omega Publications, Inc.

4. Try to relate all decimal information to real life situations. Ask the students to name times in real life when place value on the decimal side of the place value chart would be used. Examples might be in baseball statistics, track & field times, gymnastics scores, odometer on a car, or gasoline pricing at the pumps.

5. The students should be able to complete **Lesson 2-1** independently.

*Blessed is the man who perseveres under trial, because when he has stood the test,
he will receive the crown of life that God has promised to those who love Him.*
James 1:12

Lesson 3

Concepts:

    Rounding whole numbers, numeration- hundred thousandths, numeration-trillions, three-digit addition, three-digit subtraction, triangle, quadrilateral, pentagon, hexagon, octagon, nonagon, equivalent fractions.

Objectives:

1. The student will be able to round whole numbers to the nearest billion, million, hundred thousand, and hundreds' place.
2. The student will be able to identify place value through the hundred thousandths' place.
3. The student will be able to identify place value through the trillions' place.
4. The student will be able to complete three-digit addition.
5. The student will be able to complete three-digit subtraction, using the regrouping process, if necessary.
6. The student will be able to identify and label a triangle, quadrilateral, pentagon, hexagon, octagon, and nonagon.
7. The student will be able to identify equivalent fractions.

Teaching Tips:

    Stress the fact that rounding (estimating) is a skill which is used almost everyday. Give examples of everyday activities that use rounding, such as estimating prices when shopping at a store.

Materials, Supplies, and Equipment:

1. Rulers (centimeter) or measuring tapes (at least one for every 2 children)
2. *Worksheet 3*

Activities:

1. Have each student look at the centimeter ruler. They should note that the centimeter markings for 20, 30, and 40, are written larger than any other numbers. Instruct them to notice numbers 20-40. When looking at the lines which represent numbers 21-24, they are closer to the 20 than the 30. When looking at the lines which represent numbers 25-29 instruct the student that these numbers are closer to the 30. Remind the students that when they are rounding, they can picture a number line, or ruler, in their head. When rounding, the student is actually telling which number a given number is closest to. 23 is closer to 20 than 30, therefore 23 rounds to 20. 27 is closer to 30 than 20, therefore 27 rounds to 30.
2. Ask the student to illustrate these two examples by drawing number lines on a sheet of paper and showing where 23 and 27 fall in relation to the space between 20 and 30. Look at the example below:

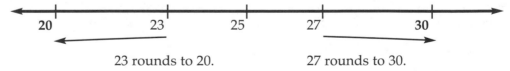

        23 rounds to 20.   27 rounds to 30.

3. Read **Lesson 3 Explanation**. Remind the students that numbers are rounded to specific places (tens, millions, hundred thousands, etc...) Practice this by making up several large numbers (through billions' place) and having the students round them to specific places.

© MCMXCIX, Alpha Omega Publications, Inc.

4. The student should be able to complete **Lesson 3-1** independently.
5. For review of **Lesson 3-5** (polygons) refer to Lesson 33.
6. For review of **Lesson 3-6** (equivalent fractions) refer to Lesson 61.

We fix our eyes not on what is seen, but on what is unseen.
For what is seen is temporary, but what is unseen is eternal.
2 Corinthians 4:18

Lesson 4

Concepts:

Compare and order of whole numbers, rounding whole numbers, numeration-hundred thousandths, numeration- trillions, three-digit addition, three-digit subtraction, equivalent fractions.

Objectives:

1. The student will be able to compare and order whole numbers.
2. The student will be able to round whole numbers to the nearest billion, million, hundred thousand, and hundreds' place.
3. The student will be able to identify place value through the hundred thousandths place.
4. The student will be able to identify place value through the trillions place.
5. The student will be able to complete three-digit addition.
6. The student will be able to complete three-digit subtraction, using the regrouping process, if necessary.
7. The student will be able to identify equivalent fractions.

Teaching Tips:

Materials, Supplies, and Equipment:

1. Play money (bills and coins)
2. Large demonstration place value chart (from **Lesson 1**)
3. *Worksheet 4*

Activities:

1. Have two students come to the front of the room. Give one student $3,900.25 in play money. Give the second student $3,009.25 in play money. Ask each student to write the amount of money they were given on the black board. Then ask the class **"Which student has the larger sum of money?"** (Student 1 with $3,900.25) Once the class, or an individual student, has responded correctly, ask them to explain how they knew that $3,900.25 is larger than $3,009.25. The student response should include some reference to the place value chart and the fact that they examined the value of each number in the dollar amounts.

2. Read **Lesson 4 Explanation** together. Remind the students that each number has a specific value on the place value chart. Take out the large demonstration place value instruction chart (from **Lessons 1 &2**). Have each student who received money now write the amount of money they received onto the place value chart. This should visually illustrate the position of each number on the place value chart.

3. Review the "Greater Than" and "Less Than" (<, >) symbols. Have the students create a mathematical sentence using these symbols and the dollar amounts written on the place value chart. The answers should be either $3,900.25 > $3,009.25 or $3.009.25 < $3,900.25.

4. The students should be able to complete **Lesson 4-1** independently.

5. For review of **Lesson 4-6** (equivalent fractions) refer to Lesson 61.

... whoever wants to become great among you must be your servant, and whoever wants to be first must be your slave just as the Son of Man did not come to be served, but to serve, and to give His life as a ransom for many.
Matthew 20:26-28

Lesson 5

Concepts:

Addition and subtraction equations, compare and order whole numbers, rounding whole numbers, numeration-hundred thousandths, four-digit addition, four-digit subtraction, lowest term fractions.

Objectives:

1. The student will be able to solve addition and subtraction equations.
2. The student will be able to compare and order whole numbers.
3. The student will be able to round whole numbers to the nearest billion, million, hundred thousands, and hundreds' place.
4. The student will be able to identify place value through the hundred thousandths place.
5. The student will be able to complete four-digit addition.
6. The student will be able to complete four-digit subtraction, using the regrouping process, if necessary.
7. The student will be able to rename fractions into lowest terms.

Teaching Tips:

One way of thinking about equations is to picture a balance or scale. The two sides of an equation are like the two pans on a scale. The equation must be balanced, equal, on both sides for the equation to be true.

Materials, Supplies, and Equipment:

1. Beans or counters.

Activities:

1. Remind the students that an equation is a number sentence where both sides of the equation are equal. A variable is a letter that stands for a number.
2. Read the Example information in **Lesson 5** and have the students work the first sample problem in **Lesson 5 Explanation** using the beans, or counters. Also have them check the answers, as shown in the examples. Look at the example below:

   Sample problem #1: $N + 9 = 30$

   ⬚⬚⬚⬚⬚⬚⬚⬚⬚   +   N   =   ⬚⬚⬚⬚⬚⬚⬚⬚⬚⬚⬚⬚⬚⬚⬚
   ⬚⬚⬚⬚⬚⬚⬚⬚⬚⬚⬚⬚⬚⬚⬚

   Ask the students **"If N is the variable, how many counters would be needed to put in its place to make the equation equal?"** (21).
3. Demonstrate that it is easy to check to see if an equation is correct. Replace N with the counters and show that both sides are equal.
4. Demonstrate more of the sample problems, if necessary. The students should be able to go from this concrete example to the abstract without difficulty. Direct the students to complete **Lesson 5-1** independently. Supervise the students as they complete the lesson.
5. For review of **Lesson 5-6** (equivalent fractions) refer to Lesson 61.

For me, to live is Christ and to die is gain.
Philippians 1:21

Lesson 6

Concepts:
Order of operations, addition and subtraction equations, compare and order whole numbers, rounding whole numbers, four-digit addition , four-digit subtraction, lowest term fractions.

Objectives:
1. The student will be able to identify the correct order of operations when presented with a multi-operational word problem.
2. The student will be able to solve addition and subtraction equations.
3. The student will be able to compare and order whole numbers.
4. The student will be able to round whole numbers to the nearest billion, million, hundred thousand, and hundreds' place.
5. The student will be able to complete four-digit addition.
6. The student will be able to complete four-digit subtraction, using the regrouping process, if necessary.
7. The student will be able to rename fractions into lowest terms.

Teaching Tips:
Stress that certain expressions (equations) may have more than one operation. When they do, the order in which the operations are performed is important because the order of operations determines the answer.

Materials, Supplies, and Equipment:
1. Calculator

Activities:
1. Write the following problem on the board: $7 \times 2^2 + 5 \times (3 \times 1) =$. Ask the students to work the problem. Discuss the different answers obtained by the students. Explain to them that the order in which the problem is worked determines the answer. Look at two of the possible answers:

Example #1 is worked in random order :	**Example #2** is worked in mathematical order :
$7 \times 2^2 + 5 \times (3 \times 1)$	$7 \times 2^2 + 5 \times (3 \times 1)$
$28 + 5 \times (3 \times 1)$	$7 \times 2^2 + 5 \times 3$
$33 \times (3 \times 1)$	$7 \times 4 + 5 \times 3$
33×3	$28 + 5 \times 3$
99	$28 + 15$
	43

2. Read **Lesson 6 Explanation** together. Go over the way to solve an equation by using the proper order of operations listed in the explanation. Go over Example #2 (above) and discuss how it was worked according to these instructions.
3. Write the following example on the board: $9 \times 5 \times (2^3 \div 8) = 45$. Ask the students to put the parentheses in the correct place so that the correct answer is 45. (Answer is: $(9 \times 5) \times (2^3 \div 8) = 45$)
4. Work the first two problems in **Lesson 6-1** as a class. Check to make sure the students understand the order of operations concept. Then assign the students to complete **Lesson 6-1** independently.
5. For review of **Lesson 6-6** (equivalent fractions) refer to Lesson 61.

Do not be anxious about anything, but in everything, by prayer and petition, with thanksgiving, present your requests to God. And the peace of God, which transcends all understanding, will guard your hearts and your minds in Christ Jesus.
Philippians 4:6-7

Lesson 7

Concepts:

Addition and subtraction properties, order of operations, addition and subtraction equations, compare and order whole numbers, five-digit addition, five-digit subtraction, compare and order fractions.

Objectives:

1. The student will be able to identify and correctly use the properties of addition and subtraction.
2. The student will be able to identify the correct order of operations when presented with a multi-operational word problem.
3. The student will be able to solve addition and subtraction equations.
4. The student will be able to compare and order whole numbers.
5. The student will be able to complete five-digit addition.
6. The student will be able to complete five-digit subtraction, using the regrouping process, if necessary.
7. The student will be able to compare and order fractions.

Teaching Tips:

The students should have little difficulty reviewing these properties of addition and subtraction.

Materials, Supplies, and Equipment:

1. Large display flash cards

Activities:

1. Prior to the lesson create demonstration flash cards which show the following information:

$$\begin{array}{r}10\\+\ 6\\\hline\end{array}\qquad\begin{array}{r}6\\+\ 10\\\hline\end{array}\qquad\qquad\begin{array}{r}4\\+\ 5\\\hline\end{array}\qquad\begin{array}{r}5\\+\ 4\\\hline\end{array}$$

These cards illustrate the Commutative (Order) Property of Addition.

$$\begin{array}{r}9\\+\ 0\\\hline\end{array}\qquad\qquad\begin{array}{r}3\\+\ 0\\\hline\end{array}\qquad\qquad\begin{array}{r}5\\+\ 0\\\hline\end{array}$$

These cards illustrate the Zero Property of Addition.

$$\begin{array}{r}10\\-\ 0\\\hline\end{array}\qquad\begin{array}{r}18\\-\ 18\\\hline\end{array}\qquad\begin{array}{r}12\\-\ 0\\\hline\end{array}\qquad\begin{array}{r}25\\-\ 25\\\hline\end{array}$$

These cards illustrate the Zero Property of Subtraction.

$$\boxed{3\ +\ (5\ +\ 2)\ =\ 10}\qquad\boxed{(3\ +\ 5)\ +\ 2\ =\ 10}$$

These cards illustrate the Associative Property of Addition.

Display these cards in random order, and ask the students to pair up the cards which belong together (shown above). Ask the students to explain why certain cards need to be grouped together (because they demonstrate a specific Addition or Subtraction Property).

© MCMXCIX, Alpha Omega Publications, Inc.

2. Review these properties by reading **Lesson 7 Explanation** together and discussing the properties listed in the explanation.
3. Have the students complete **Lesson 7-1** independently.
4. For review of **Lesson 7-6** (comparing fractions) refer to Lesson 64.

Have nothing to do with godless myths and old wives' tales; rather, train yourself to be godly. For physical training is of some value, but godliness has value for all things, holding promise for both the present life and the life to come.
1 Timothy 4:7-8

Lesson 8

Concepts:
Vertical and horizontal addition with up to 6-digits, addition and subtraction properties, addition and subtraction equations, multiplication facts, triangles, compare and order fractions.

Objectives:
1. The student will be able to complete vertical and horizontal addition problems containing up to six-digits in each addend.
2. The student will be able to identify and correctly use the properties of addition and subtraction.
3. The student will be able to identify the correct order of operations when presented with a multi-operational word problem.
4. The student will be able to solve addition and subtraction equations.
5. The student will be able to identify multiplication facts.
6. The student will be able to identify and label scalene, isosceles, equilateral, and right triangles.
7. The student will be able to compare and order fractions.

Teaching Tips:
The most common errors with addition involve misalignment of digits. Have the students check their work carefully.

Materials, Supplies, and Equipment:
1. Graph paper (if necessary)
2. *Worksheet 5*

Activities:
1. Direct the students' attention to **Lesson 8 Explanation**. Read orally.
2. This exercise should require no additional explanation if the students comprehends regrouping and basic addition (which they should by now).
3. Instruct the students to work **Lesson 8-1** independently. Allow any students who may have difficulty keeping place value columns straight to use graph paper as an aid to assist them with this problem.
4. For review of Lesson 8-5 (types of triangles) refer to Lesson 36.

The Son is the radiance of God's glory and the exact representation of His being, sustaining all things by His powerful word. After He has provided purification for sins, He sat down at the right hand of the Majesty in heaven.
Hebrews 1:3

Lesson 9

Concepts:

Vertical and horizontal subtraction with up to 6-digits, vertical and horizontal addition with up to 6-digits, addition and subtraction properties, order of operations, multiplication facts, space figures, addition of fractions with common denominators.

Objectives:

1. The student will be able to complete vertical and horizontal subtraction problems that contain up to six digits in each subtrahend or minuend.
2. The student will be able to complete vertical and horizontal addition problems that contain up to six digits in each addend.
3. The student will be able to identify and correctly use the properties of addition and subtraction.
4. The student will be able to identify the correct order of operations when presented with a multi-operational word problem.
5. The student will be able to identify multiplication facts.
6. The student will be able to identify and label space figures such as triangular prisms, rectangular pyramids, cones, and spheres.
7. The student will be able to add fractions with common denominators.

Teaching Tips:

The most common errors with addition involve misalignment of digits. Have the students check their work carefully.

Materials, Supplies, and Equipment:

1. Graph paper (if necessary)
2. *Worksheet 5*

Activities:

1. Read **Lesson 9 Explanation** orally and evaluate the example problems together.
2. Remind the students that like addition, alignment of the place value columns when subtracting is vital to arrive at the correct answer.
3. Assign the students to complete **Lesson 9-1** independently.
4. For review of **Lesson 9-7** (adding fractions) refer to Lesson 62.
5. For review of **Lesson 9-7** (equivalent fractions) refer to Lesson 61.

> *Faith is being sure of what we hope for and certain of what we do not see.*
> **Hebrews 11:1**

Lesson 10

Concepts:

Estimating sums and differences using charts, tables, & maps, vertical and horizontal subtraction with up to 6 digits, vertical and horizontal addition with up to 6 digits, addition and subtraction properties, division facts, identification of quadrilaterals, addition of fractions with common denominators.

Objectives:

1. The student will be able to estimate sums and differences in order to answers questions obtained from a chart, table, or map.
2. The student will be able to complete vertical and horizontal subtraction problems that contain up to six digits in each subtrahend or minuend.
3. The student will be able to complete vertical and horizontal addition problems that contain up to six digits in each addend.
4. The student will be able to identify and correctly use the properties of addition and subtraction.
5. The student will be able to identify division facts.
6. The student will be able to identify quadrilaterals such as rhombus, parallelograms, squares, rectangles, and trapezoids.
7. The student will be able to add fractions with common denominators.

Teaching Tips:

If students are having difficulty remembering how to round, take them aside and review rounding using play money.

Materials, Supplies, and Equipment:

Activities:

1. Point out to the students that sometimes we need exact amounts as answers and at other items we need estimates. Have them tell some instances when estimates would be appropriate. Remind the student that there are different ways to estimate depending on your needs. Today they will be rounding to the nearest thousand.
2. Direct the students to **Lesson 10 Explanation**. Look at the chart and have the students fill in the missing information by estimating the heights of each peak.
3. Rework and discuss the sample problems. Make sure each student understands that we are looking for estimated answers, not exact answers.
4. Ask the students to complete #1 on **Lesson 10-1**. Check the answer together and discuss any questions the student may have.
5. Have the student complete the rest of **Lesson 10-1** independently.
6. For review of **Lesson 10-5** (quadrilaterals) refer to Lesson 34.
7. For review of **Lesson 10-6** (adding fractions) refer to Lesson 62.
8. For review of **Lesson 10-6** (equivalent fractions) refer to Lesson 61.

A good name is better than fine perfume, and the day of death
better than the day of birth.
Ecclesiastes 7:1

Lesson 11

Concepts:

Multiplication and division of equations, six-digit subtraction, six-digit addition, measurement to the 1/8 inch, subtract fractions, writing a check

Objectives:

1. The student will be able to solve for the variable in a multiplication and division equation.
2. The student will be able to find the difference of two, six-digit number.
3. The student will be able to find the sum of two, six-digit number.
4. The student will be able to measure to the nearest 1/8 inch.
5. The student will be able to find the difference of fractions with common denominators.
6. The student will be able to write a check.

Teaching Tips:

Reinforce the idea that whatever you do to one side of the equation you do to the other. Some students divide a number by one side and multiply that same number on the other side.

Materials, Supplies, and Equipment:

1. *Worksheet 6*

Activities:

1. Review multiplication and division of equations using the following problems.

   $5 \times n = 30$ $\qquad\qquad$ $n \div 8 = 9$
   $\div 5 = \div 5$ $\qquad\qquad$ $\times 8 = \times 8$

   $n = 6$ $\qquad\qquad\qquad$ $n = 72$
   Check: $\qquad\qquad\qquad$ Check:
   $5 \times 6 = 30$ $\qquad\qquad$ $72 \div 8 = 9$

2. Tell the students that there are several ways to express the same equations. Show them the following examples:

   $5 \times n = 30$ $\quad$ or $\quad$ $5 \bullet n = 30$ $\quad$ or $\quad$ $5n = 30$

   $n \div 8 = 9$ $\quad$ or $\quad$ $n/8 = 9$

3. Have the students write these equations several ways.

   $6 \times n = 42$ $\qquad\qquad$ ($6 \bullet n = 42$ $\quad$ or $\quad$ $6n = 42$)

   $n \div 3 = 7$ $\qquad\qquad$ ($n/3 = 7$)

4. Read **Lesson 11 Explanation** with the students.

5. The students will be able to complete **Lesson 11 Practice** independently.

Love the Lord your God with all of your heart and with all of your soul
and with all of your strength.
Deuteronomy 6:5

Lesson 12

Concepts:
> Order of operations, multiplication and division of equations, six-digit subtraction, six digit addition, measurement to the 1/8 inch, subtract fractions, word problems

Objectives:
1. The student will be able to find the order of operations.
2. The student will be able to solve for the variable in a multiplication and division equation.
3. The student will be able to add and subtract four and five-digit numbers and complete a crossword puzzle.
4. The student will be able to measure to the nearest 1/8 inch.
5. The student will be able to find the difference of fractions with common denominators.
6. The student will be able to solve multiplication word problems.

Teaching Tips:
> Have the students memorize the rules for the order of operations.

Materials, Supplies, and Equipment:
1. *Worksheet 7*

Activities:
1. Read **Lesson 12 Explanation** with the students.

2. Write these two problems on the board. Ask the students: **Will the answer to these two problems be the same?**
   5 x 2 + 8 =   5(2 + 8) =

3. Select students to work the problems on the board. They will see that
   5 x 2 + 8 = 18, but 5(2 + 8) = 50

4. Encourage the students to memorize the rules for the order of operations.
5. The students will be able to complete **Lesson 12 Practice** independently.

Just for Fun:
> Give each student an index card. Have them write a two or three-step problem and answer on one side of the card. They should not include any parentheses. On the other side of the card, instruct them to recopy the problem and place the parentheses in the problem.
>
> Have the students trade cards. Instruct the students to see if they can figure out where the parentheses should go. The answers are on the other side!

These commandments I give to you today are to be upon your hearts. Impress them on your children. Talk about them when you sit at home and when you walk along the road, when you lie down and when you get up. Tie them as symbols on your hands and bind them on your foreheads. Write them on your doorframes of your houses and on your gates.
Deuteronomy 6:6-9

© MCMXCIX, Alpha Omega Publications, Inc.

Lesson 13

Concepts:

Properties of multiplication and division, order of operations, multiplication and division of equations, three-digit addition, liquid conversions, change improper fractions to mixed fractions

Objectives:

1. The student will be able to answer true and false questions regarding properties of multiplication and division.
2. The student will be able to solve for missing operation symbols using logical reasoning.
3. The student will be able to solve for the variable in a multiplication and division equation.
4. The student will be able to use estimation to find the sum.
5. The student will be able to find liquid conversions.
6. The student will be able to change improper fractions to mixed fractions or whole numbers.

Teaching Tips:

Encourage the students to memorize the properties of multiplication and division.

Materials, Supplies, and Equipment:

Activities:

1. Read **Lesson 13 Explanation** with the students.
2. Have the students write down each of these rules on notebook paper, and write a mathematical expression that demonstrates each rule. Encourage the students to memorize these rules.
3. The students will be able to complete **Lesson 13 Practice** independently.

Just for Fun:

Preparation

Give each student two index cards. On one card have them write a division or multiplication property. On the other card, have the students write a mathematical expression that demonstrates the rule. Place all of the cards face-side down on the floor. Number the cards.

Directions

Divide the class into two teams and play a matching game. When a student finds a match, remove those cards from the game and give his/her team one point. That player gets an additional turn. The team with the most points wins.

When angry, count ten before you speak; when very angry, count a hundred.
Thomas Jefferson

Lesson 14

Concepts:

Multiplication, order of operations, multiplication and division of equations, liquid conversions, change improper fractions to mixed fractions, estimation and multiplication, who am I?

Objectives:

1. The student will be able to find the product of a three-digit factor times a one-digit factor.
2. The student will be able to use the order of operations to solve the given expressions.
3. The student will be able to solve for the variable in a multiplication and division equation.
4. The student will be able to find liquid conversions.
5. The student will be able to change improper fractions to mixed fractions or whole numbers.
6. The student will be able to use estimation to find the sum.
7. Given number clues, the student will be able to use logical reasoning to uncover the secret three-digit number.

Teaching Tips:

Give the students speed drill multiplication practice every day. The students should continue practice until they can give the answers rapidly without hesitation.

Materials, Supplies, and Equipment:

Activities:

1. Read **Lesson 14 Explanation** with the students.

2. Allow the students to work the following problems with your assistance. Make sure that they are carrying properly.

$$
\begin{array}{r} 3\,4 \\ 4\,5\,7 \\ \times\ \ 6 \\ \hline 2,7\,4\,2 \end{array}
\qquad
\begin{array}{r} 3 \\ 8\,9\,0 \\ \times\ \ 4 \\ \hline 3,5\,6\,0 \end{array}
\qquad
\begin{array}{r} 1 \\ 2\,1\,8 \\ \times\ \ 2 \\ \hline 4\,3\,6 \end{array}
\qquad
\begin{array}{r} 1\,3 \\ 3\,2\,7 \\ \times\ \ 5 \\ \hline 1,6\,3\,5 \end{array}
$$

3. The students will be able to complete **Lesson 14 Practice** independently.

I am always ready to learn, but I don't always like being taught.
Winston Churchill

© MCMXCIX, Alpha Omega Publications, Inc.

Lesson 15

Concepts:

Three-digit multiplication, two-digit multiplication, compare and order fractions, linear conversions, multiplication, mixed fractions to improper fractions, order of operations, diameter and radius

Objectives:

1. The student will be able to find the product of a two-digit factor times a two-digit factor.
2. The student will be able to find their way through a fraction maze by finding the next largest fraction.
3. The student will be able to find linear conversions.
4. The student will be able to find the product of a two-digit factor times a one-digit factor.
5. The student will be able to use the order of operations and solve a given expression.
6. The student will be able to change mixed fractions improper fractions.
7. The student will be able to define a radius, diameter, of a circle and define their values.

Teaching Tips:

Give the students speed drill multiplication practice every day. The students should continue practice until they can give the answers rapidly without hesitation. Encourage the students to use zeros as placeholders as shown in **Lesson 15 Explanation**. Some students benefit from eliminating the zeros and visualizing the stair-step pattern created when they place the numbers properly. Familiarize the students with both methods.

Materials, Supplies, and Equipment:

1. *Worksheet 8*

Activities:

1. Read **Lesson 15 Explanation** with the students.

2. Allow the students to work the following problems with your assistance. Have them draw lines demonstrating the stair-step pattern.

```
    2 2              3 3
    1 1              4 7 9
      1 8 9        x   4 1
    x   3 2         ─────────
     ─────────        4 7 9
        3 7 8        1 9 1 6
      5 6 7        ─────────
    ─────────       1 9, 6 3 9
    6, 0 4 8
```

3. The students will be able to complete **Lesson 15 Practice** independently.

Pride goes before destruction, a haughty spirit before a fall.
Proverbs 16:18

© MCMXCIX, Alpha Omega Publications, Inc.

Lesson 16

Concepts:
   Estimate products, missing numbers, linear conversions, change improper fractions to mixed fractions, geometric terms, logical reasoning, missing operation signs

Objectives:
1. The student will be able to estimate products.
2. The student will be able to solve for missing numbers in a multiplication problem.
3. The student will be able to find linear conversions.
4. The student will be able to change improper fractions to mixed fractions or whole numbers.
5. Given a pictorial representation, the student will be able to write the name of the following figures: point, line, line segment, and ray.
6. Using logical reasoning, the students will arrange numbers in a puzzle so that the sum of each row is 9.
7. The student will be able to place the operation signs in the boxes to make each statement true.

Teaching Tips:
   Give the students speed drill multiplication practice every day. The students should continue practice until they can give the answers rapidly without hesitation.

© MCMXCIX, Alpha Omega Publications, Inc.

Materials, Supplies, and Equipment:

Activities:
1. Review rounding numbers to the first digit.

3 4 2 (300)	5 6 2 (600)	2 1 1 (200)	9 6 1 (1,000)
4, 6 7 0 (5,000)	6, 9 1 5 (7,000)	3, 4 1 8 (3,000)	7, 099 (7,000)

2. Read **Lesson 16 Explanation** with the students.

3. Write the following problems on the board and have the students work them with your assistance. The students should follow these steps.
   1) Round each of the two numbers to the first digit.
   2) Multiply those two numbers.
   3) Count the number of zeros in both factors and write them in the product.

6 8	8 4	2 7	3 2
x 2 2	x 3 1	x 1 5	x 5 2
70 x 20	80 x 30	30 x 20	30 x 50
7 x 2 = 14	8 x 3 = 24	3 x 2 = 6	3 x 5 = 15
Write 2 zeros.	Write 2 zeros.	Write 2 zeros.	Write 2 zeros.
1,400	2,400	600	1,500

5 9 2	3 5 2	7 3 9	8 9 1
x 3 8 0	x 1 2 4	x 2 0 5	x 6 4 9
600 x 400	400 x 100	700 x 200	900 x 600
6 x 4 = 24	4 x 1 = 4	7 x 2 = 14	9 x 6 = 54
Write 4 zeros.	Write 4 zeros.	Write 4 zeros.	Write 4 zeros.
240,000	40,000	140,000	540,000

4. The students will be able to complete **Lesson 16 Practice** independently.

All of the flowers of all the tomorrows are in the seeds of today.
Proverb

Lesson 17

Concepts:

Division, estimate products, two and three-digit multiplication, weight conversions, two-step equations, magic square, who am I?

Objectives:

1. The student will be able to divide a one-digit divisor by a four-digit dividend.
2. The student will be able to estimate and multiply two, three-digit numbers.
3. The student will be able to multiply two and three-digit numbers to solve a puzzle.
4. The student will be able to find weight conversions.
5. Given number clues, the student will be able to use logical reasoning to uncover the secret three-digit number.
6. The student will be able to solve a two-step equation.
7. Using logical reasoning, the students will arrange numbers in a puzzle so that the sum of each row is 15.

Teaching Tips:

Give the students speed drill division practice every day. The students should continue practice until they can give the answers rapidly without hesitation. Students often get confused about where to place the first digit in the quotient. Give the students repeated practice until they master this skill.

Materials, Supplies, and Equipment:

Activities:

1. Read **Lesson 17 Explanation** with the students.
2. Put the following examples on the board. Ask the students to determine where to put the first digit.

$$\overset{1}{9)\,9{,}421} \qquad \overset{2}{5)\,1{,}378} \qquad \overset{9}{6)\,5{,}800} \qquad \overset{3}{3)\,9{,}245}$$

3. Allow the students to continue solving each of the problems with your supervision. It is extremely important that the students keep their columns straight as they divide. (Answers: 1046 r. 7, 275 r. 3, 966 r. 4, 3081 r. 2)
4. Write the following problems on the board and ask the students to show three other ways to express the same problem.

$7)\overline{6{,}400}$	$6{,}400 \div 7$	$6{,}400 / 7$	$1/7$ of $6{,}400$
$4{,}795 / 5$	$5)\overline{4{,}795}$	$4{,}795 \div 5$	$1/5$ of $4{,}795$
$1/3$ of $2{,}988$	$3)\overline{2{,}988}$	$2{,}988 / 3$	$2{,}988 \div 3$

5. The students will be able to complete **Lesson 17 Practice** independently.

Success is never final, and failure never fatal.
John Wooden

© MCMXCIX, Alpha Omega Publications, Inc.

Lesson 18

Concepts:

Division, division and fractions, estimate products, multiplication and logical reasoning,

weight conversions, two-step equations, who am I?

Objectives:

1. The student will be able to divide a two-digit divisor by a three-digit dividend.
2. The student will be able to divide a one-digit divisor by a four-digit dividend.
3. The student will be able to multiply two, three-digit numbers and find the product.
4. The student will be able to multiply two and three-digit numbers to solve a puzzle.
5. The student will be able to find weight conversions.
6. Given number clues, the student will be able to use logical reasoning to uncover the secret three-digit number.
7. Given a multiplication equation, the student will solve for n.

Teaching Tips:

Give the students speed drill division practice every day. The students should continue practice until they can give the answers rapidly without hesitation.

Materials, Supplies, and Equipment:

1. *Worksheet 9*

Activities:

1. Read **Lesson 18 Explanation** with the students.
2. Put the following examples on the board. Ask the students to determine where to put the first digit.

$$\overset{1}{93\overline{)9{,}401}} \qquad \overset{2}{52\overline{)3{,}618}} \qquad \overset{9}{61\overline{)5{,}800}} \qquad \overset{3}{30\overline{)9{,}245}}$$

3. Allow the students to continue solving each of the problems with your supervision. It is extremely important that the students keep their columns straight as they divide. (Answers: 101 r.8, 69 r. 30, 95 r. 5, 308 r. 5)
4. The students will be able to complete **Lesson 18 Practice** independently.

Courage is resistance to fear, mastery of fear, not absence of fear.
Mark Twain

Lesson 19

Concepts:

Estimation and division, division and fractions, estimate products, read a thermometer, find the missing numerator, logical reasoning, equations

Objectives:

1. The student will be able to divide using estimates.
2. The student will be able to divide a one-digit divisor by a four-digit dividend.
3. The student will be able to estimate and multiply two, three-digit numbers.
4. The student will be able to read a thermometer and record the temperature.
5. The student will be able to find the missing numerator in an equivalent fraction.
6. Using logical reasoning, the students will arrange numbers in a puzzle so that the sum of each row of the pentagon equals 14.
7. The student will be able to solve for n given three of the four addends and a sum.

Teaching Tips:

Give the students speed drill division practice every day. The students should continue practice until they can give the answers rapidly without hesitation.

Materials, Supplies, and Equipment:

Activities:

1. Read **Lesson 19 Explanation** with the students.

2. Write this problem on the board and have the students work it with your supervision. Help them to determine if their trial is too large or too small. 34 rounds to 30.

$3)\overline{18}$ is 6.

$$\begin{array}{r} 6 \\ 34)\overline{1,879} \\ -\ 204 \end{array} \qquad \begin{array}{r} 5 \\ 34)\overline{1,879} \\ -170 \\ \hline 17 \end{array}$$

204 is too large.   **5 is the correct number.**

Finish working the problem. The answer is 55 r. 9

3. The students will be able to complete **Lesson 19 Practice** independently.

If you are all wrapped up in yourself, you are overdressed.
Halverson

© MCMXCIX, Alpha Omega Publications, Inc.

Lesson 20

Concepts:

Averaging with remainders, averaging with calculators, division, more division, read a thermometer, understanding Celsius, equations
Objectives - Lessons 11-20

Objectives:

1. The student will be able to find the average of four numbers.
2. The student will be able to find the average of four numbers using a calculator.
3. The student will be able to divide a two-digit divisor by a three-digit dividend.
4. The student will be able to divide a one-digit divisor by a four-digit dividend.
5. The student will be able to read a Celsius thermometer and record the temperature.
6. The student will be able to demonstrate their knowledge of Celsius temperature by matching a thermometer reading with a corresponding event.
7. The student will be able to solve for n given three of the four addends and a sum.

Teaching Tips:

Give the students speed drill division practice every day. The students should continue practice until they can give the answers rapidly without hesitation.

Materials, Supplies, and Equipment:

1. *Worksheet 10*

Activities:

1. Read **Lesson 20 Explanation** with the students.

2. Write these problems on the board and have the students work them with your supervision.

   Find the averages without a calculator.
   Round the fraction to the nearest whole number.

   389, 807, 312 (**503**) 594, 243, 800 (**546**)

   Find the averages with a calculator.
   Round the fraction to the nearest whole number.

   489, 612, 439, 302, 411 (**451**) 299, 548, 398, 799, 252 (**459**)

3. The students will be able to complete **Lesson 20 Practice** independently.

> *Teach me your way, O Lord, and I will walk in your truth; Give me*
> *an undivided heart that I may fear your name.*
> **Psalm 86:11**

Lesson 21

Concepts:
Four-digit multiplication, place value, averaging, division, pattern sequencing, estimation of money.

Objectives:
1. The student will be able to multiply four-digit numbers by four-digit numbers.
2. The student will be able to identify place value through the trillions' place.
3. The student will be able to average a given set of numbers that contain a remainder.
4. The student will be able to complete division problems that contain a two-digit divisor.
5. The student will be able to follow a sequence to complete a number pattern.
6. The student will be able to estimate dollar amounts.

Teaching Tips:
Students often have alignment problems when multiplying by more than one digit. It is helpful to use 1 centimeter graph paper or to turn regular notebook paper sideways and use the lines to align digits.

Materials, Supplies, and Equipment:
1. Graph paper or lined paper
2. *Worksheet 11*

Activities:
1. Have the students complete the following warm up problems at their desks, as you do them at the board:

117	164	208	291
x 168	x 314	x 437	x 144
936	656	1456	1164
7020	1640	6240	11640
11700	49200	83200	29100
19656	51496	90896	41904

Notice the zeros written in red. The students have difficulty remembering to put the zero here.

2. Read **Lesson 21 Explanation** with the students. Complete the example problems together.

3. The students should be able to complete **Lesson 21-1** independently.

God, I will thank you forever for what you have done. With those who worship you, I will trust you because you are good.
Psalm 52:9

Lesson 22

Concepts:

Five-digit multiplication, four-digit multiplication, place value, averaging, division, estimation of money, two-digit column addition.

Objectives:

1. The student will be able to multiply five-digit numbers by five-digit numbers.
2. The student will be able to multiply four-digit numbers by four-digit numbers.
3. The student will be able to identify place value through the Trillions' place.
4. The student will be able to average a given set of numbers that contain a remainder.
5. The student will be able to estimate dollar amounts.
6. The student will be able to complete column addition with two-digit numbers.
7. The student will be able to identify numbers that are divisible by 2 and 3.

Teaching Tips:

Students often have alignment problems when multiplying by two digits. They forget to place a zero in the ones', tens' or hundreds' place when multiplying by one of the larger factors. You may wish to use the graph paper or lined paper in an effort to help the students avoid errors.

Materials, Supplies, and Equipment:

1. Graph paper or lined paper.
2. *Worksheet 12*

Activities:

1. Read **Lesson 22 Explanation** with the students.

2. Have the students complete the following problems at their desks, as you do them at the board:

```
    1 2 3 4              3 1 5 6
  x 1 3 1 6            x 2 1 3 7
    7 4 0 4            2 2 0 9 2
  1 2 3 4 0            9 4 6 8 0
3 7 0 2 0 0          3 1 5 6 0 0
1 2 3 4 0 0 0        6 3 1 2 0 0 0
1 6 2 3 9 4 4        6 7 4 4 3 7 2
```

Notice the bold zeros. The students may have difficulty remembering to put the zero here.

3. The students should be able to complete **Lesson 22-1** independently.

Gratitude comes from having the right perspective. It's being able to look at what you have and being thankful for that, rather than longing for what you don't have.
Max Lucado

Lesson 23

Concepts:

Estimation of multiplication, five-digit multiplication, four-digit multiplication, place value, rounding whole numbers, two-digit column addition, mystery number.

Objectives:

1. The student will be able to estimate multiplication problems by rounding to the nearest tens', hundreds', or thousands' place.
2. The student will be able to multiply five-digit numbers by five-digit numbers.
3. The student will be able to multiply four-digit numbers by four-digit numbers.
4. The student will be able to identify place value through the Trillions' place.
5. The student will be able to round whole numbers.
6. The student will be able to complete column addition with two-digit numbers.
7. The student will be able to identify a mystery number by reading descriptive clues.

Teaching Tips:

Materials, Supplies, and Equipment:

Activities:

1. Read **Lesson 23 Explanation** with the students.

2. Complete several example problems with the students, as follows:

4 x 521 =	6 x 389 =	22 x 609 =
4 x 500 = 2,000	6 x 400 = 2,400	20 x 600 = 12,000

3. The students should be able to complete **Lesson 23-1** independently.

I will not sacrifice to the Lord my God that which costs me nothing.
2 Samuel 24:24

Lesson 24

Concepts:

Three-digit division, estimation of multiplication, five-digit multiplication, four-digit multiplication, rounding of whole numbers, averaging.

Objectives:

1. The student will be able to complete division problems that contain a three-digit divisor.
2. The student will be able to estimate multiplication problems by rounding to the nearest tens', hundreds', or thousands' place.
3. The student will be able to multiply five-digit numbers by five-digit numbers.
4. The student will be able to multiply four-digit numbers by four-digit numbers.
5. The student will be able to round whole numbers.
6. The student will be able to find the average of a given set of numbers.

Teaching Tips:

Using graph paper, or lined paper, will be a tremendous aid if the students are having difficulty keeping the numbers and lines straight.

Materials, Supplies, and Equipment:

1. Graph paper, or lined paper.
2. Calculator (for multiplication steps and checking)

Activities:

1. Read **Lesson 24 Explanation** together. Have the students copy the first sample problem on their graph paper. Work the problem together as you go over the explanation. Remind the students to use their knowledge of rounding and multiplication to help make the division of the 3-digit divisor easier. Calculators will make this step easier.
2. After completing the first example problem, allow one student volunteer to come to the board and explain the second example problem.
3. Allow the students to work in pairs and complete the first problem (after the example) on **Lesson 24-1**. The paired student should take turns working different steps of the problem. For example, student 1 might complete steps 1 & 2 of the division process, while student 2 completes steps 3 & 4. Once the problem is completed, one set of paired students should swap problems with another set of paired students and check each other's work. If one group has worked the problem incorrectly, then their original problem is returned to them, and they must find the error and correct it.
4. The student should be able to complete **Lesson 24-1** independently.

Therefore thou shalt love the Lord thy God, and keep His charge, and His statutes...
and His commandments, always.
Deuteronomy 11:1

Lesson 25

Concepts:
Four-digit division, three-digit division, estimation of multiplication, five-digit multiplication, compare & order whole numbers, averaging, simple equations.

Objectives:
1. The student will be able to complete division problems that contain a four-digit divisor.
2. The student will be able to complete division problems that contain a three-digit divisor.
3. The student will be able to estimate multiplication problems by rounding to the nearest tens', hundreds', or thousands' place.
4. The student will be able to multiply a five-digit number by a five-digit number.
5. The student will be able to compare and order whole numbers.
6. The student will be able to find the average of a given set of numbers.
7. The student will be able to solve simple equations.

Teaching Tips:
Using graph paper, or lined paper, will be a tremendous aid if the students are having difficulty keeping the numbers and lines straight.

Materials, Supplies, and Equipment:
1. Graph paper, or lined paper.
2. Calculator (for multiplication steps and checking)
3. *Worksheet 13*

Activities:
1. Read **Lesson 25 Explanation** together. Remind the students to use their knowledge of rounding and multiplication to help make the division of the 4-digit divisor easier. Calculators will make this step much easier.
2. Allow the students to work in pairs and complete the first problem (after the example) on **Lesson 25-1**. The paired student should take turns working different steps of the problem. For example student 1 might complete steps 1 & 2 of the division process, while student 2 completes steps 3 & 4. Once the problem is completed, one set of paired students should swap problems with another set of paired students and check each other's work. If one group has worked the problem incorrectly, then their original problem is returned to them and they must find the error and correct it.
3. The student should be able to complete **Lesson 25-1** independently.

A good name is rather to be chosen than great riches.
Proverbs 22:1

© MCMXCIX, Alpha Omega Publications, Inc.

Lesson 26

Concepts:

Division, four-digit division, three-digit division, estimation of multiplication, compare & order whole numbers, simple equations, addition logic.

Objectives:

1. The student will be able to determine if a given quotient is to high or too low for the problem.
2. The student will be able to complete division problems that contain a four-digit divisor.
3. The student will be able to complete division problems that contain a three-digit divisor.
4. The student will be able to estimate multiplication problems by rounding to the nearest tens', hundreds', or thousands' place.
5. The student will be able to compare and order whole numbers.
6. The student will be able to solve simple equations.
7. The student will be able to identify missing numbers within three-digit addition problems.

Teaching Tips:

The students should be able to grasp this concept easily after completing **Lessons 24 and 25.** The students are using their knowledge of rounding and estimating to determine if an answer is reasonable or not–either too high or too low of an answer.

Materials, Supplies, and Equipment:

Activities:

1. Read **Lesson 26 Explanation** together. Discuss the process of rounding and estimating the divisor in order to see if the quotient is reasonable.
2. Have the student complete **Lesson 26-1** independently.

Because your love is better than life, my lips will glorify you.
Psalm 63:3

© MCMXCIX, Alpha Omega Publications, Inc.

Lesson 27

Concepts:

Estimation of division, division, four-digit division, three-digit division, addition & subtraction equations, perimeter, word problems.

Objectives:

1. The student will be able to estimate division problems.
2. The student will be able to determine if a given quotient is to high or too low for the problem.
3. The student will be able to complete division problems that contain a four-digit divisor.
4. The student will be able to complete division problems that contain a three-digit divisor.
5. The student will be able to solve addition and subtraction equations.
6. The student will be able to calculate the perimeter of a given shape or object.
7. The student will be able to add decimal numbers.
8. The student will be able to convert written numbers to standard numbers.
9. The student will be able to use a calculator to solve given problems.

Teaching Tips:

Review rounding before beginning the lesson.

Materials, Supplies, and Equipment:

1. Calculator, if necessary for multiplication and checking.

Activities:

1. Read **Lesson 27 Explanation** together. Discuss and work the sample problem.

2. Use these additional problems if extra practice is needed:

   4,854 ÷ 7 =   4,189 ÷ 7 =   7,241 ÷ 9 =

   (Answers: 700, 600, 800). You may have the students round each problem to the thousand, hundred, or ten to create several additional practice problems.

3. The students should be able to complete **Lesson 27-1** independently, with little difficulty.

> *The fear of the Lord is the beginning of knowledge, but fools despise wisdom and discipline.*
> **Proverbs 1:7**

Lesson 28

Concepts:

    Problem solving with division, estimation of division, division, four-digit division, addition & subtraction equations, perimeter, using information in a chart.

Objectives:

1. The student will be able to complete problems solving tasks that require the use of division.
2. The student will be able to estimate division problems.
3. The student will be able to determine if a given quotient is too high or too low for the problem.
4. The student will be able to complete division problems that contain a four-digit divisor.
5. The student will be able to solve addition and subtraction equations.
6. The student will be able to solve word problems using information contained in a chart.

Teaching Tips:

    It may be helpful to review the "key words" contained in word problems that indicate what functions should be performed. For example: "difference" usually signals subtraction, "sum" means addition, and so on.

Materials, Supplies, and Equipment:

Activities:

1. A review of the basic steps of problem solving might be useful before beginning the lesson. They are 1. Understand;   2. Plan;   3. Work;   4. Answer/Check.

2. Read **Lesson 28 Explanation** orally.

3. Discuss how to interpret remainders, should they occur when dividing (may refer to *Horizon Book 5*, Lesson 50). Review both whole number remainders and remainders expressed as fractions. In some word problems the answer found by division will need to be rounded off to correctly answer the question. For example if the question asks for the number of one dozen egg cartons needed to completely pack 30 eggs the correct answer would not be 2 1/2 but 3 cartons.

4. Have the students complete **Lesson 28-1** independently.

Remember your Creator in the days of your youth, before the days of trouble come...
Ecclesiastes 12:1a

Lesson 29

Concepts:

Giving change, problem solving with division, division, order of operations, addition of fractions with common denominators, area.

Objectives:

1. The student will be able to give correct change after performing a given purchase or transaction.
2. The student will be able to complete problems solving tasks that require the use of division.
3. The student will be able to estimate division problems.
4. The student will be able to solve a problem by choosing the correct order of operations.
5. The student will be able to add and reduce fractions with common denominators.
6. The student will be able to calculate the area of a given shape or object.
7. The student will be able to determine if a given quotient is too high or too low for the problem.

Teaching Tips:

Most students know their coins and bills but cannot count back change. Try to give examples of times when a student would need to count back change without the assistance of a calculator or computer (concessions stands at a ball field, cashiering during a power outage, making sure a cashier gave you the correct change) The students need to know how to verbally count back the change. For example: If the total was $5.25 and the customer gave the cashier a $10.00 bill, the student would say: "Your total was $5.25. Three quarters makes $6.00, and five makes $10.00."

Materials, Supplies, and Equipment:

1. Play money and coins

Activities:

1. Review the value of coins- pennies, nickels, dimes, quarters and half-dollars. Then ask the following types of questions:
   1 quarter, 5 dimes. How much altogether?
   17 pennies, 3 dimes, 5 pennies. How much altogether?
   3 quarters, 1 dime, 3 pennies. How much altogether?
2. Read **Lesson 29 Explanation** together. Go through each step and actually do the problem with the aid of play money and coins. Have several students experience counting the change. Create several new problems and allow several more students to count change. Be sure to practice how to verbally count back the change (read
   the example listed above in the Teaching Tip).
3. Pair the students, and have them work the first problem on **Lesson 29-1** together with the play money and coins, demonstrating and verbally counting back the change correctly. Check their answers. The first problem is an example and has been answered for them. They can demonstrate this one and the next problem as the two practice problems.
4. The students should be able to complete the rest of **Lesson 29-1** independently.

... for He bore the sin of many and made intercession for the transgressors.
Isaiah 53:12b

Lesson 30

Concepts:

Ordering from a menu, order of operations, sequencing patterns, rays, lines, line segments, planes, time conversions, addition of fractions with common denominators, area.

Objectives:

1. The student will be able to solve problems that require the student to order from a menu.
2. The student will be able to solve a problem by choosing the correct order of operations.
3. The student will be able to follow a sequence to complete a number pattern.
4. The student will be able to identify a ray, line, line segment, and plane.
5. The student will be able to complete time conversions that involve the use of seconds, minutes, hours, and days.
6. The student will be able to add fractions with common denominators.
7. The student will be able to calculate the area of a given shape or object.

Teaching Tips:

Be as creative as possible with this lesson. It is an important life skill.

Materials, Supplies, and Equipment:

1. Takeout menus from a local restaurant.
2. Calculators, if needed.

Activities:

1. Read **Lesson 30 Explanation** together.
2. Pass out menus from a local restaurant. Chose one or more students to place orders and then have the class calculate the cost of each order. Have several students come to the board and explain how they solved each problem.
3. Divide the student into groups of three or four. Instruct them to select one person to play waiter, or waitress, and write down the individual orders. Then each student is to calculate the cost of their order and how much the waitress/waiter should be tipped (20%). This is a great opportunity to discuss how to calculate an appropriate tip when eating out. Have the groups swap orders and check each other's calculations for accuracy.
4. The student should be able to complete **Lesson 30-1** independently.

You will seek me and find me when you seek me with all your heart.
Jeremiah 29:13

Lesson 31

Concepts:
Geometric terms, addition, word problems, multiplication and division equations, even and odd numbers, and multiplication.

Objectives:
1. The student will be able to define in pictures, symbols, and words the following geometric terms: point, line, line segment, ray, plane, intersecting lines, parallel lines, and perpendicular lines.
2. The student will be able to find the sum of two or more six-digit numbers.
3. The student will be able to use information in a chart to solve word problems.
4. The student will be able to solve a multiplication and division equation.
5. The student will be able to connect even and odd number in order to complete a picture.
6. The student will be able to solve multiplication problems expressed in several different ways.

Teaching Tips:
Using concrete examples will help the students understand the geometric terms.

Materials, Supplies, and Equipment:

Activities:
1. Read **Lesson 31 Explanation** orally with the students. Ask them to give examples of each of these geometric terms. Some examples might be:
   <u>point</u> - period on a poster; <u>line</u> - horizon; <u>line segment</u> - top of the door; <u>ray </u> - airplane trail; <u>plane</u> - ceiling or floor; <u>intersecting lines </u> - two roads that cross; <u>parallel lines </u> - railroad tracks; <u>perpendicular lines</u> - the cross.
2. Practice writing each term in pictures and symbols.
3. Students should be able to complete **Lesson 31 Practice** independently.

Education makes people easy to lead but difficult to drive;
easy to govern but impossible to enslave.
Henry Brougham

© MCMXCIX, Alpha Omega Publications, Inc.

Lesson 32

Concepts:

Define angles, classify angles, measure angles, geometric terms, order of operations, decimal place value, word problems, and finding sums and differences.

Objectives:

1. The student will be able to define, classify, and measure a given angle.
2. The student will be able to tell if an angle is acute, obtuse, or a right angle.
3. Given the measurement for an angle, the student will be able to construct the angle.
4. The student will be able to draw and label the following: intersecting lines, parallel lines, perpendicular lines, points, lines, line segments, rays, and planes.
5. The student will apply the order of operations to a problem with three or more steps.
6. The student will be able to demonstrate their knowledge of decimal place value.
7. The student will be able to use information in a chart to solve word problems.
8. The student will be able to place addition or subtraction signs in number sentences to obtain a positive answer.

Teaching Tips:

Working with concrete examples helps the students better conceptualize the information. It is also valuable for retention.

Materials, Supplies, and Equipment:

1. Geoboards and rubber bands (one per student)
2. Protractor (one per student)
3. *Worksheet 14*

Activities:

1. Ask the students to define an angle. **An angle is two rays that share a common endpoint.**
2. Tell the students to use two rubber bands and make one angle on their geoboard.
3. Ask the students to share their angles with the class. Ask them if they can think of a way to classify the different angles. Have them classify them into groups with similar characteristics.
4. Read **Lesson 32 Explanation** and see how mathematicians classify angles.
5. Demonstrate measuring angles with a protractor. Allow the students to measure several angles with your supervision before they begin the lesson.
6. Students should be able to complete **Lesson 32 Practice** independently.

It is not the I.Q. but the I will that is important in education.
Unknown

Lesson 33

Concepts:
Identify polygons, angles, geometric terms, addition, column addition, change.

Objectives:
1. The student will be able to find the number of vertices, number of sides, and number of diagonals in the following polygons: triangle, quadrilateral, pentagon, hexagon, octagon, and decagon.
2. The student will be able to determine if a given figure is a polygon.
3. The student will be able to draw an example of the following angles: acute, obtuse, right, and straight. The student will be able to tell the measurement of each of the angles drawn.
4. Given a geometric drawing, the student will be able to define the following: intersecting lines, parallel lines, perpendicular lines, and points.
5. The student will be able to find the difference of two seven-digit numbers.
6. The student will be able to use column addition to find sums.
7. Given the amount of purchase and payment given, the student will be able to determine the change due using the least number of coins and bills possible.

Teaching Tips:
Working with concrete examples helps the students better conceptualize the information. It is also valuable for retention.

Materials, Supplies, and Equipment:
1. Geoboards (one per student)
2. 15 rubber bands per student
3. *Worksheet 15*

Activities:
1. Read **Lesson 33 Explanation** with the students.
2. Read the definition for polygons. Have each student create their own polygon on the geoboard. Make sure that each polygon meets the requirements of the definition.
3. Read the definition for regular polygons. Have each student create their own regular polygon on the geoboard. Make sure each polygon meets the requirements of a REGULAR polygon.
4. Have each student find the number of vertices, sides, and diagonals of their regular polygons.
5. Students should be able to complete **Lesson 33 Practice** independently.

He who has the Son has life; He who does not have the Son of God does not have life.
1 John 5:12

Lesson 34

Concepts:

Quadrilaterals, angles, geometric terms, polygons, addition, column addition.

Objectives:

1. Given a quadrilateral, the student will be able to find define the angles and sides.
2. The student will be able to demonstrate their knowledge of angles by answering questions about a given figure.
3. The student will be able to match the following terms and illustrations: intersecting lines, parallel lines, perpendicular lines, points, lines, line segments, rays and planes.
4. Given the following polygons, the student will be able to tell the number of sides: triangle, octagon, decagon, quadrilateral, hexagon, and pentagon.
5. The student will be able to find the sum of two three-digit numbers.
6. The student will be able to use column addition to find sums.

Teaching Tips:

Materials, Supplies, and Equipment:

1. Geoboards (one per student)
2. 15 rubber bands per student
3. *Worksheet 16*

Activities:

1. Read **Lesson 34 Explanation** with the students. Have each student make the following quadrilaterals on their geoboards: square, rectangle, parallelogram, trapezoid, and rhombus.
2. Students should be able to complete **Lesson 34 Practice** independently.

Now if we died with Christ, we believe that we will also live with him.
Romans 6:8

Lesson 35

Concepts:

Congruence, polygons, geometric shapes, protractor, word problems, equations.

Objectives:

1. The student will be able to find congruent lines, angles, and polygons.
2. The student will be able to find all of the possible definitions for a rectangle, square, trapezoid, and rhombus.
3. The student will be able to match pictures to the most common definition of the following: rhombus, square, rectangle, octagon, hexagon, trapezoid, pentagon, and decagon.
4. The student will be able to measure an angle with a protractor and determine its measurement. The student will be able to tell if the angle is acute, obtuse, or right.
5. The student will be able to answer word problems involving money.
6. The student will be able to choose from four answers and determine the answer to an equation.

Teaching Tips:

Materials, Supplies, and Equipment:

1. Geoboards
2. Rubber bands
3. *Worksheet 17*

Activities:

1. Read **Lesson 35 Explanation** with the students.
2. Have the students make congruent segments on their geoboards. Make sure that the students realize that the lines must be the same length, but the lines can run horizontally or vertically.
3. Have the students make congruent angles on their geoboards. Make sure that the students realize that the angles must have the same measure, but they can face any direction.
4. Have the students make congruent triangles on their geoboards. Make sure that the students realize that the lines and angles must be the congruent, but the triangles can face any direction.
5. Have the students make polygons on their geoboards that are symmetrical.
6. Have the students make polygons on their geoboards that are not symmetrical.
7. Students should be able to complete **Lesson 35 Practice** independently.

For my Father's will is that everyone who looks to the Son and believes in Him shall
have eternal life, and I will raise him up on the last day.
John 6:40

Lesson 36

Concepts:

Triangles, polygons, geometric shapes, sides, vertices, and diagonals, equations, word problems.

Objectives:
1. Given three different types of triangles, the student will be able to name the triangle using letters and tell if it is isosceles, equilateral, or scalene.
2. The student will be able to find and color the following shapes: equilateral triangle, trapezoid, rectangle, pentagon, octagon, isosceles triangle, hexagon, and square.
3. The student will be able to recognize the following figures: square, rhombus, scalene triangle, rectangle, equilateral triangle, octagon, hexagon, and isosceles triangle.
4. The student will be able to tell the number of sides, vertices, and diagonals of the following: triangle, square, rectangle, and octagon.
5. The student will be able to solve subtraction equations.
6. The student will be able to answer word problems using data from a table.

Teaching Tips:

Materials, Supplies, and Equipment:
1. Geoboards
2. Rubber bands
3. *Worksheet 18*

Activities:
1. Have the students each make a triangle on their geoboard.
2. Have the students share their triangles. Ask them to group the triangles according similar attributes.
3. Read **Lesson 36 Explanation** with the students. Did the students classify their triangles using a similar method to the one described in the lesson?
4. Students should be able to complete **Lesson 36 Practice** independently.

For he will command his angels concerning you to guard you in all your ways.
Psalm 91:11

Lesson 37

Concepts:
Angles, geometric terms, polygons, equations, rounding, time definitions.

Objectives:
1. Given the measurement of two angles of a triangle, the student will be able to find the third angle.
2. The student will be able to define the following terms: congruent segments, congruent angles, congruent polygons, regular polygons, and lines of symmetry.
3. The student will be able to draw the following shapes: right triangle, trapezoid, rectangle, pentagon, octagon, hexagon, rhombus, and square.
4. The student will be able to solve multiplication and division equations.
5. The student will be able to round numbers to the nearest hundred and shade those numbers to solve a puzzle.
6. The student will be able to place the following words in the appropriate sentences using context clues: bicentennial, millennium, century, decade, BC, and AD.

Teaching Tips:
Students will readily understand that the sum of the measures of all the angles of a triangle equal 180 when they see the concrete example given below.

Materials, Supplies, and Equipment:

Activities:
1. The three angles of any triangle can be combined to make a straight angle which is 180.
2. Demonstrate this by tearing off the three corners of a triangle and putting them back together on a straight line. The students can see in a concrete way that the three angles in a triangle equal 180.

3. Read **Lesson 37 Explanation** with the students.
4. Students should be able to complete **Lesson 37 Practice** independently.

Come near to God and he will come near to you.
James 4:8a

Lesson 38

Concepts:
> Circles, diameter and radius, triangles, types of triangles, quadrilaterals, regular polygons, equations, century.

Objectives:
1. The student will be able to find and name the following parts on a diagram: diameter, chord, radii, and central angles.
2. Given the diameter, the student will be able to find the radius.
3. Given the measurement of two angles of a triangle, the student will be able to find the third angle.
4. The student will be able to define the following triangles: isosceles, equilateral, and scalene.
5. The student will be able to place the following figures in order from largest to smallest: dodecagon, decagon, nonagon, octagon, heptagon, hexagon, pentagon, quadrilateral, and triangle.
6. The student will be able to find regular polygons and circle them.
7. The student will be able to solve multiplication and division equations.
8. Given the year, students will be able to tell what century the year is in.

Teaching Tips:
> Allow plenty of time to learn to use a compass.

Materials, Supplies, and Equipment:
1. 1 compass (per child) & 1 ruler (per child)
2. *Worksheet 19*

Activities:
1. Read **Lesson 38 Explanation** orally with the students.
2. Distribute a compass to each student and a ruler.
3. Demonstrate how to draw a circle using a compass. Point out the center point and how each point on the circle is equidistant from that point. Label the circle using the diagram below.

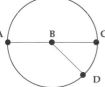

4. Allow each child to draw a circle and label it. Tell them that you want circles of different sizes.
5. Ask each child to measure the diameter and radius of their circle in centimeters.
6. Place a chart on the board and have the students come to the board and place the measurements from their circle.

Radius	Diameter

7. What did the students notice about the radius and diameter?
   (The radius x 2 equals the diameter)

8. Ask the students the following questions about their circle:
   Name the circle. **(Circle B)**
   Name the diameter. **(AC)**
   Name the three radii. **(AB, BC, BD)**
   Name the acute central angle. **(∠CBD)**
   Name the obtuse central angle **(∠ABD)**

9. The students should be able to complete **Lesson 38 Practice** independently.

Do not imitate what is evil but what is good.
3 John 11a

Lesson 39

Concepts:

Face, vertices and edges, space figures, circles, triangles, equations, mystery numbers.

Objectives:

1. Given a picture of a triangular prism, triangular pyramid, and cube, the student will be able to find the number of faces, vertices, and edges.
2. Given pictures, the student will be able to define the following: rectangular prism, hexagonal prism, cylinder, and octagonal prism.
3. The student will be able to find and name the following parts on a diagram: diameter, chord, radii, and obtuse and acute central angles.
4. The student will be able to find equilateral triangles, isosceles triangles, scalene triangles and hexagons in a picture.
5. Given the measurement of two angles of a triangle, the student will be able to find the third angle.
6. The student will be able to solve division equations.
7. Given number clues, the student will be able to identify the mystery number.

Teaching Tips:

Leave the solid space figures in the room with the names on them.
Review the names on a daily basis.

Materials, Supplies, and Equipment:

1. Solid space figures
2. *Worksheet 20*

Activities:

1. Read **Lesson 39 Explanation** orally with the students.
   Review the types of space figures.
2. Show the students the various solid space figures identifying them by name.
   Ask the students to find the number of faces, edges, and vertices on each figure.
3. The students should be able to complete **Lesson 39 Practice** independently.

Trust in Him at all times, O people; pour out your hearts to Him, for God is our refuge.
Psalm 62:8

Lesson 40

Concepts:
> Circle graphs, space figures, circles, equations, triangle, number patterns.

Objectives:
1. The student will be able to label a circle graph given data.
2. The student will be able to match the definition and drawing of the following figures: cube, sphere, rectangular pyramid, rectangular prism, triangular pyramid, triangular prism, cone, and cylinder.
3. The student will demonstrate their knowledge of circles by drawing a radius, diameter, central angle, and chord as described in directions.
4. The student will be able to solve division equations.
5. Given the measurement of two angles of a triangle, the student will be able to find the third angle.
6. Given a number pattern, the student will be able to tell the next three numbers.

Teaching Tips:
> Pie, or circle graphs, can be shown with numbers in each slice of the pie or as percentages in the slices of the pie. Make sure the students understand that all the sections of the graph must add up to 100 if using actual numbers, or 100% if using percentages. If the pie graph shows fractions, then all fractions should add up to 1 whole. (Remind them that there should never be a percentage total more than 100%, or a fraction total larger than 1 whole.) Also remember that pie graphs can show breakdowns on numbers which are larger than 100 or smaller than 100. If this is the case, they must be able to convert this information to percentages or fractions, if needed.

Materials, Supplies, and Equipment:
1. Ruler
2. Colored pencils or crayons.
3. Paper plate

Activities:
1. Read **Lesson 40 Explanation** together.
2. Have the students keep track of their activities for 24 hours.
3. Have the students group similar activities together.
4. Have them determine what percentage of their day was spent eating, sleeping, going to school etc.
5. Have the student graph the information on the pie plate. Compare results.
6. The students should be able to complete **Lesson 40 Practice** independently.

He is good; His love endures forever.
2 Chronicles 5:13b

Lesson 41

Concepts:

Multiples, circle graphs, solids, circles, diameter, radius, chord, central angle, addition and subtraction properties, order of operations, giving change.

Objectives:

1. The student will be able to identify multiples of a given number.
2. The student will be able to read and interpret circle graphs.
3. The student will be able to identify and label given solid forms.
4. The student will be able to draw, identify, and label the diameter, radius, chord, and central angle of a circle.
5. The student will be able to correctly identify and apply the addition and subtraction properties.
6. The student will be able to correctly interpret the order of operations for a given equation.
7. The student will be able to give correct change from a given purchase or transaction.

Teaching Tips:

By this time the students should know the multiplication tables through the 11's with no difficulty. They may need additional practice with the 12's tables.

Materials, Supplies, and Equipment:

Activities:

1. Read **Lesson 41 Explanation** together. Discuss the times tables which show patterns, like the 2's, 5's, 10's, and 11's. Remind the students that these multiples are easy to remember because of these patterns.
2. Assign **Lesson 41-1** for independent work. The students should have no difficulty with this assignment.

The way of the upright is to depart from evil:
He that keepeth his way preserveth his soul.
Proverbs 16:17

Lesson 42

Concepts:

Prime and composite numbers, circle graphs, multiples, six-digit addition, four-digit by four-digit multiplication, reading a table.

Objectives:

1. The student will be able to identify prime and composite numbers.
2. The student will be able to read and interpret circle graphs
3. The student will be able to identify multiples of a given number.
4. The student will be able to add six-digit numbers.
5. The student will be able to complete multiplication problems which contain four-digit factors.
6. The student will be able to read and interpret information presented in table form.

Teaching Tips:

Remember that the number 1 is not a prime nor a composite number. It is a unique number because it is a factor of every number.

Materials, Supplies, and Equipment:

1. Hole punchers (one per student, or one per pair of students if necessary)
2. Multiplication chart as shown below:

1	2	3	4	5	6
7	8	9	10	11	12
13	14	15	16	17	18
19	20	21	22	23	24
25	26	27	28	29	30
31	32	33	34	35	36
37	38	39	40	41	42
43	44	45	46	47	48
49	50	51	52	53	54
55	56	57	58	59	60
61	62	63	64	65	66
67	68	69	70	71	72
73	74	75	76	77	78
79	80	81	82	83	84
85	86	87	88	89	90
91	92	93	94	95	96
97	98	99	100	101	102

3. *Worksheet 21*

Activities:

1. Read the definitions of a prime and a composite number shown in the beginning of **Lesson 42 Explanation**. Ask the students to **"Name numbers that they know are prime numbers."** Once you have received a few correct answers, write these numbers on the board and ask the students **"What do these numbers all have in common?"** The responses should include that all of the prime numbers, with the exception of the number 2, are odd numbers. Explain that a prime number will never be an even number because all even numbers are multiples of 2.
   By definition, a prime number could never be an even number.

© MCMXCIX, Alpha Omega Publications, Inc.

2. Give each student a copy of the table shown in the above materials section. Have the students punch out all the numbers which are multiples of 2 (not including 2 itself). Then have the students punch out all the multiples of 3 (except for 3 itself), the multiples of 5 (except for 5), and so on. When finished only prime numbers should be "unpunched." Have a copy of the original chart made into a transparency. After the students have punched all of the composite numbers out, look at the original sheet on the overhead. Compare the punched sheets to the original copy. Ask the students why they think that no prime numbers were in the last column of the sheet? (This is because all the numbers were even numbers.) Ask them if there is another column that fell into this same pattern (column 4). Discuss any additional patterns they see.

3. Read the rest of **Lesson 42 Explanation**. Discuss the sample problems. Have the students draw examples to illustrate the following numbers: 11, 8, & 13.

4. Assign **Lesson 42-1** as independent work.

There is a way that seems right to man; but the end leads to death.
Proverbs 16:25

Lesson 43

Concepts:

Factor trees, multiples, solids, addition and subtraction properties, order of operations, giving change.

Objectives:

1. The student will be able to create and complete factor trees for given numbers.
2. The student will be able to identify multiples of a given number.
3. The student will be able to read and interpret circle graphs.
4. The student will be able to identify and label given solid forms.
5. The student will be able to correctly identify and apply the addition and subtraction properties.
6. The student will be able to correctly interpret the order of operations for a given equation.
7. The student will be able to give correct change from a given purchase or transaction.

Teaching Tips:

Materials, Supplies, and Equipment:

1. Prime number "punch sheet" from **Lesson 42**, if necessary.
2. *Worksheet 22*

Activities:

1. Review prime and composite numbers. Read **Lesson 43 Explanation** together. Explain that every number can be broken down into prime factors.
   Look at the sample problems shown. Also complete factor trees for the following numbers as additional practice: 15, 25, & 100. Be sure to point out that no matter where you start factoring the tree, in the end, all the prime factors should be the same. Look at the examples below as an illustration:

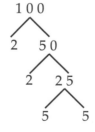

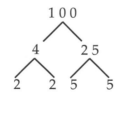

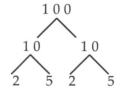

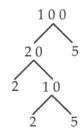

2. Assign **Lesson 43-1** for independent work.

The Lord longs to be gracious to you; He rises to show you compassion. For the Lord is a God of justice. Blessed are all who wait for Him!
Isaiah 30:18

Lesson 44

Concepts:

Exponents, prime and composite numbers, factor trees, multiples, six-digit addition, four-digit by four-digit multiplication, reading a table.

Objectives:

1. The student will be able to write, calculate, and interpret exponential information.
2. The student will be able to identify prime and composite numbers.
3. The student will be able to create and complete factor trees for given numbers.
4. The student will be able to identify multiples of a given number.
5. The student will be able to add six-digit numbers.
6. The student will be able to complete multiplication problems which contain four digit factors.
7. The student will be able to read and interpret information presented in table form.

Teaching Tips:

Materials, Supplies, and Equipment:

1. *Worksheet 23*

Activities:

1. Choose two or three students in the class that have long given names, and go by nicknames. For example: a student with a given name of Christopher but goes by Chris. Have them come to the board and write their whole name and under it, their nickname. Explain that "Chris" and Christopher are the same person, it is simply easier, and shorter, to call him Chris. Demonstrate that using exponents is much like calling a number by his/her nickname.

   Instead of writing 2 x 2 x 2 x 2, we can write 2^4.
2. Read **Lesson 44 Explanation** together as a class. Make sure the students understand that any number can be raised to a power.
3. The student should complete **Lesson 44-1** independently.

I have loved you with an everlasting love; I have drawn you with loving-kindness.
Jeremiah 31:3b

Lesson 45

Concepts:

Square roots, exponents, prime and composite numbers, factor trees, six-digit subtraction, five-digit by five-digit multiplication, logic problems.

Objectives:

1. The student will be able to write, calculate, and interpret square roots.
2. The student will be able to write, calculate, and interpret exponential information.
3. The student will be able to identify prime and composite numbers.
4. The student will be able to create and complete factor trees for given numbers.
5. The student will be able to subtract six-digit numbers.
6. The student will be able to complete multiplication problems which contain five-digit factors.
7. The student will be able to correctly complete a given logic problem.

Teaching Tips:

Materials, Supplies, and Equipment:

1. Snap blocks
2. Calculator
3. *Worksheet 24*

Activities:

1. Read **Lesson 45 Explanation** together as a class. Use the snap blocks to demonstrate the sample problems shown in the lesson explanation. Have the students "play" with the snap cubes and find other squares & square roots.

2. Use the calculators at tools to find the square roots of given numbers. Explain the student can make educated guesses when looking for a square root. They can then use the calculator as a resource. For example: When looking for the square root of 121 think about the times tables. If the students know that 10 is the square root of 100, then the square root of 121 should be close to 10. In fact the square root of 121 is 11. Practice find the square root of the following numbers as a class: 289, 324, 10,000 (Answers: 17^2, 18^2, 100^2).
3. Assign **Lesson 45-1** as independent work.

Restrain your voice from weeping and your eyes from tears, for your
work will be rewarded declares the Lord.
Jeremiah 31:16b

© MCMXCIX, Alpha Omega Publications, Inc.

Lesson 46

Concepts:

Greatest Common Factor (GCF), square roots, exponents, prime and composite, six-digit subtraction, five-digit by five-digit multiplication.

Objectives:

1. The student will be able to find the greatest common factor of a give set of numbers.
2. The student will be able to write, calculate, and interpret square roots.
3. The student will be able to write, calculate, and interpret exponential information.
4. The student will be able to identify prime and composite numbers.
5. The student will be able to subtract six-digit numbers.
6. The student will be able to complete multiplication problems which contain five digit factors.

Teaching Tips:

The students should remember greatest common factor from the previous studies of fractions.

Materials, Supplies, and Equipment:

Activities:

1. Read **Lesson 46 Explanation** orally with the students. Most of the students should have no difficulty with this concept due to prior studies. Work with those that do individually.
2. Assign **Lesson 46-1** for independent work.

Administer true justice; show mercy and compassion to one another...
In your hearts do not think evil of each other.
Zechariah 7:9b-10

Lesson 47

Concepts:

Least Common Multiple (LCM), GCF, square roots, exponents, division with a three-digit divisor, three-digit estimation, two-digit column addition.

Objectives:

1. The student will be able to find the least common multiple of two given numbers.
2. The student will be able to find the greatest common factor of a give set of numbers.
3. The student will be able to write, calculate, and interpret square roots.
4. The student will be able to write, calculate, and interpret exponential information.
5. The student will be able to complete division problems which contain a three-digit divisor.
6. The student will be able to estimate three-digit addition problems.
7. The student will be able to complete column addition of two-digit numbers.

Teaching Tips:

The students should also remember least common multiple from previous fractional work.

Materials, Supplies, and Equipment:

Activities:

1. Read **Lesson 47 Explanation** orally. The students probably have not seen the prime factorization method for finding LCM. Concentrate on this portion of the lesson explanation since most of the students will remember LCM from their fractional studies.
2. Assign **Lesson 47-1** for independent work.

Heaven and earth will pass away, but my words will never pass away.
Mark 13:31

Lesson 48

Concepts:

Scientific Notation, LCM, GCF, square roots, division with three-digit divisors, three-digit estimation, two-digit column addition.

Objectives:

1. The student will be able to interpret and calculate information in scientific notation.
2. The student will be able to find the least common multiple of two given numbers.
3. The student will be able to find the greatest common factor of a give set of numbers.
4. The student will be able to write, calculate, and interpret square roots.
5. The student will be able to complete division problems which contain a three-digit divisor.
6. The student will be able to estimate three-digit addition problems.
7. The student will be able to complete column addition of two-digit numbers.

Teaching Tips:

A review of exponents might be helpful before beginning this lesson.

Materials, Supplies, and Equipment:

1. Calculators
2. *Worksheet 25*

Activities:

1. Write the following chart on the board and ask the students to carefully examine it:

26	2.6×10^1
352	3.52×10^2
1956	1.956×10^3
13,000	1.3×10^4
150,000	1.5×10^5
1,650,000	1.65×10^6

Ask them **"Do you notice a pattern in this chart?"** They should notice that all of the numbers have been changed into an equation and that the zeros have been dropped off by moving the decimal point over and multiplying by powers of ten. Explain that these numbers have been converted into Scientific Notation. In scientific notation a numbers is expressed a number between 1 and 10, which is multiplied by ten raised to a certain power. For example 26 is written as 2.6 (a number between 1 and 10) and multiplied by 10^1. Look at the number 1,650,000. It is rewritten as 1.65 (again a number between 1 and 10) and multiplied by 10^6. Explain that the main reason for using scientific notation is to provide a more efficient way for people in technical fields to express and work with very large numbers.

2. Read **Lesson 48 Explanation** together as a class. Have the students use their calculators as directed in the explanation to create a number which is too large for the display. Continue with the explanation to discuss the fact that large fractional numbers may also be converted into scientific notation.

3. Write the following numbers on the board and have the students convert them into scientific notation:

$$567{,}000; \quad 0.0000357; \quad 9{,}750{,}000{,}000$$

(Answers: 5.67×10^5; 3.57×10^{-5}; 9.75×10^9).

4. The students should complete **Lesson 48-1** as independent work.

Love the Lord your God with all you heart and with all your soul and with all your strength and with all your mind, and Love your neighbor as yourself.
Luke 10:27

Lesson 49

Concepts:

Base 2, scientific Notation, LCM, GCF, division with four-digit divisors, four-digit estimation, renaming fractions.

Objectives:

1. The student will be able to calculate and interpret numbers in Base 2 form.
2. The student will be able to interpret and calculate information in scientific notation.
3. The student will be able to find the least common multiple of two given numbers.
4. The student will be able to find the greatest common factor of a give set of numbers.
5. The student will be able to complete division problems which contain a four-digit divisor.
6. The student will be able to estimate four-digit addition problems.
7. The student will be able to rename given fractions into lowest terms.

Teaching Tips:

Getting the student to think abstractly is difficult at times. Using manipulatives can be very helpful. Some student will need the concrete example a manipulative will provide, others will be confused by it and a simple place value chart will be sufficient for them.

Materials, Supplies, and Equipment:

1. Snap cubes or place value cubes
2. *Worksheet 26*

Activities:

1. Ask the students what system of exchange our place value system is based on. (How may items do you need to have before an exchange can take place in our number system?) The students should respond that our number systems based on 10. Explain that we can create any new number system based on any number: 5, 7, 9, 12, or any other number. Explain that this lesson is going to discuss a counting system based on an exchange rate of 2.
2. Read **Lesson 49 Explanation** orally. Use the snap blocks or place value blocks to illustrate the diagrams show in the explanation.
3. Have the student draw a Base 2 place value chart onto a piece of paper for them to use as a conversion chart. Practice converting the numbers shown on the last place value chart in the explanation. Have the students create and convert additional numbers.
4. Work numbers 1 and 2 together in **Lesson 49-1**. Check to see which students are grasping the concept and which are not. For those who understand base 2, allow them to complete **Lesson 49-1**. Help those students who may need additional help in completing **Lesson 49-1**.

He is the Rock, His works are perfect, and all His ways are just.
A faithful God who does no wrong, upright and just is He.
Deuteronomy 32:4

Lesson 50

Concepts:

Pictographs, Base 2m, scientific Notation, LCM, division with a four-digit divisor, four-digit estimation, renaming fractions.

Objectives:

1. The student will be able to read and interpret information presented in pictographs.
2. The student will be able to calculate and interpret numbers in Base 2 form.
3. The student will be able to interpret and calculate information in scientific notation.
4. The student will be able to find the least common multiple of two given numbers.
5. The student will be able to complete division problems which contain a four-digit divisor.
6. The student will be able to estimate four-digit addition problems.
7. The student will be able to rename given fractions into lowest terms.

Teaching Tips:

Pictographs can be great fun. Try to think of different pictures to use for the graphic on the pictograph. Most students will enjoy drawing these pictures.

Materials, Supplies, and Equipment:

1. Colored pencils or crayons
2. Rulers

Activities:

1. Read **Lesson 50 Explanation** together. Answer the example problems together. Create a class pictograph which shows the number of students in your class that have pets. Have the students use 1 stick person as the unit of measurement. 1 whole stick person should equal 2 students. If you would like to show the number of pets owned by the students in your class, or type of pets owned by the students in your class, this would also work. If you choose to do this, have the students use 1 cat picture (dog, fish, etc...) to represent 2 animals. Have the student use the rulers and colored pencils/crayons to create a neatly colored and straight graph. Stress that pictographs, and all graphs, need to be neat so that there is no difficulty interpreting the information contained in the graph.
2. The students should be able to complete **Lesson 50-1** independently.

They remembered that God was their Rock, that God Most High was their Redeemer.
Psalm 78:35

Lesson 51

Concepts:

Place value with decimals, pictographs, Base 2, Scientific Notation, quadrilaterals, three-digit estimation, giving change.

Objectives:

1. The student will be able to identify place value through the thousandths' place.
2. The student will be able to read and interpret information presented in a pictograph.
3. The student will be able to change numbers from base 2 to base 10.
4. The student will be able to read, write, and calculate scientific notation.
5. The student will be able to identify specific quadrilaterals.
6. The student will be able to estimate subtraction problems that contain three digits.
7. The student will be able to give the correct amount of change due from a given purchase or transaction.

Teaching Tips:

Materials, Supplies, and Equipment:

Activities:

1. Read **Lesson 51** orally. Discuss the fact that the place value chart is infinite. The answer to the question "What is the next column of the place value chart after the hundred thousandths column?" is the millionths column.
2. Assign **Lesson 51-1** for independent work.

For by grace are you saved through faith; and not of yourselves: it is the gift of God:
Not of works, lest any man should boast.
Ephesians 2:8

Lesson 52

Concepts:
Comparing decimals, pictographs, Base 2, quadrilaterals, three-digit estimation, giving change.

Objectives:
1. The student will be able to compare and order decimals through the hundred thousandths' place.
2. The student will be able to identify place value through the thousandths' place.
3. The student will be able to read and interpret information presented in a pictograph.
4. The student will be able to use Base 2.
5. The student will be able to identify specific quadrilaterals.
6. The student will be able to estimate subtraction problems that contain three digits.
7. The student will be able to give the correct amount of change due from a given purchase or transaction.

Teaching Tips:
Place Value charts (for reference only)

Materials, Supplies, and Equipment:

Activities:
1. Read **Lesson 52 Explanation** together. Look at the race times shown in the example box. Have each student write these times on a place value chart. Follow the steps outlined in the explanation of **Lesson 51** and compare the numbers to see which runner has the best time (the lowest number). Once the lowest, or smallest, number is identified, have the students find the next lowest number. Follow this process until all of the numbers are ordered from the fastest time to the slowest time. Look at the answer section to **Lesson 52 Explanation**. Check to make sure that each student's response is correct.
2. The students might need a review of the "greater than," "less than" signs before working **Lesson 52-1**. Once this review has been done, the students should be able to complete **Lesson 52-1** independently with little difficulty.

Know that man is not justified by observing the law, but by faith in Jesus Christ. So we, too, have put our faith in Christ Jesus that we may be justified by faith in Christ and not by observing the law, because by observing the law no one will be justified.
Galatians 2:16

Lesson 53

Concepts:
Adding decimals, comparing decimals, pictographs, measuring angles, four-digit estimation, logic problem.

Objectives:
1. The student will be able to add decimals.
2. The student will be able to compare and order decimals through the hundred thousandths' place.
3. The student will be able to identify place value through the thousandths' place.
4. The student will be able to read and interpret information presented in a pictograph.
5. The student will be able to find the measure of a missing angle.
6. The student will be able to estimate subtraction problems that contain four digits.
7. The student will be able to complete a given logic problem.

Teaching Tips:

Materials, Supplies, and Equipment:
1. Place value chart
2. Graph paper or lined paper
3. *Worksheet 27*

Activities:
1. Read **Lesson 53 Explanation** together. Have the student write the sample problem down on their place value chart or on the graph paper (lined paper). This will help them to keep the columns straight. Have them bring the decimal down first and then add or subtract the numbers. Remind them that adding decimals is exactly like adding or subtracting other numbers; the only difference is the presence of the decimal.
2. The student should be able to complete **Lesson 53-1** independently.

Thus saith the Lord, Let not the wise man glory in his wisdom, neither let the mighty man glory in this might, let not the rich man glory in his riches: But let him that glorieth glory in this, that he understandeth and knoweth me, that I am the Lord which exercises loving kindness, judgment, and righteousness in the earth:
for in these things I delight, saith the Lord.
Jeremiah 9:23-24

Lesson 54

Concepts:
Subtracting decimals, comparing decimals, measuring angles, four-digit estimation, logic problems.

Objectives:
1. The student will be able to subtract decimals.
2. The student will be able to add decimals.
3. The student will be able to compare and order decimals through the hundred thousandths' place.
4. The student will be able to identify place value through the thousandths' place.
5. The student will be able to find the measure of a missing angle.
6. The student will be able to estimate subtraction problems that contain four digits.
7. The student will be able to complete a given logic problem.

Teaching Tips:
Review **Lesson 53** before beginning **Lesson 54**.

Materials, Supplies, and Equipment:
1. Place value chart (if necessary)
2. Graph paper or lined paper (if necessary)

Activities:
1. Read **Lesson 54 Explanation** together. Complete the example problem together by having the student write the problem on his/her graph paper or place value chart if necessary. The students should have little difficulty with this lesson. If problems arise monitor the student to see what the problem is. More than likely it is a lack of the subtraction process (borrowing) than anything to do with the decimal information.
2. The student should be able to complete **Lesson 54-1** independently.

Set your minds on things above, not on earthly things.
Colossians 3:2

Lesson 55

Concepts:
Rounding decimals, subtracting decimals, adding decimals, comparing decimals, renaming fractions, simple multiplication, mathematical terms.

Objectives:
1. The student will be able to round decimals to the indicated place.
2. The student will be able to subtract decimals.
3. The student will be able to add decimals.
4. The student will be able to compare and order decimals to the hundred thousandths' place.
5. The student will be able to rename fractions.
6. The student will be able to complete simple multiplication problems.
7. The student will be able to identify given mathematical terms.

Teaching Tips:
Review the rounding of whole numbers before beginning **Lesson 55.**

Materials, Supplies, and Equipment:
1. Dry erase board or laminated poster board
2. Dry erase markers or Overhead markers
3. Play money (coins)

Activities:
1. Read **Lesson 55 Explanation** together. Have each student draw a number line on his/her paper. Draw a number line on the dry erase board (or laminated poster board) for the students to see. Remind them that when rounding numbers you are deciding whether a given number is closer to the number just above it or below it in numerical sequence. Have the students look at the example number line and the steps involved in the rounding process. Remind them that the magic number in rounding is 5. Anything below 5 rounds down. Anything 5 or above 5 rounds up. This should not be a difficult concept because the students have done this with whole numbers.
2. If the students need additional examples, use the play money. Place 0.62 cents on a student's desk. Ask the student if that amount of money is closer to having 0 cents or having a dollar. (The student should respond that it is closer to a dollar.) Make a money number line on the dry erase board just like the number line drawn in **Activity 1**. Place 0.62 on the number line to show that it is more than half way and larger than 0.50. For this reason it is rounded up to a dollar. You may wish to show several other money examples, if it helps the students.
3. The student should be able to complete **Lesson 55-1** independently

Serve wholeheartedly, as if you were serving the Lord, not men, because you know that the Lord will reward everyone for whatever good he does, whether he is slave or free.
Ephesians 6:7-8

© MCMXCIX, Alpha Omega Publications, Inc.

Lesson 56

Concepts:

Column addition with decimals, rounding decimals, adding decimals, subtracting decimals, renaming fractions, simple division, mathematical terms.

Objectives:

1. The student will be able to complete column addition that contains whole and decimal numbers.
2. The student will be able to round decimals.
3. The student will be able to subtract decimals.
4. The student will be able to add decimals.
5. The student will be able to rename fractions.
6. The student will be able to complete simple division problems.
7. The student will be able to identify given mathematical terms.

Teaching Tips:

The students should have no difficulty with column addition at this age.

Materials, Supplies, and Equipment:

Activities:

1. Direct the students' attention to **Lesson 56 Explanation**. Read orally.
2. This exercise should require no additional explanation if the students comprehend regrouping.
3. Allow the student to complete **Lesson 56-1** independently.

Therefore, if anyone is in Christ, he is a new creation; the old has gone, the new has come!
2 Corinthians 5:17

Lesson 57

Concepts:

Roman Numerals, column addition with decimals, rounding decimals, subtracting decimals, word problems with decimals, congruent figures/shapes, Logic problem-magic square.

Objectives:

1. The student will be able to read and write Roman numerals.
2. The student will be able to complete column addition that contains whole and decimal numbers.
3. The student will be able to round decimals.
4. The student will be able to subtract decimals.
5. The student will be able to complete word problems that contain decimal information.
6. The student will be able to complete a magic square.
7. The student will be able to identify congruent and non-congruent figures.

Teaching Tips:

Stressing the use of Roman Numerals in every day life will help when teaching this concept. Have the students name the different areas and items which contain or use Roman Numerals. This concept is much easier to understand once the student understands that Roman Numerals follow place value just like regular standard (Arabic) numbers. Each Roman Numeral has it's place on the place value chart.

Materials, Supplies, and Equipment:

1. Place value chart
2. Index cards
3. *Worksheet 28*

Activities:

1. Read **Lesson 57 Explanation** together. Have each student write down the basic Roman numerals (given in the text) on an index card. These may be used as a reference while instructing.
2. Demonstrate how each Roman Numeral has a place value and coordinates with the place value chart.

    Example:

	Hundreds	Tens	Ones
XXI = 19		X	IX
		1	9
CXXV = 125	C	XX	V
	1	2	5

    Make up several numbers, have the students make up numbers also, and place them on the place value chart (like above) as both Roman numerals and Standard Arabic numbers.

3. Use the index cards to create a Roman numeral concentration game for the students. If you would like, the students can pair up and create their own concentration games in pairs. Chose several Roman numerals and write them on cards (each numeral needs to be written on two cards to make a pair or "match".)
    Allow the students to play several games of Concentration.

4. The students should be able to complete **Lesson 57-1** independently.

Do you not know that your body is a temple of the Holy Spirit, who is in you,
whom you have received from God? You are not your own; you were
bought at a price. Therefore honor God with your body.
1 Corinthians 6:19-20

Lesson 58

Concepts:

Mean, Mode & Median, column addition with decimals, rounding decimals, word problem with decimals, logic problem - magic number, congruent figures/shapes.

Objectives:

1. The student will be able to calculate the mean, mode, and median of a given set of numbers.
2. The student will be able to complete column addition that contains whole and decimal numbers.
3. The student will be able to round decimals.
4. The student will be able to complete word problems that contain decimal information.
5. The student will be able to complete a magic square.
6. The student will be able to identify congruent and non-congruent figures.

Teaching Tips:

Mean, Range, Median, and Mode are all statistical terms that the students have worked with very little. Calculating a mean is no different than calculating an average. You may want to review averaging (and averaging with remainders) before beginning the lesson. The students, however, should have no difficulty with this lesson.

Materials, Supplies, and Equipment:

1. Calculator

Activities:

1. Read **Lesson 58 Explanation** together.
   Go over the definitions of Range and Mean orally.

   Have the students calculate the range and mean of the following data:

   > 90, 100, 105, 107, 88, 92
   >
   > Range - 19,   Mean - 97.

2. For additional practice you may give the students a set of his/her grades from one subject area and have him/her calculate the range and mean of them.
3. The student should be able to complete **Lesson 58-1** independently.

Do not be misled: Bad company corrupts good character.
1 Corinthians 15:33

Lesson 59

Concepts:

Mean, Mode & Median, column addition with decimals, rounding decimals, missing number addition, symmetry, equivalent fractions, logic problem.

Objectives:

1. The student will be able to calculate the mean, mode, and median of a given set of numbers.
2. The student will be able to complete column addition that contains whole and decimal numbers.
3. The student will be able to round decimals.
4. The student will be able to find the missing numbers in a given addition problem.
5. The student will be able to draw the appropriate lines of symmetry for a given figure.
6. The student will be able to identify equivalent fractions.
7. The student will be able to find a mystery numbers when given clues about that number.

Teaching Tips:

A review of **Lesson 58** might be helpful before beginning **Lesson 59**.

Materials, Supplies, and Equipment:

1. Calculator

Activities:

1. Have the students look at the first 10 books of the Old Testament. How many chapters are in each book? This data is shown below:

   Genesis - 50
   Exodus - 40
   Leviticus - 27
   Numbers - 36
   Deuteronomy - 34
   Joshua - 24
   Judges - 21
   Ruth - 4
   1 Samuel - 31
   2 Samuel - 24

   Ask the students which books have the same number of chapters? Joshua & 2 Samuel both have 24. Explain that if we are looking at this information as a set of data, 24 would be the mode.

2. Read **Lesson 59 Explanation** together. Explain that the mode is simply the number that appears <u>most frequently</u> in a set of data. Stress that there will not always be a mode. The second example problem illustrates this. There may also be several numbers that appear more than once, but you are looking for the number that appears <u>the most</u>.

© MCMXCIX, Alpha Omega Publications, Inc.

3. Have the students calculate the mode of the following data:
   89, 23, 75, 45, 98, 65, 89, 75, 17, 75
   Mode - 75

4. Have the students calculate the range and mean of the same set of data:
   Range - 81,   Mean - 65

5. Explain that the median of a set of numbers is the number which appears in the middle of the set. Use the information below as a reference:
   89, 80, 79, 70, 65, 60, 40

   Have the students put their left index finger on the first number and their right index finger on the last number. Simultaneously move both fingers one number at a time until the student reaches the middle number. The middle number is 70. 70 is the median of this set of data.

6. Use the books of the bible data listed above as a reference.
   Find the median number
   of this data. With this data there will be 2 numbers left in the middle.
   As explained in **Lesson 59 Explanation**, have the students calculate the mean of these two numbers to get the median number.

7. If additional practice is still needed, give the students a set of their grades, or use the same grades given to them in **Lesson 59**, and have them calculate the median number.

8. Have the students complete **Lesson 59-1** independently.

I can do everything through Christ who gives me strength.
Philippians 4:13

Lesson 60

Concepts:

Problem Solving - too much/too little information, mean, mode & median, column addition with decimals, rounding decimals, missing number subtraction, similar figures, equivalent fractions.

Objectives:

1. The student will be able to determine if a word problem has too much or too little information
2. The student will be able to calculate the mean, mode, and median of a given set of numbers.
3. The student will be able to complete column addition that contains whole and decimal numbers.
4. The student will be able to round decimals.
5. The student will be able to find the missing numbers in given subtraction problems.
6. The student will be able to identify similar figures.
7. The student will be able to identify equivalent fractions.

Teaching Tips:

The students should have little, or no, difficulty with this concept. This should be treated as additional practice with word problem strategies for the average student.

Materials, Supplies, and Equipment:

Activities:

1. Read **Lesson 60 Explanation**.
2. Discuss the sample problems in the explanation.
3. Assign **Lesson 60-1** for independent work.

Just as you received Christ Jesus as Lord, continue to live in him,
rooted and built up in him, strengthened in the faith as you were taught,
and overflowing with thankfulness.
Colossians 2:6

© MCMXCIX, Alpha Omega Publications, Inc.

Lesson 61

Concepts:

Simplify fractions, decimal column addition, symmetry, division equations, mean, median, and mode, rounding

Objectives:

1. The student will be able to simplify fractions.
2. The student will be able to place decimals in a column and add.
3. Given one half of a symmetrical design, the student will be able to complete the other side.
4. The student will be able to solve 2 step equations that include division.
5. Given a group of numbers, the student will be able to find the mean, median, and mode.
6. The student will be able to round numbers to the nearest ones, tenths, hundredths, thousandths, and ten thousandths.

Teaching Tips:

Students often write an equivalent fraction that is not in the lowest terms. If they find the GCF first, this error can be avoided.

Materials, Supplies, and Equipment:

Activities:

1. Read **Lesson 61 Explanation** with the students.
2. Write these numbers on the board and have the students lists all of the factors of the two numbers and circle the factors they both share.

     6   ①②③⑥
     18   ①②③⑥ 9

3. Find the greatest common factor that the two share.

     6 is the greatest common factor of 6 and 18

4. To write the simplest form fraction of 6/18, divide the numerator and the denominator by the GCF.

$$\frac{6}{18} \quad \frac{\div 6}{\div 6} \quad \frac{1}{3}$$

5. **Just for Fun**

     Give each student two index cards. Have them write a fraction that is not in simplest terms on one card and
     the same fraction written in simplest on the other card. Have the students turn over all of the cards face-side down on the floor. Now the students are ready to play Fraction Concentration.

     <u>Here's How</u> Player one turns over two cards. If the cards are a match, the player gets one point and removes the cards from the board. The player may continue taking turns until no matches are found. If the cards are not a match, the player turns the cards back over and it is the next player's turn.
     Play continues until all of the matches are found.
     The winner is the player with the most points.

6. The students should be able to complete **Lesson 61 Practice** independently.

We live by faith, not by sight.
2 Corinthians 5:7

Lesson 62

Concepts:

LCD, simplify fractions, mean, mode, and median, four-digit multiplication, order whole numbers, three step number sentence, round decimals

Objectives:

1. The student will be able to add and subtract fractions with common denominators.
2. The student will be able to simplify fractions.
3. Given a group of numbers, the student will be able to find the mean, median, and mode.
4. The student will be able to find the product when given two, four-digit numbers.
5. The student will be able to order whole numbers from least to greatest.
6. Given a three step number sentence, the student will be able to find the solution.
7. The student will be able to round decimals to the nearest whole number.

Teaching Tips:

Students often try and add the numerators and denominators when they are first introduced to adding fractions. Use a concrete example to start the explanation to avoid this problem.

Materials, Supplies, and Equipment:

1. 3 paper plates
2. *Worksheet 29*

Getting Ready:

Draw lines on 3 paper plates dividing them into four equal parts.

Activities:

1. Display one of the paper plates. Have a student shade 1/4 of the paper plate and cut it out.
2. Display another paper plate. Have a student shade 2/4 of the paper plate and cut it out.
3. Ask the students: **What is the sum of 2/4 and 1/4 ? 3/4**
   Place the shaded 1/4 and 2/4 over the whole paper plate. It will be easy to see that 3/4 of the paper plate is covered.
4. Display the whole paper plate and the shaded 2/4. Place the 2/4 over the 4/4 and ask the students: **What is the** difference of 4/4 and 2/4? 2/4 or 1/2
5. Read **Lesson 62 Explanation** with the students.
6. The students should be able to complete **Lesson 62 Practice** independently.

Everyone and everything around you is a teacher.
Ken Keyes Jr.

© MCMXCIX, Alpha Omega Publications, Inc.

Lesson 63

Concepts:
LCD, add and subtract fractions with common denominators, simplify fractions, mean, mode, and median, four-digit multiplication, mystery number

Objectives:
1. Given two fractions, the student will be able to find the least common denominator.
2. The student will be able to find the sum or difference given two fractions with common denominators.
3. The student will be able to simplify fractions.
4. Given a group of numbers, the student will be able to find the mean, median, and mode.
5. The student will be able to find the product when given two, four-digit numbers.
6. Given number clues, the student will be able to find the mystery number.

Teaching Tips:
Start by teaching the students to write out all of the multiples of both numbers when finding the LCM. After they grasp the concept show them the abbreviated form taught in **Lesson 63 Explanation**.

Materials, Supplies, and Equipment:
1. *Worksheet 30*

Activities:
1. Find the LCM of 3 and 4.
   What are the first 10 multiples of 3? 3, 6, 9, (12) 15, 18, 21, (24) 27, 30
   What are the first 10 multiples of 4? 4, 8, (12) 16, 20, (24) 28, 32, 36, 40
   The common multiples of 3 and 4 are 12 and 24.
   The least common multiple is 12.
2. Find the LCM of 5 and 7.
   What are the first 10 multiples of 5? 5, 10, 15, 20, 25, 30, (35) 40, 45, 50
   What are the first 10 multiples of 7? 7, 14, 21, 28, (35) 42, 49, 56, 63
   The common multiples of 5 and 7 are 35.
   The least common multiple is 35.
3. Read **Lesson 63 Explanation** with the students. This is a quicker way to find the LCM and should be introduced after the students have a thorough understanding of the whole process.
4. The students should be able to complete **Lesson 63 Practice** independently.

Failure is impossible.
Susan B. Anthony

Lesson 64

Concepts:

Compare fractions, LCD, add and subtract fractions with common denominators, five digit multiplication, rounding, define: decade, millennium, and century

Objectives:

1. The student will be able to compare two fractions with different denominators.
2. Given two fractions, the student will be able to find the least common denominator.
3. The student will be able to find the sum or difference given two fractions with common denominators.
4. The student will be able to find the product of two, five-digit numbers.
5. The student will be able to estimate by rounding numbers to the nearest thousand.
6. The student will be to demonstrate knowledge of the terms millennium, decade, and century by placing them in the proper sentences.

Teaching Tips:

Materials, Supplies, and Equipment:

Activities:

1. Read **Lesson 64 Explanation** with the students. Work several of the examples below to reinforce the concepts of the lesson.

   Compare 2/3 and 1/2 by renaming them as like fractions.

   $$\frac{2 \times 2}{3 \times 2} = \frac{4}{6}$$

   $$\frac{1 \times 3}{2 \times 3} = \frac{3}{6}$$

   2/3 > 1/2

   Compare 2/7 and 21/28 by renaming them as like fractions.

   $$\frac{2 \times 4}{7 \times 4} = \frac{8}{28}$$

   $$\frac{3 \times 7}{4 \times 7} = \frac{21}{28}$$

   2/7 < 21/28

2. After the students are familiar with this process, teach them the short-cut method given below.
   Cross multiply 2 x 4 to get the first product.
   Cross multiply 3 x 3 to get the second product.
   Compare:

   $$\frac{2}{3} \diagdown\diagup \frac{3}{4} \qquad \begin{array}{l} 3 \times 3 = 9 \\ 4 \times 2 = 8 \end{array}$$

   Since the second product is larger, the second fraction is larger. 2/3 < 3/4

3. The students should be able to complete **Lesson 64 Practice** independently.

There is no excellence without difficulty.
Ovid

Lesson 65

Concepts:
Subtract fractions with different denominators, compare fractions, LCD, add or subtract fractions with common denominators, place value

Objectives:
1. The student will be able to add and subtract fractions with different denominators.
2. The student will be able to determine if a fraction is 1/2 or greater.
3. The student will be able to compare two fractions.
4. Given two fractions, the student will be able to find the least common denominator.
5. The student will be able to find the sum or difference given two fractions with common denominators.
6. The student will be able to demonstrate knowledge of place value by finding indicated place values.

Teaching Tips:
If the students find the LCM before adding or subtracting, the computations will be much easier because the numbers are smaller.

Materials, Supplies, and Equipment:
1. *Worksheet 31*

Activities:
1. Read **Lesson 65 Explanation** with the students.
   Work several of the examples below to reinforce the concepts of the lesson.

1/4 + 1/3
The denominators are NOT the same.

Multiples of 4: 4, 8, 12	1/4 = 3/12	3/12
Multiples of 3: 3, 6, 12	1/3 = 4/12	+ 4/12
		7/12

1/3 − 1/6
The denominators are NOT the same.

Multiples of 3: 3, 6, 9	1/3 = 2/6	2/6
Multiples of 6: 6		− 1/6
		1/6

2. The students should be able to complete **Lesson 65 Practice** independently.

If we don't ever take chances, we won't reach the rainbows.
Collin McCarty

© MCMXCIX, Alpha Omega Publications, Inc.

Lesson 66

Concepts:
Mixed number to improper fraction, add and subtract fractions with different denominators, compare fraction, LCD, place value

Objectives:
1. The student will be able to change a mixed number to an improper fraction.
2. The student will be able to add and subtract fractions with different denominators.
3. The student will be able to compare two fractions.
4. Given two fractions, the student will be able to find the least common denominator.
5. The student will be able to demonstrate knowledge of place value by finding indicated place values.

Teaching Tips:

Materials, Supplies, and Equipment:
1. *Worksheet 32*

Activities:
1. Read **Lesson 66 Explanation** with the students.
   Work several of the examples below to reinforce the concepts of the lesson.
   Change each mixed fraction to an improper fraction.

   $3\ 1/5 =$ _____ $8\ 2/7 =$ _____ $9\ 7/8 =$ _____ $9\ 5/9 =$ _____
   $\qquad\quad 16/5 \qquad\qquad\qquad 58/7 \qquad\qquad\qquad\quad 79/8 \qquad\qquad\qquad\quad 86/9$

   $8\ 4/7 =$ _____ $5\ 7/8 =$ _____ $17\ 1/3 =$ _____ $12\ 3/4 =$ _____
   $\qquad\quad 60/7 \qquad\qquad\qquad 47/8 \qquad\qquad\qquad\quad 52/3 \qquad\qquad\qquad\quad 51/4$

2. The students should be able to complete **Lesson 66 Practice** independently.

We grow into things that fill our thoughts.
Emmett Fox

© MCMXCIX, Alpha Omega Publications, Inc.

Lesson 67

Concepts:
Improper to mixed fraction, mixed to improper, add and subtract fractions with different denominators, compare fractions, divide large numbers

Objectives:

1. The student will be able to change an improper fraction to a mixed number.
2. The student will be able to change a mixed number to an improper fraction.
3. The student will be able to add and subtract fractions with different denominators.
4. The student will be able to compare two fractions.
5. The student will be able to divide a five-digit number by a three-digit number.

Teaching Tips:

Materials, Supplies, and Equipment:

1. *Worksheet 33*

Activities:

1. Read **Lesson 67 Explanation** with the students.
   Work several of the examples below to reinforce the concepts of the lesson.
   Change each improper fraction to a mixed fraction.

17/5 = _____	16/4 = _____	29/7 = _____	19/2 = _____
3 2/5	4	4 1/7	9 1/2
27/4 = _____	39/9 = _____	12/2 = _____	78/9 = _____
6 3/4	4 3/9 = 4 1/3	6	7 6/9 = 7 2/3

2. The students should be able to complete **Lesson 67 Practice** independently.

   My son, keep my words and store up my commands within you.
   Keep my commands and you will live: guard my teachings as the apple of your eye.
   Proverbs 7:1-2

Lesson 68

Concepts:
Add and subtract mixed numbers with different denominators, mixed to improper, add and subtract fractions with different denominators, compare fractions, decimal place value

Objectives:
1. The student will be able to add and subtract mixed numbers with different denominators.
2. The student will be able to change mixed fractions to improper fractions.
3. The student will be able to add and subtract fractions with different denominators.
4. The student will be able to compare two fractions.
5. Given a number in written form, the student will be able to write it in the number form.

Teaching Tips:
Adding mixed numbers can seem overwhelming to the student at first because there are so many steps. Write the steps on the board to help them see every part of the process clearly.

Materials, Supplies, and Equipment:
1. *Worksheet 34*

Activities:
1. Read **Lesson 68 Explanation** with the students. Write these steps on the board.
   1. Add or subtract the fraction part first. Find the common denominator.
   2. Rename the numerators.
   3. Add or subtract the fraction.
   4. Add or subtract the whole numbers.
   5. Simplify the fraction if necessary.
2. Work the examples below to reinforce the concepts of the lesson.

$$\begin{array}{r} 4\ 1/2 \\ +\ 3\ 1/2 \\ \hline 7\ \ 2/2 = 1\ whole = 8\ whole\ pies \end{array}$$

$$\begin{array}{rcl} 5\ 1/2 & = & 5\ 3/6 \\ -\ 1\ 1/6 & = & 1\ 1/6 \\ \hline & & 4\ 2/6\ =\ 4\ 1/3 \end{array}$$

3. The students should be able to complete **Lesson 68 Practice** independently.

I will destroy the wisdom of the wise; the intelligence of the intelligent I will frustrate.
Isaiah 29:14

© MCMXCIX, Alpha Omega Publications, Inc.

Lesson 69

Concepts:
Add mixed numbers and rename sums, add and subtract mixed numbers with different denominators, mixed fractions, divide large numbers, place value, word problems

Objectives:
1. The student will be able to add mixed numbers and rename sums.
2. The student will be able to add and subtract mixed numbers with different denominators.
3. The student will be able to match mixed fractions to their corresponding improper fraction.
4. The student will be able to divide a five-digit number by a three-digit number.
5. Given a number in written form, the student will be able to write it in the number form.
6. The student will be able to solve word problems that involve fractions.

Teaching Tips:
Adding mixed numbers can seem overwhelming to the student at first because there are so many steps. Write the steps on the board to help them see every part of the process clearly.

Materials, Supplies, and Equipment:
1. *Worksheet 35*

Activities:
1. Read **Lesson 69 Explanation** with the students. Write these steps on the board.
   1. Add the fraction part first. Find the common denominator.
   2. Rename the numerators.
   3. Add the fraction.
   4. Add the whole numbers.
   5. If the answer is an improper mixed fraction, make it a proper mixed fraction.
   6. Simplify if necessary.
2. Work the examples below to reinforce the concepts of the lesson. Find the sum. Rename any improper answers to mixed numbers.

$$
\begin{array}{r}
9\ 1/3 \\
+\ \ 8\ 2/3 \\
\hline
17\ 3/3 \\
18
\end{array}
\qquad
\begin{array}{r}
3\ 3/4 \\
+\ \ 8\ 4/5 \\
\hline
11\ 31/20 \\
12\ 11/20
\end{array}
\qquad
\begin{array}{r}
9\ 11/12 \\
+\ \ 4\ 3/4 \\
\hline
13\ 20/12 \\
14\ 8/12 = 14\ 2/3
\end{array}
$$

3. The students should be able to complete **Lesson 69 Practice** independently.

Whatever is true, whatever is noble, whatever is right, whatever is pure,
whatever is lovely, whatever is admirable –
if anything is excellent or praiseworthy think about such things.
Philippians 4:8

© MCMXCIX, Alpha Omega Publications, Inc.

Lesson 70

Concepts:

Subtract mixed numbers renaming whole numbers, add mixed numbers and renaming sums, mixed fraction, add larger numbers, decimal place value, decimal column addition

Objectives:

1. The student will be able to subtract mixed numbers renaming the whole numbers.
2. The student will be able to add mixed numbers and rename sums.
3. The student will be able to match mixed fractions to their corresponding improper fraction.
4. The student will be able to add two six-digit numbers.
5. The student will be able to order decimals from least to greatest.
6. Given a vertical list of decimal numbers, the student will be able to line up the decimal points and find the sum.

Teaching Tips:

Subtracting mixed numbers can seem overwhelming to the student at first because there are so many steps. Write the steps on the board to help them see every part of the process clearly.

Materials, Supplies, and Equipment:

Activities:

1. Read **Lesson 70 Explanation** with the students. Write these steps on the board.
   1. Subtract the fraction part first. Find the common denominator.
   2. Rename the numerators.
   3. If the fraction in the subtrahend is too small, borrow from the whole number.
   4. Rename the whole number and the new fraction.
   5. Subtract the fraction.
   6. Subtract the whole numbers.
   7. Simplify if necessary.
2. Work the examples below to reinforce the concepts of the lesson.
   Find the difference. Simplify if necessary.

12 1/3	16 1/2	18 2/7
− 2 5/6	− 8 5/8	− 9 5/6
9 3/6	7 7/8	8 19/42
9 1/2		

3. The students should be able to complete **Lesson 70 Practice** independently.

It is good that I am going away. Unless I go away, the counselor will not come to you; but if I go, I will send Him to you.
John 16:7b

Lesson 71

Concepts:

Multiply decimals, subtract mixed numbers, add mixed numbers, add six-digit numbers, factor trees, word problems

Objectives:

1. The student will be able to multiply a decimal by a whole number.
2. The student will be able to subtract two mixed fractions with different denominators.
3. The student will be able to add two mixed fractions with different denominators.
4. The student will be able to add two six-digit numbers.
5. The student will be able to complete a factor tree.
6. The student will be able to complete word problems that involve multiplication of decimals.

Teaching Tips:

Allow the students many opportunities to work with concrete examples before they solve written problems.

Materials, Supplies, and Equipment:

Activities:

1. Use a 100 tile to begin this lesson.
   a. We know that multiplication is repeated addition, so 0.56 x 3 = 0.56 + 0.56 + 0.56

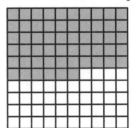 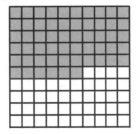

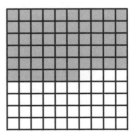

   b. If we add the number of individual tiles in each of these hundred tiles, we find the sum is 2.01.
   c. If we multiply, 0.56 the product is 1.68.

$$\begin{array}{r} 0.56 \\ \underline{\times\ \ 3} \\ 1.68 \end{array}$$

2. Ask the students **"When we multiply, how do we know where to put the decimal point?"**
   a. Show them these examples, and see if they can eventually determine where the decimal point will go. See if they can generalize and come up with a rule.
   (In each example, the number of decimal places in the product is equal to the number of places in the decimal factor.)

   b.
0.9	0.18	0.62	7.1	0.31
x 7	x 3	x 2	x 4	x 6
6.3	0.54	1.24	28.4	1.86

3. Read **Lesson 71 Explanation** with the students.
4. The students should be able to complete **Lesson 71 Practice** independently.

No temptation has overtaken you but such as is common to man; and
God is faithful, who will not allow you to be tempted beyond what you are able;
but with the temptation will provide the way of escape also,
that you may be able to
endure it.
1 Corinthians 10:13

Lesson 72

Concepts:

Multiply decimals, subtract mixed numbers, add mixed numbers, subtract six-digit numbers, factor trees, word problems

Objectives:

1. The student will be able to multiply two decimals.
2. The student will be able to subtract two mixed fractions with different denominators.
3. The student will be able to add two mixed fractions with different denominators.
4. The student will be able to subtract two six-digit numbers.
5. The student will be able to complete a factor tree.
6. The student will be able to complete word problems that involve multiplication of decimals.

Teaching Tips:

Students often start counting the decimal places from the left instead of the right.

Materials, Supplies, and Equipment:

1. *Worksheet 36*

Activities:

1. Tell the students **"Today we are going to multiply a decimal by a decimal. Watch as I work these problems and see if you can figure out how I know where to put the decimal place."**
   (In each example, the number of decimal places in the product is equal to the number of places in both factors.)

2. a.
   ```
        6. 2          3 8. 2          0.1 6
      x  0. 7        x   3. 4        x 0.2 8
        4.3 4        1 2 9.8 8       0.0 4 4 8
     (2 places)     (2 places)      (4 places)
   ```

3. Read **Lesson 72 Explanation** with the students. The students will be able to complete **Lesson 72 Practice** independently.

   But, I say to you love your enemies and pray for those who persecute you.
   Matthew 5:44

Lesson 73

Concepts:
Divide decimals, multiply two decimals, multiply a decimal by a whole number, subtract two mixed fractions, subtract six-digit numbers, prime numbers, angles

Objectives:
1. The student will be able to divide a decimal by a whole number.
2. The student will be able to multiply two decimals.
3. The student will be able to multiply a decimal by a whole number.
4. The student will be able to subtract two mixed fractions with different denominators.
5. The student will be able to subtract two six-digit numbers.
6. The student will be able to shade prime numbers and find their way through a maze.
7. The student will be able to match the following terms and pictures: acute, obtuse, right or straight angles.

Teaching Tips:
Encourage the students to place the decimal point in the quotient BEFORE they begin the division process.

Materials, Supplies, and Equipment:
1. *Worksheet 37*

Activities:
1. Read **Lesson 73 Explanation** with the students. Remind the students that the decimal point in the quotient is to be placed directly above the decimal point in the dividend.
2. Work the following example problems with the students before they begin working independently.

$$5\overline{)60.95} = 12.19 \qquad 7\overline{)308.91} = 44.13 \qquad 9\overline{)613.08} = 68.12$$

3. The students will be able to complete **Lesson 73 Practice** independently.

Don't complain or argue in anything you do.
Philippians 2:14

Lesson 74

Concepts:

Extending quotients, divide decimals, multiply two decimals, multiply a decimal by a whole number, divisibility, geometric shapes

Objectives:

1. The student will be able to extend the quotient, and divide a decimal by a whole number.
2. The student will be able to divide a decimal by a whole number.
3. The student will be able to multiply a decimal by a whole number.
4. The student will be able to multiply two decimals.
5. Given a number, the student will be able to determine if it is divisible by 2, 3, 5, or 10.
6. Given a picture of the following figures, the student will be able to define the figure: parallelogram, trapezoid, pentagon, rhombus, rectangle, and square.

Teaching Tips:

Encourage the students to place the decimal point in the quotient BEFORE they begin the division process.

Materials, Supplies, and Equipment:

Activities:

1. Read **Lesson 74 Explanation** with the students. Remind the students that the decimal point in the quotient is to be placed directly above the decimal point in the dividend.

2. Many students ask how many zeros they should add to the dividend. Explain that there are many reasons for extending the dividend. Sometimes it is necessary to answer the question in a word problem, or they may need to see if an answer is repeating. (More repeating decimals in Lesson 75.) You need to determine the number of zeros to add based on the question you are answering.

3. Work several of the examples below to reinforce the concepts of the lesson.

Divide to the tenths.

$$\begin{array}{r} 0.6 \\ 5\overline{)3} \end{array} \qquad \begin{array}{r} 0.8 \\ 10\overline{)8} \end{array} \qquad \begin{array}{r} 4.5 \\ 4\overline{)1\,8} \end{array}$$

Divide to the hundredths.

$$\begin{array}{r} 0.75 \\ 4\overline{)3} \end{array} \qquad \begin{array}{r} 1.50 \\ 12\overline{)1\,2\,6} \end{array} \qquad \begin{array}{r} 0.32 \\ 25\overline{)8} \end{array}$$

Divide to the thousandths.

$$\begin{array}{r} 0.375 \\ 8\overline{)3} \end{array} \qquad \begin{array}{r} 0.125 \\ 8\overline{)1} \end{array} \qquad \begin{array}{r} 0.875 \\ 8\overline{)7} \end{array}$$

4. The students will be able to complete **Lesson 74 Practice** independently.

Don't tell your secrets to a gossip unless you want them broadcast to the world.
Proverbs 20:19

Lesson 75

Concepts:

Fractions to decimals, extend the quotient, divide decimals, multiply decimals, equivalent fractions, column addition

Objectives:

1. The student will be able to change a fraction to a decimal.
2. The student will be able to extend the quotient, and divide a decimal by a whole number.
3. The student will be able to divide a decimal by a whole number.
4. The student will be able to multiply two decimals.
5. The student will be able to find equivalent fractions.
6. The student will be able to put decimals in a column and add.

Teaching Tips:

The students may stop dividing before they see the pattern of repeating digits. Encourage them to continue dividing until the entire pattern comes up twice.

Materials, Supplies, and Equipment:

1. One calculator per student
2. *Worksheet 38*

Activities:

1. Begin this lesson with a calculator activity. Tell the students that when dividing they will find some decimals that repeat. Tell them to divide the following numbers and to look for a number or a series of numbers that repeat and place a bar over the repeating part of the decimal.

   $1 \div 3 = 0.3333333333333$ (**3 repeats**) We write 0.3.

   $5 \div 11 = 0.45454545$ (**45 repeats**) We write 0.45.

   $1 \div 18 = 0.0555555555$ (**5 repeats**) We write 0.05.
   (Remind the students to add the initial zero before the 5's!)

   $5 \div 6 = 0.\ 8333333333$ (**3 repeats**) We write 0.83.
   (Remind the students to add the initial 8 before the 3's!)

   $9 \div 11 = 8181818181$ (**81 repeats**) We write 0.81.

2. Read **Lesson 75 Explanation** with the students.
3. The students will be able to complete **Lesson 75 Practice** independently.

> *Take no part in the worthless pleasures of evil and darkness.*
> *Instead, rebuke them and bring them out into the light.*
> **Ephesians 5:11**

© MCMXCIX, Alpha Omega Publications, Inc.

Lesson 76

Concepts:
Divide decimals, compare fractions and decimals, repeating decimals, divide a whole number by a decimal, exponents, multiple operations

Objectives:
1. The student will be able to divide a decimal by a whole number and round the quotient.
2. The student will be able to compare fractions and decimals.
3. The student will be able to change a fraction into a decimal and properly mark a repeating decimal.
4. The student will be able to divide a whole number by a decimal and complete a crossword puzzle.
5. The student will be able to complete an exponent table.
6. The student will be able to complete a series of operations in the proper order.

Teaching Tips:
You may want to review rounding before starting the lesson.

Materials, Supplies, and Equipment:
1. *Worksheet 39*

Activities:

1. Read **Lesson 76 Explanation** with the students. Work several of the examples below to reinforce the concepts of the lesson.

2. Divide to the thousandths. Round the quotients to the hundredth and tenth.

$$7)\overline{9.000} = 1.285$$

   1.285 rounded to the hundredth is 1.29.
   1.285 rounded to the tenth is 1.3.

3. Divide to the thousandths. Round the quotients to the hundredth and tenth.

$$11)\overline{9.000} = 0.8181$$

   0. 818 rounded to the hundredth is 0. 82
   0.818 rounded to the tenth is 0. 8.

4. The students will be able to complete **Lesson 76 Practice** independently.

And why do you look at the speck in your brother's eye,
but do not notice the log that is in your own eye?
Matthew 7:3

Lesson 77

Concepts:
> Powers of ten, rounding decimals, repeating decimals, square roots, addition, place value

Objectives:
1. The student will be able to move the decimal point to the right or left when asked to multiply or divide by powers of ten.
2. The student will be able to change a fraction to a decimal and round to the nearest tenth.
3. The student will be able to change a fraction to a decimal and write the decimal as a repeating decimal or round it to the tenths.
4. The student will be able to find the square root of perfect squares.
5. The student will be able to add two three-digit numbers.
6. The student will be able to demonstrate knowledge of place value by completing a table.

Teaching Tips:

Materials, Supplies, and Equipment:
1. One calculator per student
2. *Worksheet 40*

Activities:
1. Begin this lesson with a calculator activity.
   Have the students punch in the number 34.98.
   Complete the following operations on this number.
   a. multiply times 10 (**349.8**)
   b. multiply times 100 (**3498**)
   c. multiply times 1,000 (**34,980**)
   d. divide by 10 (**3. 498**)
   e. divide by 100 (**0. 3498**)
   f. divide by 1000 (**0. 03498**)

2. Read **Lesson 77 Explanation** with the students. Have them circle the decimal point in each column so they can visually see that it moves one place to the left or right depending upon the operation.
3. The students will be able to complete **Lesson 77 Practice** independently.

Therefore, laying aside falsehood, speak truth, each one of you, with his neighbor,
for we are members of one another.
Ephesians 4:25

© MCMXCIX, Alpha Omega Publications, Inc.

Lesson 78

Concepts:

Equivalent division problems, divide decimal, powers of ten, compare fractions and decimals, square roots, subtraction, multiply decimals

Objectives:

1. The student will be able to find equivalent division problems.
2. The student will be able to divide a decimal by a decimal.
3. The student will be able to move the decimal point to the right or left when asked to multiply or divide by powers of ten.
4. The student will be able to compare a fraction and a decimal.
5. The student will be able to find the square root of perfect squares.
6. The student will be able to subtract two three-digit numbers.
7. The student will be able multiply a decimal by a whole number and complete multiplication wheels.

Teaching Tips:

Train the students to move the decimal point in the divisor and dividend BEFORE they start working the problem.

Materials, Supplies, and Equipment:

Activities:

1. Read **Lesson 78 Explanation** with the students. Work several of the examples below to reinforce the concepts of the lesson.

$$2.1\overline{)9.87} \quad = 4.7$$
$$0.51\overline{)5.049} \quad = 9.9$$
$$6.2\overline{)22.94} \quad = 3.7$$
$$4.6\overline{)1.794} \quad = 0.39$$

2. The students will be able to complete **Lesson 78 Practice** independently.

This is My commandment, that you love one another, just as I have loved you.
John 15:12

Lesson 79

Concepts:

Interpret remainders, divide decimals, powers of ten, rounding decimals, multiply

Objectives:

1. Given division word problems, the student will be able to interpret remainders.
2. The student will be able to divide a decimal by a decimal.
3. The student will be able to move the decimal point to the right or left when asked to multiply or divide by powers of ten.
4. The student will be able to divide a whole number by a decimal and round the quotient to the nearest hundredth.
5. The student will be able to multiply a three-digit number by a two-digit number.

Teaching Tips:

After the students understand the basic concepts presented in this lesson, have them write four of their own problems to demonstrate the use of each type of remainder.

Materials, Supplies, and Equipment:

1. *Worksheet 41*

Activities:

1. Read **Lesson 79 Explanation** with the students. Help the students think of other types of problems that require the use of each type of remainder. After they understand the basic concepts presented in this lesson, have them write four of their own problems to demonstrate the use of each type of remainder.
2. The students will be able to complete **Lesson 79 Practice** independently.

But the Helper, the Holy Spirit, whom the Father will send in My name,
He will teach you all things, and bring to your remembrance all that I said to you.
John 14:26

Lesson 80

Concepts:

Coordinate graphing, interpret remainders, equivalent division problems, powers of ten, addition, multiplication

Objectives:

1. Given coordinate points, the student will be able to complete a coordinate graph.
2. Given division word problems, the student will be able to interpret remainders.
3. The student will be able to find equivalent division problems.
4. The student will be able to move the decimal point to the right or left when asked to multiply or divide by powers of ten.
5. The student will be able to add two six-digit numbers.
6. The student will be able to multiply a three-digit numbers by a two-digit number.

Teaching Tips:

Many fun coordinate picture books may be found at your local teacher store. The students will enjoy plotting coordinates to reveal various pictures.

Materials, Supplies, and Equipment:

1. 1 centimeter graph paper
2. *Worksheet 42*

Activities:

1. Read **Lesson 80 Explanation** together. Have the students use the centimeter graph paper to plot the following coordinates: (4,1) (5,5) (2,5). Connect the coordinates in the order they were given. Ask the students to identify the shape. It should reveal a triangle. Most students will have no difficulty with this lesson due to prior experience with coordinate graphs and graphing.
2. The students should be able to complete **Lesson 80 Practice** independently.
3. Have the students create their own coordinate picture on a piece of graph paper and write down the coordinates on an index card. Collect these and use them as a student center in the room during your study of graphs. The students will love doing these during their spare time.
4. Try to find some multi-level coordinate pictures to keep on hand for extra work. These take a lot of time to complete and the students can work on them in their spare time.

Draw near to God and he will draw near to you.
James 3:8a

Lesson 81

Concepts:

Multiplication of fractions, interpreting remainders, dividing by decimals, base 2, making change, time zones

Objectives:

1. The student will be able to multiply fractions.
2. The student will be able to interpret remainders.
3. The student will be able to divide by a decimal number.
4. The student will be able to convert base 2 numbers into base 10 numbers.
5. The student will be able to give the correct change due from a given transaction or purchase.
6. The student will be able to identify and accurately label time zones with in the United States.

Teaching Tips:

If needed, allow the student many opportunities to work with concrete examples before they solve written problems.

Materials, Supplies, and Equipment:

1. *Worksheet 43*

Activities:

1. Students learn to multiply fractions quite easily, but it takes working many concrete example before they really understand the application of the concept. Use the concrete examples that follow or develop your own to insure the students are not simply following rote learning without any understanding of the concept.
2. Display the picture below and ask the students to shade 1/3 times 1/2.

1/2 x 1/3 = 1/6

Explain to the students that you are looking for the area of the diagram where 1/3 of the whole rectangle and 1/2 of the whole rectangle intersect. The diagram below shows this information.

1/2 x 1/3 = 1/6

3. Display the picture below and ask the students to shade 1/3 times 2/4.

1/3 x 2/4 = 2/12 = 1/6

Again, remind the students that you are looking for the area of the diagram where 2/4 of the diagram and 2/3 of the diagram intersect.

4. Display the picture below and ask the students to shade 1/8 times 1/2.

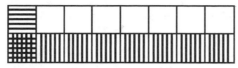

$$1/8 \times 1/2 = 1/16$$

5. Read **Lesson 81 Explanation** with the students.
6. The students will be able to complete **Lesson 81-1** independently.

When the Son of Man comes in His glory, and all the angels with Him, He will sit on His throne in heavenly glory. All the nations will be gathered before Him, and He will separate the people one from another as a shepherd separates the sheep from the goats.
Matthew 24:31-32

Lesson 82

Concepts:

Multiplication of fractions and whole numbers, multiplication of fractions, interpreting remainders, dividing by decimals, base 2, making change, rounding to the nearest tenth

Objectives:

1. The student will be able to multiply a fraction and a whole number.
2. The student will be able to multiply fractions.
3. The student will be able to interpret remainders.
4. The student will be able to divide by a decimal number.
5. The student will be able to convert base 2 numbers into base 10 numbers.
6. The student will be able to give the correct change due from a given transaction or purchase.
7. The student will be able to round given numbers to the nearest tenth.

Teaching Tips:

Most students will be able to operate in the abstract arena at this point. For those that are having difficulty, however, allow the students many opportunities to work with concrete examples before the solve written problems.

Materials, Supplies, and Equipment:

Activities:

1. Read **Lesson 82 Explanation** with the students.
2. Share concrete examples of this type of problem with the students.
   A few examples follow:
   a. Place 10 pencils on the table.
   b. Ask the students to find 4/5 of the 10 pencils.
   c. Help them to first divide the pencils into 5 even groups, then determine how many pencils are in two groups.

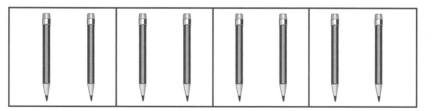

4/5 of 10 equals 8

3. Have the students create a few problems of their own. Allow them to pair up and solve each other's problems.
4. The student will be able to complete **Lesson 82-1** independently.

For the sinful nature desires what is contrary to the Spirit, and the Spirit what is contrary to the sinful nature. They are in conflict with each other, so that you do not do what you want.
Galatians 5:17-18

© MCMXCIX, Alpha Omega Publications, Inc.

Lesson 83

Concepts:

Multiplication of mixed numbers, multiplication of fractions and whole numbers, multiplication of fractions, interpreting remainders, column addition with decimals, calculating discounts, comparing and ordering decimals

Objectives:

1. The student will be able to multiply mixed numbers.
2. The student will be able to multiply a fraction and a whole number.
3. The student will be able to multiply fractions.
4. The student will be able to interpret remainders.
5. The student will be able to complete column addition with decimal numbers.
6. The student will be able to calculate 10% discounts.
7. The student will be able to compare and order decimals.

Teaching Tips:

Students sometimes have difficulty with these type of problems because they combine so many different skills. Help the student to see the problem in stages, or steps. Encourage them to work slowly and carefully to insure accuracy. It might be productive to practice converting improper fractions before beginning the lesson.

Materials, Supplies, and Equipment:

1. Rulers (centimeter) or measuring tapes (at least one for every 2 children)
2. *Worksheet 44*

Activities:

1. Read **Lesson 83 Explanation** with the students.
2. Write the following steps on the board:
   Step 1: Change the mixed numbers into improper fractions.
   Step 2: Multiply the numerators.
   Step 3: Multiply the denominators.
   Step 4: Change the improper fraction to a mixed number.

3. Have the students complete the practice problem shown below using the steps shown above.

   $$1\ 1/3 \times 2\ 1/4$$
   Answer: $36/12 = 3$

4. The students should be able to complete **Lesson 83-1** independently.

For you have delivered me from death and my feet from stumbling that I may walk before God in the light of life.
Psalm 56:13

Lesson 84

Concepts:
 Simplifying fractions, multiplication of mixed numbers, multiplication of fractions and whole numbers, multiplying fractions, calculating discounts, comparing and ordering decimals

Objectives:
 1. The student will be able to simply fractions by using "cross-simplification" or the "factor cross out method."
 2. The student will be able to multiply mixed numbers.
 3. The student will be able to multiply a fraction and a whole number.
 4. The student will be able to multiply fractions.
 5. The student will be able to calculate 10% discounts.
 6. The student will be able to compare and order decimals.

Teaching Tips:

Materials, Supplies, and Equipment:
 1. Calculator, for multiplication of large numbers only.
 2. *Worksheet 45*

Activities:

 1. Write the following problem on the board and instruct the students to solve and write the answer in lowest terms.

 33/75 x 55/63 =
 Answer: 1815/4725 = 121/315

 The students should have difficulty renaming the answer into lowest terms due to the size of the answer.

 2. Demonstrate to the students that by cross-simplification, the answer can be renamed into lowest terms before the multiplication process, therefore making the process of solving the problem much easier. Instruct the student to look at the numerators and denominators which are diagonal from each other. If the numbers share a common factor, then divide by that factor.

 a. both may be divided by 3.

 $$\frac{\overset{11}{\cancel{33}}}{75} \times \frac{55}{\underset{21}{\cancel{63}}} =$$

 b. both may be divided by 5.

 $$\frac{\overset{11}{\cancel{33}}}{\underset{15}{\cancel{75}}} \times \frac{\overset{11}{\cancel{55}}}{\underset{21}{\cancel{63}}} = \frac{121}{315}$$

 c. the answer is in lowest terms.

 3. Read **Lesson 84 Explanation** together.
 4. The students should be able to complete **Lesson 84-1** independently.

 Be exalted, O God, above the heavens; let your glory be over all the earth.
 Psalm 57:5

© MCMXCIX, Alpha Omega Publications, Inc.

Lesson 85

Concepts:

Reciprocals, simplifying fractions, multiplication of mixed numbers, multiplication of fractions and whole numbers, subtraction of decimals, addition problems, addition equations

Objectives:

1. The student will be able to identify the reciprocal of a given fraction.
2. The student will be able to simply fractions by using "cross-simplification" or the "factor cross out method."
3. The student will be able to multiply mixed numbers.
4. The student will be able to multiply a fraction and a whole number.
5. The student will be able to subtract decimals.
6. The student will be able to complete addition problems which contain missing numbers.
7. The student will be able to solve addition equations.

Teaching Tips:

This is an extremely easy lesson to comprehend. The students should have no difficulty at all.

Materials, Supplies, and Equipment:

Activities:

1. Read **Lesson 85 Explanation** with the students.
2. Answer any questions the student may have.
3. Assign **Lesson 85-1** to be completed independently.

... put off your old self, which is being corrupted by its deceitful desires; to be made new in the attitude of your minds, and to put on the new self, created to be like God in true righteousness and holiness.
Ephesians 4:22-24

Lesson 86

Concepts:

Division of a whole number by a fraction, reciprocals, simplifying fractions, multiplication of mixed numbers, subtraction of decimals, subtraction problems, subtraction equations

Objectives:

1. The student will be able to divide a whole number by a fraction.
2. The student will be able to identify the reciprocal of a given fraction.
3. The student will be able to simply fractions by using "cross-simplification" or the "factor cross out method."
4. The student will be able to multiply mixed numbers.
5. The student will be able to subtract decimals.
6. The student will be able to complete subtraction problems which contain missing numbers.
7. The student will be able to solve subtraction equations.

Teaching Tips:

Reviewing reciprocals before beginning the lesson might be helpful. It might be helpful to remind the students that a whole number may be converted to a fraction by placing the number over 1 (6 = 6/1).

Materials, Supplies, and Equipment:

1. Two (2) large chocolate bars.

Activities:

1. Place the chocolate bars on a table where all students can see them. Tell the students that you are making a pie which requires 2/3 of a chocolate bar. Ask the students to figure out how many chocolate pies you can make if each pie requires 2/3 of a bar and you have 2 whole bars. Allow the students to discuss, calculate, the answer. Once the students have arrived at their answers share the answers and have each student explain how they arrived at that answer.
2. Read the first example shown in **Lesson 86 Explanation** with the students. The correct answer to the student problem is shown in **Lesson 86 Explanation** (Three (3) pies can be made from the 2 whole chocolate bars). Did any student know how to correctly solve the problem?
3. Complete **Lesson 86 Explanation** with the students. Discuss the process of writing an equation and solving it using reciprocals and placing a 1 under the whole number in order to convert it into a fraction.
4. Assign **Lesson 86-1** as independent work.

The thief comes only to steal and kill and destroy; I have come that they
may have life, and have it to the fullest.
John 10:10

© MCMXCIX, Alpha Omega Publications, Inc.

Lesson 87

Concepts:

Division of a fraction by a fraction, division of a whole number by a fraction, reciprocals, simplifying fractions, multiplication, intersecting, parallel and perpendicular lines, multiplication equations

Objectives:

1. The student will be able to divide a fraction by a fraction.
2. The student will be able to divide a whole number by a fraction.
3. The student will be able to identify the reciprocal of a given fraction.
4. The student will be able to simply fractions by using "cross-simplification" or the "factor cross out method."
5. The student will be able to solve multiplication problems which contain missing numbers.
6. The student will be able to identify and construct intersecting, parallel, and perpendicular lines.
7. The student will be able to solve multiplication equations.

Teaching Tips:

Remind the students that a whole number can be written as a fraction by placing the number over 1 (4 = 4/1). Also remind the students that even a whole number has a reciprocal.

Materials, Supplies, and Equipment:

1. *Worksheet 46*

Activities:

1. Read **Lesson 87 Explanation** with the students. Explain to the students that when dividing, they are really multiplying by the reciprocal of the fraction to find the products.
2. Complete the following problems together as additional practice:

5/9 ÷ 3/7 =	4/8 ÷ 1/2 =	6/12 ÷ 1/3 =

Answers: 35/27 = 1 8/27   8/8 = 1   18/12 = 1 1/2

3. The student will be able to complete **Lesson 87-1** independently.

In this world you will have trouble, But take heart! I have overcome the world.
John 16:33b

Lesson 88

Concepts:
Division of a fraction by a whole number, division of a fraction by a fraction, division of a whole number by a fraction, reciprocals, division, perimeter, division equations

Objectives:
1. The student will be able to divide a fraction by a whole number.
2. The student will be able to divide a fraction by a fraction.
3. The student will be able to divide a whole number by a fraction.
4. The student will be able to identify the reciprocal of a given fraction.
5. The student will be able to solve division problems which contain missing numbers.
6. The student will be able to find the perimeter of a given object or figure.
7. The student will be able to solve division equations.

Teaching Tips:
Remind the students that a whole number can be written in an equivalent fraction by placing the number over 1. 5 = 5/1.

Materials, Supplies, and Equipment:

Activities:
1. Read **Lesson 88 Explanation** together with the students. Discuss the example problems written in the explanation with the students.
2. The students will be able to complete **Lesson 88-1** independently.

... make my joy complete by being like-minded, having the same love,
being one in spirit and purpose.
Philippians 2:1b-2

Lesson 89

Concepts:

Estimation of fractions, division of a fraction by a whole number, division of a fraction by a fraction, division of a whole number by a fraction, area, four-digit addition

Objectives:

1. The student will be able to estimate with fractions.
2. The student will be able to divide a fraction by a whole number.
3. The student will be able to divide a fraction by a fraction.
4. The student will be able to divide a whole number by a fraction.
5. The student will be able to find the area of a given object or figure.
6. The student will be able to add four-digit numbers.

Teaching Tips:

Materials, Supplies, and Equipment:

1. 2 apples
2. 1 orange/tangerine
3. 5 candy bars

Activities:

1. Have three students come to the front of the room. Give one student a whole apple and 3/4 of another apple. Give the second student 4 candy bars and 1/4 of another candy bar. Give the third student a little more than 1/2 of an orange (or tangerine. You need a fruit which can be sectioned so that it is slightly more than 1/2). Then ask the students **"How much fruit/candy does each student have when rounded to the nearest whole number?"**
   The answers are as follows:
   Student 1: 2 apples;   Student 2: 4 candy bars;   Student 3: 1 orange/tangerine.
   Explain that estimating with fractions is exactly like rounding with decimals (because fractions and decimals are really the same thing in different forms). Draw a number line if necessary to illustrate that 1 3/4 is closer to 2 than 1; 4 1/4 is closer to 4 than 5; and the tangerine wedge is closer to 1 than 0.
2. Read **Lesson 89 Explanation** with the students. Carefully review the clues shown for rounding of fractions. Then work the example problems together which show how rounding fractions can be used in estimating equations.
3. Assign problem 1 in **Lesson 89-1** to be worked independently by all students. Allow them one or two minutes to complete the problem and then check all answers for accuracy. For those students that understand the estimation of fractions, assign the rest of **Lesson 89-1** as independent work. For those students that need additional assistance, work one or two more problems in Lesson 89-1 with them and provide the additional explanation which is needed before assigning the reaming problems as independent work.

Have nothing to do with godless myths and old wives' tales;
rather, train yourselves to be godly.
1 Timothy 4:7

Lesson 90

Concepts:
Division by a mixed number, estimation of fractions, division of a fraction by a whole number, division of a fraction by a fraction, volume, four-digit subtraction, bar graphs

Objectives:
1. The student will be able to divide by a mixed number.
2. The student will be able to estimate with fractions.
3. The student will be able to divide a fraction by a whole number.
4. The student will be able to divide a fraction by a fraction.
5. The student will be able to find the volume of a given item or figure.
6. The student will be able to subtract a four-digit number.
7. The student will be able to create a bar graph data given in numerical form.

Teaching Tips:
Review **Lesson 89** before beginning this lesson. You might also wish to review the conversion of a mixed number to an improper fraction. Some students may find Lesson 90 difficult because so many different processes are involved in solving each equation. Stress that the students work carefully and slowly at first until they get the steps down. Remember to take advantage of cross-simplification, if possible.

Materials, Supplies, and Equipment:
1. Pattern blocks, if necessary
2. *Worksheet 47*

Activities:
1. Read **Lesson 90 Explanation** with the students.
2. Have the students work the example problem on paper as you are reading it in the example problem. If necessary, use pattern blocks to create a concrete example of the problem while working it. Complete the following problems for additional practice:

$$11 \ 1/2 \div 1 \ 1/4 = \qquad 16 \ 1/4 \div 4 \ 1/2 = \qquad 20 \ 10/24 \div 5 \ 1/3 =$$

Answers: $92/10 = 9 \ 1/5$ $\qquad 130/36 = 3 \ 11/18 \qquad 1470/384 = 3 \ 53/64$

3. Assign **Lesson 90-1** as independent work.

What is man that you are mindful of him? The son of man that you care for him? You have made him a little lower than the angels; you crowned him with glory and honor and put everything under his feet.
Hebrews 2:6b-8a

© MCMXCIX, Alpha Omega Publications, Inc.

Lesson 91

Concepts:

Standard measure, dividing by mixed numbers, estimating fractions, division of fractions, numeration, quadrilaterals, factor trees.

Objectives:

1. The student will be able to identify, measure, read, write, and label given items using Standard (Customary) measurements of inches, half inches, quarter inches, eighth inches, and sixteenth inches.
2. The student will be able to divide by a mixed number.
3. The student will be able to estimate with fractions.
4. The student will be able to divide a fraction by a whole number.
5. The student will be able to identify numbers through the trillions' place.
6. The student will be able to identify quadrilaterals.
7. The student will be able to complete factor trees.

Teaching Tips:

Most of the students will not have difficulty with the concept of measuring to the 16th of an inch. Be sure to use rulers that have the 16th markings.

Materials, Supplies, and Equipment:

1. Rulers (one per student)
2. Nails of various sizes
3. *Worksheet 48*

Activities:

1. Read **Lesson 91 Explanation** together as a class.
2. Have the students use their rulers to measure the various sized nails which you have brought to class. Allow them to work together in pairs, if desired. The students need to measure nails of several different sizes, therefore they will need to move around and trade nails.
3. Allow the students to measure different items within the classroom such as books, pens, pencils, etc…
4. Assign **Lesson 91-1** as independent work.

And hope does not disappoint us, because God has poured out His love into our hearts by the Holy Spirit, whom He has given us.
Romans 5:5

Lesson 92

Concepts:

Standard weight, standard measurement, division of mixed numbers, estimation of fractions, numeration, quadrilaterals, prime and composite numbers.

Objectives:

1. The student will be able to identify, measure, read, write, and label given items using Standard (Customary) measurement units of weight.
2. The student will be able to identify, measure, read, write, and label given items using Standard (Customary) measurements of inches, half inches, quarter inches, eighth inches, and sixteenth inches.
3. The student will be able to divide by a mixed number.
4. The student will be able to estimate with fractions.
5. The student will be able to identify numbers through the trillions' place.
6. The student will be able to identify quadrilaterals.
7. The student will be able to identify prime and composite numbers.

Teaching Tips:

The students have worked with weight enough to know the basic units of measurement for Standard measurement. You may want to have a few sample products on display to demonstrate the weight comparisons.

Materials, Supplies, and Equipment:

1. Sample weight products (if desired)
2. Scales
3. Ounce and pound weights
4. *Worksheet 49*

Activities:

1. Read **Lesson 92 Explanation** together.
2. Remind them of the units of measure which are included in the Customary (Standard) System of measurement. Have them look over the sample products, scales, and weights. Compare the examples given to the samples present in the room. Have the students estimate the weight of other objects in the room and compare them to the samples and examples.
3. Practice converting several weight measurements for a refresher exercise.
4. Assign **Lesson 92-1** for independent work.

*You have turned my mourning into joyful dancing. You have taken away
my clothes of mourning and clothed me with joy.*
Psalm 30:11

© MCMXCIX, Alpha Omega Publications, Inc.

Lesson 93

Concepts:

Standard liquid measure, Standard weight, Standard measure, division of mixed numbers, six-digit addition, angle measurement, exponents.

Objectives:

1. The student will be able to identify, measure, read, write, and label given items using Standard (Customary) measurement units of liquid measure.
2. The student will be able to identify, measure, read, write, and label given items using Standard (Customary) measurement units of weight.
3. The student will be able to identify, measure, read, write, and label given items using Standard (Customary) measurements of inches, half inches, quarter inches, eighth inches, and sixteenth inches.
4. The student will be able to divide by a mixed number.
5. The student will be able to add six-digit numbers.
6. The student will be able to find the measurement of a given angle.
7. The student will be able to convert a whole number into an exponential number.

Teaching Tips:

If possible, have the students review the relationships between the gallon, quart, pint, and cup units by making containers available for the students to manipulate. For example, have the students demonstrate that a pint container can fill 2 cups; a quart container can fill 2 pints; or a gallon container can fill 4 quart containers. These are not difficult concepts, but may need to be reviewed with the students.

Materials, Supplies, and Equipment:

1. Measuring containers in the following sizes: cups, pints, quarts, and gallons.
2. Access to water, or some non-staining liquid.
3. *Worksheet 50*

Activities:

1. Discuss the different measuring contains and allow the student to compare them by passing them around the room. (This can be omitted if you have completed the teaching tip listed above).
2. Read **Lesson 93 Explanation** together
3. The student should be able to complete **Lesson 93-1** independently. Allow them to use the liquid container only if a manipulative is absolutely necessary. The students need to be able to think abstractly by this point.

I will answer them before they even call to me. While they are still talking to me about their needs, I will go ahead and answer their prayers!
Isaiah 65:24, NLT

Lesson 94

Concepts:

Standard temperature, standard liquid measure, standard weight, standard measurement, six-digit subtraction, degrees in a triangle, exponents

Objectives:

1. The student will be able to read, and write temperatures given in Fahrenheit degrees.
2. The student will be able to identify, measure, read, write, and label given items using Standard (Customary) measurement units of liquid measure.
3. The student will be able to identify, measure, read, write, and label given items using Standard (Customary) measurement units of weight.
4. The student will be able to identify, measure, read, write, and label given items using Standard (Customary) measurements of inches, half inches, quarter inches, eighth inches, and sixteenth inches.
5. The student will be able to solve six-digit additional problems.
6. The student will be able to find the measurement of a given angle.
7. The student will be able to read, write, and calculate the value of exponents.

Teaching Tips:

Materials, Supplies, and Equipment:

1. A Fahrenheit thermometer

Activities:

1. Read **Lesson 94 Explanation** together. Review the boiling point and freezing point of water at the appropriate Fahrenheit temperatures.
2. Assign **Lesson 94-1** as independent work.

At that time Jesus said "I praise you, Father, Lord of heaven and earth, because you have hidden these things from the wise and learned, and revealed them to little children."
Matthew 11:25

Lesson 95

Concepts:

Metric conversions, standard temperature, standard liquid measure, standard weight, six-digit subtraction, square roots, addition of mixed numbers with different denominators.

Objectives:

1. The student will be able to identify, measure, read, write, and label given items using Metric units of measurement.
2. The student will be able to read, and write temperatures given in Fahrenheit degrees.
3. The student will be able to identify, measure, read, write, and label given items using Standard (Customary) measurement units of liquid measure.
4. The student will be able to identify, measure, read, write, and label given items using Standard (Customary) measurement units of weight.
5. The student will be able to solve six-digit subtraction problems.
6. The student will be able to calculate the square root of a number.
7. The student will be able to add mixed numbers with different denominators.

Teaching Tips:

Remember: The Metric system is a system of weights and measures which is based on a unit of 10. The basic unit of length is called a meter (m), the basic unit of weight is called a gram (g), and the basic unit of capacity is called a liter (l). All three of these units use the same prefixes to indicate a specific amount of length, weight, or liquid. Look at the conversion chart below. The prefixes are in order from the largest to the smallest going from left to right.

			<u>Basic Unit</u>		1.	2.
Kilo	Hecto	Deka	(meter, liter or gram)	deci	centi	milli

If we were measuring length the chart above would show 12 millimeters. Because the metric system is based on units of 10, we can convert from one measurement to another measurement (Ex: millimeter to centimeter) by simply moving a decimal because our decimal system is also based on 10. We show 12 millimeters on the conversion chart by writing the last digit of the measurement in the millimeter box. Remember from your decimal studies that if a decimal is not given in a number, we know that it is a whole number and that the decimal goes at the end. For this reason, the decimal and the number "12" is placed in the millimeter box to indicate that the original measurement was in millimeters. We are converting to centimeters so simply move the decimal one space to the left into the centimeter box. 12 millimeters = 1.2 centimeters. Check this on a ruler to see if it is correct.

Materials, Supplies, and Equipment:

1. Variety of soda cans, 1 & 2 liter soda bottles
2. Meter ruler with centimeter & millimeter markings
3. Large Metric conversion chart drawn on either an overhead transparency or a large dry erase board
4. Dry erase markers or overhead markers (depending on what is being used)
5. *Worksheet 51*

Activities:

1. Read **Lesson 95 Explanation** orally. The students should remember this conversion chart and explanation from prior studies. Discuss the conversion chart by using the large instruction conversion chart on the board or overhead. Discuss the prefix names. Allow the students to draw a conversion chart on their papers to keep if necessary.

2. Complete the example conversion on the large class conversion chart. Allow the students to create additional sample problems and work them together. Use the meter stick to demonstrate any conversions made with length conversions.

3. Assign **Lesson 95-1** for class work. Walk around to assess understanding and assist students that may need help.

He existed before everything else began, and he holds all creation together.
Colossians 1:17, NLT

Lesson 96

Concepts:

Metric weight, Standard temperature, Standard liquid measure, six-digit subtraction, square roots, addition of mixed numbers with different denominators.

Objectives:

1. The student will be able to identify, measure, read, write, and label given items using Metric measurement units of weight.
2. The student will be able to identify, measure, read, write, and label given items using Metric units of measurement.
3. The student will be able to read, and write temperatures given in Fahrenheit degrees and convert them to Celsius degrees.
4. The student will be able to identify, measure, read, write, and label given items using Standard (Customary) measurement units of liquid measure.
5. The student will be able to solve six-digit subtraction problems.
6. The student will be able to calculate the square root of a given number.
7. The student will be able to add mixed numbers with different denominators.

Teaching Tips:

Before beginning the lesson, show the students an object that weighs about a kilogram (a book) and also show them another object that weighs about one milligram (like a paper clip or feather). This gives a concrete reinforcement of the difference between the weights.

Materials, Supplies, and Equipment:

1. Large instructional Metric conversion chart from Lesson 95
2. Individual student Metric conversion charts.
3. Metric liquid containers, Metric measuring rulers and sticks, and Metric weights and scales, if possible.
4. *Worksheet 52*

Activities:

1. Review **Lesson 95** on the conversions of metric measurements using the conversion chart.
2. Discuss the three different basic units of the Metric system (grams, liters, and meters). Use the Metric weights, liquid measurements, and rulers to reiterate and demonstrate the differences, if necessary. Give examples of various gram amounts (1 g is about the weight of a paper clip, etc.) and measurements by weighing items in the classroom like a paper clip, a book, or a child (if you have a the proper type of Metric scale). You might want to allow the students to break into groups and "play" with items which weigh various weights in order to "feel" the different weights.
3. Read **Lesson 96 Explanation** together. Complete the example problems.
4. Stress the importance of the weight difference and equivalences (1 kilogram = 1,000 grams).

Nothing in all creation is hidden from God's sight. Everything is uncovered and laid bare before the eyes of him to whom we must give account.
Hebrews 4:13

Lesson 97

Concepts:
   Metric liquid measure, Metric weight, Metric measurement, Standard temperature, Scientific Notation, subtraction of mixed numbers, 10% discounts.

Objectives:
   1. The student will be able to identify, measure, read, write, and label given items using Metric measurement units of liquid measure.
   2. The student will be able to identify, measure, read, write, and label given items using Metric measurement units of weight.
   3. The student will be able to identify, measure, read, write, and label given items using Metric units of measurement.
   4. The student will be able to read, and write temperatures given in Fahrenheit degrees.
   5. The student will be able to interpret and calculate information in scientific notation.
   6. The student will be able to subtract mixed numbers which require the renaming (borrowing) of the whole number.
   7. The student will be able to calculate a 10% discount.

Teaching Tips:

Materials, Supplies, and Equipment:
   1. Large instructional Metric conversion chart form Lesson 96
   2. Metric liquid containers
   3. *Worksheet 53*

Activities:
   1. Review **Lesson 96** by going over the conversion chart. Discuss the three different basic units of the Metric System (grams, liters and meters). Use the liquid containers to compare size differences. Remember that you may always opt for a center which allows the students to experiment with the different measurement items.
   2. Read **Lesson 97** together and complete the sample problems.
   3. The student should be able to complete **Lesson 97-1** independently.

Let us then approach the throne of grace with confidence, so that we may receive mercy and find grace to help us in our time of need.
Hebrews 4:16

Lesson 98

Concepts:

Metric temperature, Metric liquid measure, Metric weight, Metric measurement, Scientific Notation, Subtraction of mixed numbers, 10% discounts.

Objectives:

1. The student will be able to read and write temperatures in Celsius degrees.
2. The student will be able to identify, measure, read, write, and label given items using Metric measurement units of liquid measure.
3. The student will be able to identify, measure, read, write, and label given items using Metric measurement units of weight.
4. The student will be able to identify, measure, read, write, and label given items using Metric units of measurement.
5. The student will be able to interpret and calculate information in scientific notation.
6. The student will be able to subtract mixed numbers which require the renaming (borrowing) of the whole number.
7. The student will be able to calculate a 10% discount.

Teaching Tips:

The students should understand the concept of temperature and should need no additional assistance with this concept.

Materials, Supplies, and Equipment:

Activities:

1. Read **Lesson 98 Explanation**.
2. Assign **Lesson 98-1** as independent work.

Come near to God and He will come near to you.
James 4:8

Lesson 99

Concepts:

Problem solving - drawing a picture, Metric temperature, Metric liquid measurement, Metric weight, Base 2, two step equations, multiplication.

Objectives:

1. The student will be able to complete a given mathematical problem using the problem solving strategy of drawing a picture.
2. The student will be able to read and write temperatures in Celsius degrees.
3. The student will be able to identify, measure, read, write, and label given items using Metric measurement units of liquid measure.
4. The student will be able to identify, measure, read, write, and label given items using Metric measurement units of weight.
5. The student will be able to calculate and interpret numbers in Base 2 form.
6. The student will be able to solve two step equations.
7. The student will be able to multiply a four-digit number by a two-digit number.

Teaching Tips:

Explain to the students that drawing pictures when completing difficult problems can make things easier to comprehend and decipher.

Materials, Supplies, and Equipment:

Paper & pencil

Activities:

1. Read **Lesson 99 Explanation** as a class. Discuss the different ways this problem may be resolved. Look at both example solutions and explain why they arrive at the same answer by using different mathematical strategies based on a knowledge of mathematical rules and information.
2. Complete **Lesson 99-1** independently as class work. Assist any student that needs further teaching intervention.

I can do all things through Christ who strengthens me.
Philipians 4:13

Lesson 100

Concepts:

Bar graphs, Metric temperature, Metric liquid measure, Base 2, two step equations, multiplication, logic problems.

Objectives:

1. The student will be able to read and interpret information presented in both vertical and horizontal bar graphs.
2. The student will be able to read and write temperatures in Celsius degrees.
3. The student will be able to identify, measure, read, write, and label given items using Metric measurement units of liquid measure.
4. The student will be able to calculate and interpret numbers in Base 2 form.
5. The student will be able to solve two step equations.
6. The student will be able to multiply a four-digit number by a two-digit number.
7. The student will be able to complete a given logic problem.

Teaching Tips:

Graphs are used to help answer questions. They show data, or information, in a visual form. Many times graphs are the best way to show information that contains numbers. Bar graphs, line graphs, pictographs, circle graphs, and coordinate graphs are the types of graphs we will discuss in the following lessons.

Materials, Supplies, and Equipment:

1. Rulers
2. Colored pencils or crayons

Activities:

1. Read **Lesson 100 Explanation** together. Discuss the parts of the graph: the dollar amounts on the side of the graph, the items listed on the bottom of the graph and the corresponding bar liens. Discuss the proper way to read a graph.
2. Conduct a survey within the classroom. Ask the students to identify five of their favorite Bible stories. Then have the class vote on their favorite story when choosing from the 5 stories named. Once voting is complete, have the students tally the information and present it in a bar graph. The graph should be neatly drawn and colored.
3. The student should be able to complete **Lesson 100-1** independently.

Let a man so consider us, as servants of Christ and stewards of the mysteries of God.
1 Corinthians 4:1

Lesson 101

Concepts:

Perimeter, area, Fahrenheit, Celsius, multi-step word problems, multiply decimals, multiply fractions

Objectives:

1. The student will be able to find the perimeter and area of rectangles and squares.
2. The student will be able to read each Fahrenheit thermometer and write the temperature.
3. The student will be able to read each Celsius thermometer and write the temperature.
4. The student will be able to solve a multi-step problem by determining the correct order of operations.
5. The student will be able to multiply a two-digit decimal by a whole number and find the product.
6. The student will be able to multiply two fractions.

Teaching Tips:

Give the students the opportunity to apply the information they are learning. Have them measure objects in the learning center and find their perimeter and area.

Materials, Supplies, and Equipment:

1. 1 tape measure per child
2. *Worksheet 54*

Activities:

1. Read **Lesson 101 Explanation** orally with the students.
2. Review measuring with a tape measure.
3. Allow the students to work with partners and measure the perimeter of 4 objects in the room. They must include a drawing of the object, the measurement of each side, and the perimeter of the object.
4. Have the children share one of their drawings with the class.
5. Have the students use the same drawings and find the area of the objects. Emphasize that when we label area, we use square units. (m^2, cm^2, mm^2)
6. The students should be able to complete **Lesson 101–1** independently.

Just for Fun:

Have the students guess which room in the learning center has the largest perimeter. What do they think the perimeter will be? Go out and measure, and determine who had the closest estimate.

The angel said to the women, "Do not be afraid, for I know that you are looking for Jesus, who was crucified. He is not here; he has risen, just as he said."
Matthew 28:5

Lesson 102

Concepts:

Area of a parallelogram, perimeter, area of a rectangle and square, area of other polygons, multiplication, multiply fractions, add decimals, multiply decimals

Objectives:

1. The student will be able to find the area of a parallelogram.
2. The student will be able to find the perimeter of rectangles and squares.
3. The student will be able to find the area of irregular shapes.
4. The student will be able to read Celsius thermometers and write the temperature.
5. The student will be able to add decimals.
6. The student will be able to multiply two fractions.
7. The student will be able to multiply a two-digit decimal by a whole number and find the product.

Teaching Tips:

Some students confuse the height of a parallelogram with the measurement of a side. Point out the difference.

Materials, Supplies, and Equipment:

1. Paper and scissors
2. *Worksheet 55*

Activities:

1. Draw a parallelogram on the piece of paper and cut it out.

2. Draw a perpendicular line from the base to the top as shown.

3. Cut along the perpendicular line.

4. Attach the triangle to the other side of the parallelogram.

5. After this visual presentation, students will understand that since the product of the base and height equals the area of a rectangle, it also equals the area of a parallelogram.
6. Review the formula $A = bh$
7. Solve this example problem with the students.
   $b = 15$ cm $h = 9$ cm   area = 15 cm x 9 cm area = 135 cm^2
8. The students should be able to complete **Lesson 102–1** independently.

And now these three remain: faith, hope and love. But the greatest of these is love.
1 Corinthians 13:13

Lesson 103

Concepts:
Area of a triangle, area of a parallelogram, area of other polygons, multiplication, multiply fractions, add decimals, multiply decimals

Objectives:
1. The student will be able to find the area of a triangle.
2. The student will be able to find the area of a parallelogram.
3. Given the area of polygons and the length of the two or three sides, the student will find the length of one or more sides.
4. The student will be able to find the area of polygons.
5. Given two five-digit factors the students will be able to find the products. The student will be able to arrange the products from largest to smallest.
6. The student will be able to multiply two fractions.
7. The student will be able to add decimals.
8. The student will be able to multiply four-digit decimals by two-digit decimals and find the product.

Teaching Tips:
Emphasize that when we label area, we use square units. (m^2, cm^2, mm^2)

Materials, Supplies, and Equipment:
1. Paper, scissors
2. *Worksheet 56*

Activities:
1. Draw a parallelogram on the piece of paper and cut it out.

2. Cut the parallelogram in half along the diagonal. Show the students that there are two identical triangles.

3. Review the formula for a parallelogram: $A = bh$. Logically we can see that the formula for the area of a triangle must equal $A = bh/2$.
4. Read **Lesson 103-1** orally with the students. Solve the example problem together.
5. The students should be able to complete **Lesson 103–1** independently.

Assemble the people–men, women, and children, and the aliens living in your towns –
so they can listen and learn to fear the Lord your God and follow
carefully all of the words of this law.
Deuteronomy 31:12

© MCMXCIX, Alpha Omega Publications, Inc.

Lesson 104

Concepts:

Area of a circle, area of a triangle, area of a parallelogram, area of irregular figures, multiply fractions, logical reasoning

Objectives:

1. The student will be able to find the area of a circle given the radius.
2. The student will be able to find the area of a circle given the diameter.
3. The student will be able to find the area of a triangle.
4. The student will be able to find the area of parallelograms.
5. The student will be able to find the area of irregular figures.
6. The student will be able to multiply two fractions.
7. The student will be able to use logical reasoning to pair sets of factors to obtain given products.

Teaching Tips:

Emphasize that when we label area, we use square units. (m^2, cm^2, mm^2)

Materials, Supplies, and Equipment:

1. *Worksheet 57*

Activities:

1. Read **Lesson 104 Explanation** with the students.
2. Write the following problem on the board and help the students find a solution.

    $A = \pi r^2$ (r = 4 cm)

    $\approx 3.14\,(4\ cm \times 4\ cm)$

    $\approx 3.14\,(16\ \text{square centimeters})$

    $\approx 50.24\ \text{square centimeters}$

3. The students should be able to complete **Lesson 104–1** practice independently.

Who of you by worrying can add a single hour to his life?
Luke 12:25

Lesson 105

Concepts:

Volume of a cube, area of a circle, area of a triangle and parallelogram, division, divide decimals, rename fractions

Objectives:

1. The student will be able to find the volume of a cube.
2. The student will be able to find the area of a circle given the radius or diameter.
3. The student will be able to find the area of a triangle and parallelogram.
4. The student will be able to divide by a three-digit number.
5. The student will be able to divide by a three-digit decimal.
6. The student will be able to rename fractions.

Teaching Tips:

Working with centimeter cubes will help the students understand the concept of volume. Emphasize that when we label volume, we use cubed units. (m^3, cm^3, mm^3)

Materials, Supplies, and Equipment:

1. Centimeter cubes

Activities:

1. Read **Lesson 105 Explanation** orally with the students. Familiarize the students with the formula for finding the volume of three-dimensional figure.
   (Volume = base x height)
2. Give each student 18 centimeter cubes. Have each student construct a figure similar to the illustration below.

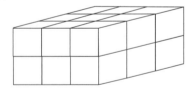

3. Have the students remove the top nine cubes to expose the base. To find the top surface area of the base, have the students apply the formula:
   $A = lw$; $A = (3 \text{ cm} \times 3 \text{ cm})$; $A = 9 \text{ cm}^2$.
4. Put the nine cubes back where they came from.
5. To find the volume of the figure, apply the formula:
   $V = bh$; $b = 9 \text{ cm}^2$; $h = 2 \text{ cm}$;
   $V = 9 \text{ cm}^2 \times 2 \text{ cm}$; $V = 18 \text{ cm}^3$
6. Have the students count the blocks to verify that the answer using the formula and the answer using the centimeter cubes match.
7. Continue to work with the students making other three-dimensional figures and finding the volume until they thoroughly understand the concept and are comfortable with the formula.
8. The students should be able to complete **Lesson 105–1** practice independently.

For where your treasure is, there your heart will be also.
Luke 12:34

Lesson 106

Concepts:
Volume of a cylinder, volume of a cube, area of a circle, area of a triangle, mystery number, divide decimals, bar graphs

Objectives:
1. The student will be able to find the volume of a cylinder.
2. The student will be able to find the volume of a three dimensional figure.
3. The student will be able to find the area of a circle given the radius or diameter.
4. The student will be able to find the area of a triangle.
5. Given number clues, the student will be able to find a mystery number.
6. The student will be able to divide a decimal by a two-digit whole number.
7. The student will be able to read a bar graph and answer questions.

Teaching Tips:
Emphasize that when we label volume, we use cubed units. (m^3, cm^3, mm^3)

Materials, Supplies, and Equipment:
1. *Worksheet 58*

Activities:
1. Read **Lesson 106 Explanation** orally with the students. Point out that the formula for finding the volume of a three-dimensional figure and the formula for finding the volume of a cylinder is the same. Ask the students to state how the formula for finding the base is different in the two examples.

    ($A = \pi r^2$; A = length x width)

2. Complete problems one and two on **Lesson 106–1** with the students. Have them complete the other problems independently.

   The business of a teacher is not to supply information–but to raise a thirst.
   William Lyons Phelps

Lesson 107

Concepts:
Surface area, volume of a cube, area of a circle, radius and diameter, divide decimals

Objectives:
1. The student will be able to find the surface area of a three-dimensional figure.
2. The student will be able to find the volume of a three dimensional figure.
3. The student will be able to draw a figure given its area and width.
4. Given the radius or diameter of a circle, the student will be able to draw the circle and find its area.
5. The student will be able to divide a decimal by a decimal.
6. The student will be able to rename fractions.

Teaching Tips:
Use the centimeter blocks to give the students a concrete example of surface area.

Materials, Supplies, and Equipment:
1. Centimeter blocks
2. *Worksheet 59*

Activities:
1. Give each student 12 centimeter blocks and ask them to build a figure like the one below.

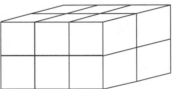

2. Tell the students that they are going to find the surface area of this figure. In other words, the area of just the outside of the figure.

3. Write on the board:

   1. top and bottom   2 (3 cm x 2 cm) = 12 cm²
   2. front and back   2 (3 cm x 2 cm) = 12 cm²
   3. sides   2 (2 cm x 2 cm) = 8 cm²

                            Total   = 32 cm²

4. Have the students look at the figure they have constructed to verify that the surface area is 32 cm².
5. Read **Lesson 107 Explanation** orally with the students. Point out that we are finding the **area** so the answer will be expressed in **cm²**.
6. The students should be able to complete **Lesson 107–1** practice independently.

Winners make goals; losers make excuses.
Anonymous

Lesson 108

Concepts:

Formulas, surface area, area of a circle, radius and diameter, volume of a cube, logical reasoning, divide fractions

Objectives:

1. The student will be able to use the formulas for finding perimeter, area, and volume to solve problems.
2. The student will be able to find the surface area of a three-dimensional figure.
3. Given the radius or diameter of a circle, the student will be able to draw the circle and find its area.
4. Given the length, width, and height of a figure, the student will be able to find the volume.
5. Using logical reasoning, the student will be able to arrange given numbers in boxes to find a product.
6. The student will be able to divide fractions.

Teaching Tips:

Post the formulas in your learning center and encourage the students to memorize them.

Materials, Supplies, and Equipment:

Activities:

1. Read **Lesson 108 Explanation** orally with the students. Point out that when we are finding the **perimeter**, the answer is expressed in **cm**. When we are finding the **area**, the answer is expressed in **cm²**. When we are finding **volume**, the answer is expressed in **cm³**.
2. Work the example problems on the board.
3. The students should be able to complete **Lesson 108–1** practice independently.

No matter how deep the stain of your sins, I can take it out and make you as clean as freshly fallen snow. Even if you are stained as red as crimson, I can make you white as wool.
Isaiah 1:18

Lesson 109

Concepts:

> World time zones, area of triangles, area of rectangles, surface area, volume of a cylinder, multiply decimals, fractions to decimals

Objectives:

1.   Given a time zone map of the world, the student will be able to tell the time in various cities around the world.
2.   The student will be able to find the areas of two triangles and determine which triangle has the greater area.
3.   The student will be able to find the areas of two rectangles and determine which triangle has the greater area.
4.   The student will be able to find the surface area of a three-dimensional figure.
5.   Given the radius and height of a cylinder, the student will be able to find the volume of the cylinder.
6.   The student will be able to multiply a decimal times a whole number.
7.   The student will be able to change fractions into decimals.

Teaching Tips:

> Show the students how they can use the globe to help them determine what time it is in various parts of the world.

Materials, Supplies, and Equipment:

1.   World atlas or time zone map
2.   *Worksheet 60*

Activities:

1.   Read **Lesson 109 Explanation** orally with the students and complete **Lessons 109–1** practice as a class.

> ***People may doubt what you say, but they will believe what you do.***
> **Anonymous**

Lesson 110

Concepts:

Two-step word problems, time zones, surface area, add improper fractions, divide decimals, divide mixed fractions, rename fractions

Objectives:

1. The student will be able to determine what operations to use to solve two-step word problems.
2. The student will be able to answer questions about their time zone and other time zones.
3. The student will be able to find the surface area of a three-dimensional figure.
4. The student will be able to find fractions that when added equal 5.
5. The student will be able to divide a decimal by a decimal.
6. The student will be able to divide two mixed fractions.
7. The student will be able to rename fractions in lowest terms.

Teaching Tips:

Encourage the students to the read word problems several times before they determine the mathematical operations.

Materials, Supplies, and Equipment:

Activities:

1. Read **Lesson 110 Explanation** orally with the students.
   Encourage the students to work on **Lesson 110–1** practice with a partner

On hearing his words some of the people said, "Surely this man is the Prophet."
Others said, "He is Christ!"
John 7:40-41

Lesson 111

Concepts:

Measuring with a protractor, problem solving, area of triangles, time zones, LCM, dividing fractions, ordering decimals

Objectives:

1. The student will be able to measure angles with a protractor.
2. The student will be able to solve multiple step problems.
3. The student will be able to find the base, height, and area of a triangle.
4. Given two numbers, the student will be able to find the least common multiple.
5. The student will be able to divide fractions.
6. The student will be able to order decimals from least to greatest.

Teaching Tips:

Give students many opportunities to practice using a protractor, compass, and straightedge to make geometric designs and constructions.

Materials, Supplies, and Equipment:

1. Protractors and straightedge (one per student)

Activities:

1. Read **Lesson 111 Explanation** orally with the students.
2. Review using a protractor.
3. Allow the students to work with partners. Have one student draw an acute angle. Have the other student measure it with a protractor. Switch roles. Have one student draw an obtuse angle. Have the other student measure it with a protractor.
4. Have the students share their angles with the class.
5. The students should be able to complete **Lesson 111-1** independently.

Just for Fun:

Have the students use their protractor and straight edge to create designs. One example follows: Use a protractor to draw points around the circle 20 degrees apart. Connect the points on the diameter to the points on the circle in the pattern reflected in the design below.

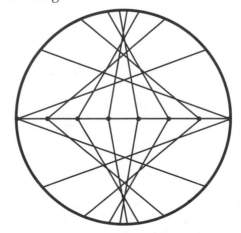

I attribute my success to this: I never gave nor took an excuse.
Florence Nightingale

Lesson 112

Concepts:

Measuring angles in a circle, measuring angles, word problems, time zones, prime numbers, divide fractions

Objectives:

1. The student will be able to use a protractor to measure angles in a circle.
2. The student will be able to measure angles with a protractor.
3. The student will be able to solve multiple step problems.
4. The student will be able to use a time zone map and determine what time it is in different locations.
5. Given a maze of numbers, the student will be able to find prime numbers and move through the maze from start to finish.
6. The student will be able to divide fractions.

Teaching Tips:

Give students many opportunities to practice using a protractor, compass, and straightedge to make geometric designs and constructions.

Materials, Supplies, and Equipment:

1. Protractor, straightedge, compass (one per student)
2. *Worksheet 61*

Activities:

1. Read Lessons **112-1 Explanation** with the students.
2. Allow the students to work with partners. Have one student draw a circle with a compass and divide it into four parts. Have the other student use a protractor to measure each angle in the circle. Emphasize to the students that when all the angles are added together that they should equal 360 degrees. Switch roles.
3. Have the students share their circle drawings with the class.
4. The students should be able to complete **Lesson 112 -1** independently.

Self-motivation is the only motivation that works.
Steve Chandler

Lesson 113

Concepts:
Drawing angles, angles in a circle, word problems, exponents, divide decimals, weight

Objectives:
1. The student will be able to draw an angle to a specified number of degrees using a protractor.
2. The student will be able to use a protractor to measure angles in a circle.
3. The student will be able to complete multiple step problems.
4. When given a number in exponential form, the student will be able to list the following: factors, products, exponents, and number of zeros.
5. The student will be able to divide decimals.
6. The student will be able to approximate the weight of specific objects.

Teaching Tips:
Give students many opportunities to practice using a protractor, compass, and straight edge to make geometric designs and constructions.

Materials, Supplies, and Equipment:
1. Protractor and straightedge (one per student)

Activities:
1. Read Lessons **113-1 Explanation** with the students.
2. Have the students draw a 30-degree angle and a 100-degree angle with a protractor and straight edge.
3. The students should be able to complete **Lesson 113-1** independently.

I will praise God's name in song and glorify him in thanksgiving.
Psalm 69:30

© MCMXCIX, Alpha Omega Publications, Inc.

Lesson 114

Concepts:

Constructing perpendicular bisectors, draw angles, angles in a circle, measure angles, exponents, dividing decimals

Objectives:

1. Given a line, the student will be able to draw a perpendicular bisector.
2. The student will be able to draw angles to a specified number of degrees using a protractor.
3. The student will be able to use a protractor to measure angles in a circle.
4. The student will be able to measure an angle using a protractor.
5. The student will be able to find the value of numbers written in the form of exponents.
6. The student will be able to divide decimals.

Teaching Tips:

Give students many opportunities to practice using a protractor, compass, and straight edge to make geometric designs and constructions.

Materials, Supplies, and Equipment:

1. Compass, straightedge (one per student)

Activities:

1. Read **Lesson 114-1 Explanation** with the students.
2. Have the students draw a 6 cm vertical line on a piece of paper. Have them draw a perpendicular bisector of that line.
3. The students should be able to complete **Lesson 114-1** practice independently.

I will praise you, O Lord, with all my heart; before the "gods"
I will sing your praise.
Psalm 138:1

Lesson 115

Concepts:

Bisect angles, perpendicular bisectors, draw angles, angles in a circle, square roots, metric measure

Objectives:

1. The student will be able to draw a perpendicular bisector of a given angle.
2. The student will be able to draw a perpendicular bisector of the sides of a triangle.
3. The student will be able to draw angles to a specified number of degrees using a protractor.
4. The student will be able to use a protractor to measure angles in a circle.
5. The student will be able to find the square root of a given number.
6. The student will be able to convert metric measures.

Teaching Tips:

Give students many opportunities to practice using a protractor, compass, and straight edge to make geometric designs and constructions.

Materials, Supplies, and Equipment:

1. Compass, straightedge (one per student)
2. *Worksheet 62*

Activities:

1. Read **Lesson 115 Explanation** orally with the students.
2. Allow the students to work with partners. Have one student draw an angle and measure it with a protractor. Have the other student use a protractor to draw a bisector of the angle. Switch roles.
3. After the students are comfortable drawing a bisector using a protractor, have one student draw an angle. Have the other student use a compass and straight edge to bisect the angle. Switch roles.
4. The students should be able to complete **Lesson 115-1** practice independently.

We are not put on this earth primarily to see through one another,
but to see each other through.
Peter Devries

Lesson 116

Concepts:

Construct a hexagon, bisect angles, perpendicular bisectors, draw angles, square roots, metric measure

Objectives:

1. The student will be able to construct a hexagon.
2. The student will be able to draw a perpendicular bisector of a given angle.
3. The student will be able to draw a perpendicular bisector of a given angle inside a circle.
4. The student will be able to draw angles to a specified number of degrees using a protractor.
5. The student will be able to find the square root of a given number.
6. The student will be able to convert metric measures.

Teaching Tips:

Give students many opportunities to practice using a protractor, compass, and straight edge to make geometric designs and constructions.

Materials, Supplies, and Equipment:

1. Compass, straightedge (one per student)
2. *Worksheet 63*

Activities:

1. Read **Lesson 116 Explanation** orally with the students.
2. Allow the students to practice constructing regular hexagons of different sizes.
3. The students should be able to complete **Lesson 116–1** practice independently.

Clap your hands, all you nations; shout to God with cries of joy.
How awesome is the Lord Most High, the great King
over all the earth!
Psalm 47:1,2

Lesson 117

Concepts:
Construct an equilateral triangle, draw a hexagon, bisect angles, exponents, multiplication

Objectives:
1. The student will be able to construct an equilateral triangle.
2. The student will be able to construct a hexagon.
3. The student will be able to bisect an angle using a protractor.
4. The student will be able to bisect an angle using a compass.
5. The student will be able to write larger numbers in exponent form.
6. The student will be able to multiply numbers and complete a crossword puzzle.

Teaching Tips:
Give students many opportunities to practice using a protractor, compass, and straight edge to make geometric designs and constructions.

Materials, Supplies, and Equipment:
1. Compass, straightedge (one per student)
2. *Worksheet 64*

Activities:
1. Read **Lesson 117 Explanation** orally with the students.
2. Allow the students to practice constructing equilateral triangles of different sizes.
3. The students should be able to complete **Lesson 117-1** practice independently.

Just for Fun:
1. Equilateral triangles are used in quilt patterns, on signs, on wallpaper etc. Have the students look for equilateral triangles in designs at home.
2. Give the students opportunities to draw their own equilateral triangle patterns. Two examples follow:

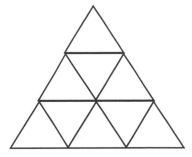 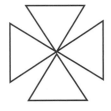

Be bold in what you stand for and careful of what you stand for.
Ruth Boorstin

Lesson 118

Concepts:
Construct right triangles, draw a hexagon, bisect angles, exponents, multiplication

Objectives:

1. The student will be able to construct a right triangle.
2. The student will be able to construct an equilateral triangle.
3. The student will be able to construct a hexagon and use the hexagon to create a new quilt pattern.
4. The student will be able to bisect an angle using a compass.
5. The student will be able to write decimals and exponents in standard form.
6. The student will be able to multiply numbers and complete a riddle.

Teaching Tips:

Give students many opportunities to practice using a protractor, compass, and straight edge to make geometric designs and constructions.

Materials, Supplies, and Equipment:

1. Compass, straightedge (one per student)

Activities:

1. Read **Lesson 118 Explanation** orally with the students.
2. Allow the students to practice constructing different types of right triangles.
3. The students should be able to complete **Lesson 118-1** practice independently.

Just for Fun:

1. Right triangles come in many different shapes and sizes.
   Challenge the students to draw as many different types of right triangles as possible.
   A few examples follow:

When he had led them out to the vicinity of Bethany, he lifted up his hands and blessed them. While he was blessing them, he left them and was taken up into heaven. Then they worshiped him and returned to Jerusalem with great joy. And they stayed continually at the temple, praising God.
Luke 24:50-53

Lesson 119

Concepts:

Construct a square, construct an equilateral triangle, multiplication, averaging, fluid measures

Objectives:

1. The student will be able to construct a square.
2. The student will be able to construct a right triangle.
3. The student will be able to construct an equilateral triangle.
4. The student will be able to multiply a three-digit number times a two-digit number.
5. The student will be able find the average of three or more numbers.
6. The student will be able to convert liquid measures.

Teaching Tips:

Give students many opportunities to practice using a protractor, compass, and straight edge to make geometric designs and constructions.

Materials, Supplies, and Equipment:

1. Compass, straightedge (one per student)
2. *Worksheet 65*

Activities:

1. Read **Lesson 119 Explanation** orally with the students.
2. Allow the students to practice constructing different types of squares.
3. The students should be able to complete **Lessons 119-1** practice independently.

*Amen! Praise and glory and wisdom and thanks and honor and power and
strength be to our God for ever and ever. Amen!*
Revelations 7:12

© MCMXCIX, Alpha Omega Publications, Inc.

Lesson 120

Concepts:

Construct a parallelogram, construct a square, construct a right triangle, construct an equilateral triangle, multiplication, measuring distance

Objectives:

1. The student will be able to construct a parallelogram.
2. The student will be able to construct a square.
3. The student will be able to construct a right triangle.
4. The student will be able to construct an equilateral triangle.
5. The student will be able to multiply a four-digit number times a two-digit number.
6. The student will be able to convert linear measures.

Teaching Tips:

Give students many opportunities to practice using a protractor, compass, and straight edge to make geometric designs and constructions.

Materials, Supplies, and Equipment:

1. Compass, straightedge (one per student)

Activities:

1. Read **Lesson 120 Explanation** orally with the students.
2. Allow the students to practice constructing different types of parallelograms.
3. The students should be able to complete **Lesson 120-1** practice independently.

Just for Fun:

Give the students a large piece of construction paper and have them design a flag using some of the shapes they have learned to construct with a compass, protractor, and straightedge. Have the students color the flags and display them in your learning center.

Be joyful always; pray continually; give thanks in all circumstances,
for this is God's will for you in Christ Jesus.
1 Thessalonians 5:16

Lesson 121

Concepts:

Simple ratios, column addition with decimals, addition & subtraction of fractions with common denominators, area of a parallelogram, word problems, discounts, 5-digit addition

Objectives:

1. The student will be able to write simple ratios.
2. The student will be able to complete column addition with decimal numbers.
3. The student will be able to add and subtract fractions with common denominators.
4. The student will be able to find the area of a parallelogram.
5. The student will be able to complete word problems which require the use of money.
6. The student will be able to find a 20% discount.
7. The student will be able to complete five-digit addition.

Teaching Tips:

The students should be able to easily see the relationship between a ratio & a fraction.

Materials, Supplies, and Equipment:

Activities:

1. Have 5 students come to the front of the room. Pick 3 girls and 2 boys, if possible. Ask the students:

    "How many girls are in the group?"(3)

    "How many boys are in the group?" (2)

    "What is the ratio of boys to girls?" (3 to 2, 3/2, or 3 : 2).

2. Read **Lesson 121** orally. Read the sample problems and discuss them.
3. Assign **Lesson 121-1** as independent work.

O Lord, you are my God; I will exalt you and praise your name,
for in perfect faithfulness you have done marvelous things,
things planned long ago.
Isaiah 25:1

© MCMXCIX, Alpha Omega Publications, Inc.

Lesson 122

Concepts:

Equal ratios, simple ratios, addition of decimals, addition & subtraction of fractions with common denominators, area of a parallelogram, word problems, discounts.

Objectives:

1. The student will be able to multiply in order to find equal ratios.
2. The student will be able to write simple ratios.
3. The student will be able to add decimals.
4. The student will be able to add and subtract fractions with common denominators.
5. The student will be able to find the area of a parallelogram.
6. The student will be able to complete word problems which require the use of money.
7. The student will be able to find a 20% discount.

Teaching Tips:

The students have studied equivalent fractions for many years and should see the relationship between ratios and fractions.

Materials, Supplies, and Equipment:

1. *Worksheet 67*

Activities:

1. Read **Lesson 122 Explanation** with the students.
2. The students will be able to complete **Lesson 122-1** as independent work.
3. If an additional assignment is needed, the students can be instructed to make their own ratio charts and exchange them with fellow students to solve.

> *Be very careful how you live, not as unwise but as wise, making the*
> *most of every opportunity, because the days are evil.*
> **Ephesians 5:15 - 16**

Lesson 123

Concepts:
Equal ratios, simple ratios, subtraction of decimals, equivalent fractions, area of a triangle.

Objectives:
1. The student will be able to divide fractions to find equal ratios.
2. The student will be able to multiply in order to find equal ratios.
3. The student twill be able to write simple ratios.
4. The student will be able to subtract decimals.
5. The student will be able to find equivalent fractions.
6. The student will be able to find the area of a triangle.

Teaching Tips:
Students will need little guidance with this concept.

Materials, Supplies, and Equipment:
1. *Worksheet 67*

Activities:
1. Read **Lesson 123 Explanation** with the students.
2. The student will be able to complete **Lesson 123-1** as independent work.

And we know that in all things God works for the good of those who love Him,
who have been called according to His purpose.
Romans 8:28

Lesson 124

Concepts:

Cross products, equal ratios, simple ratios, equivalent fractions, area of a triangle.

Objectives:

1. The student will be able to find cross products.
2. The student will be able to divide to find equal ratios.
3. The student will be able to multiply to find equal ratios.
4. The student will be able to write simple ratios.
5. The student will be able to find equivalent fractions.
6. The student will be able to find the area of a triangle.

Teaching Tips:

The students should have little difficulty with this concept.

Materials, Supplies, and Equipment:

1. Calculator (for multiplication only), if needed

Activities:

1. Read **Lesson 124 Explanation** as a class.
2. Discuss situations where a person would want to use a proportion, such as making scaled models.
3. Assign **Lesson 124-1** as independent work.

4. As an additional assignment, for more advanced students, have them draw a proportional scale model of something they have such as a car, a swing set, their room. They will need to measure the original item and then show all the conversions for the model. A more extensive project would be for them to actually make the model in addition to drawing the plans.

I am the good shepherd; I know my sheep and my sheep know me just as the Father knows me and I know the Father and I lay down my life for the sheep.
John 10:14 - 15

Lesson 125

Concepts:

Cross products to solve for N, cross products, equal ratios, comparing fractions, area of a circle, metric temperature, logic problems.

Objectives:

1. The student will be able to use cross products to solve for N.
2. The student will be able to find cross products.
3. The student will be able to divide to find equal ratios.
4. The student will be able to multiply to find equal ratios.
5. The student will be able to compare fractions.
6. The student will be able to find the area of a circle.
7. The student will be able to read temperatures in Celsius degrees.
8. The student will be able to solve a given logic problem.

Teaching Tips:

This lesson is similar to finding equivalent fractions. The students should have no difficulty with this concept.

Materials, Supplies, and Equipment:

1. *Worksheet 68*

Activities:

1. Read Lesson **125** orally with the students.
2. Discuss the similarities between using cross products to solve for a value and finding equivalent fractions.
3. Complete the first problem on Lesson **125-1** together to insure student understanding.
4. Assign the rest of Lesson **125-1** as independent work.

My soul glorifies the Lord and my spirit rejoices in God my Savior...
Luke 1:46b-47

© MCMXCIX, Alpha Omega Publications, Inc.

Lesson 126

Concepts:
Ratio and percent, cross products to solve for N, cross products, equal ratios, comparing fractions, area of a triangle, metric temperature.

Objectives:
1. The student will be able to identify ratios and percents.
2. The student will be able to use cross products to solve for N.
3. The student will be able to find cross products.
4. The student will be able to divide to find equal ratios.
5. The student will be able to compare fractions.
6. The student will be able to find the area of a triangle.
7. The student will be able to read temperatures in Celsius degrees.

Teaching Tips:
It might be beneficial to review the relationship between fractions, percents, and decimals before beginning this new lesson.

Materials, Supplies, and Equipment:

Activities:
1. Read **Lesson 126 Explanation** with the students.
2. Demonstrate the process of dividing the denominator into the numerator in order to find the percentage equivalent for each ratio. Use the example of 4\5.

$$\begin{array}{r} 0.80 \\ 5\overline{)4.00} \end{array} \qquad 0.80 = 80/100 \text{ or } 80\%$$

3. Have the students complete the following practice problems on their own:

   4/10 = ?%   27/50 = ?%   15/20 = ?%

   40%   54%   75%

4. Assign **Lesson 126-1** as independent work.

The angel of the Lord encamps around those who fear him, and he delivers them.
Psalm 34:7

Lesson 127

Concepts:
Probability, ratio & percent, cross products to solve for N, cross products, addition & subtraction of fractions with different denominators, volume of a cylinder, bar graphs.

Objectives:
1. The student will be able to find the probability of a single event or situation occurring.
2. The student will be able to calculate ratio and percent.
3. The student will be able to use cross products to solve for N.
4. The student will be able to calculate cross products.
5. The student will be able to add and subtract fractions with different denominators.
6. The student will be able to find the volume of a cylinder.
7. The student will be able to draw, read, and interpret information presented in a bar graph.

Teaching Tips:

Materials, Supplies, and Equipment:
1. Marbles - two red, one white, one green, and one blue (or any other colors as long as there are 2 the same color and all the rest are different).
2. Cup
3. Box or hat

Activities:
1. Show the students the 4 different colored marbles. Put the 4 marbles into the cup. Ask the students to tell you what colors marble you could pull out if you reach in and grab one. Allow time for student response. Remind them that there are only 4 marbles in the cup.
   Ask them your chances of pulling out a blue one. (1/4)
   Ask them the chances of pulling out a red marble (1/4).
   Explain that probability of pulling out a red marble is the same as pulling out a blue marble (and the rest of the colors as well) because there is only one of each color.
2. Add the additional red marble into the cup and now ask the students to tell you the chance (probability) of pulling out a red marble. (2/5)
   The odds have just increased because you now have 2 red ones instead of one.
3. Read **Lesson 127 Explanation orally**. Discuss each example problem carefully.
4. If additional practice is needed, conduct this same example exercise in your room. Give some type of treat. Have the students write their name on an index card, or small piece of paper. Place all of the names in a hat or box. Have each student calculate their chance, probability, of winning. Draw one out, or have a student draw one out.
5. The student should be able to complete **Lesson 127-1** independently.

The eyes of the Lord are on the righteous and his ears are attentive to their cry...
Psalm 34:15

Lesson 128

Concepts:

Probability, ratio & percent, cross products, addition & subtraction of mixed numbers with different denominators, volume of a cylinder, line graphs.

Objectives:

1. The student will be able to find the probability that an event or events will occur.
2. The student will be able to calculate ratio and percent.
3. The student will be able to use cross products to solve for N.
4. The student will able to add and subtract mixed numbers with different denominators.
5. The student will be able to find the volume of a cylinder.
6. The student will be able to draw, read, and interpret information presented in a line graph.

Teaching Tips:

Materials, Supplies, and Equipment:

1. A deck of cards

Activities:

1. Repeat the "name in the box" activity from Lesson 127. This time choose only 6 names (4 boys and 2 girls). Write these 6 names on the board and ask the students what the probability is that a girls' name will be drawn (2/6 = 1/3). Then ask what the probability is that a boy s' name will be drawn (4/6 = 2/3).

2. Read **Lesson 128 Explanation** orally.
3. Take the deck of playing cards and have the students tell you the probability of drawing various cards from the deck. For example, ask what the probability is that a jack will be drawn (4/52). Then ask the probability of drawing a jack of spades (1/52). Do this a few times to make sure that the students grasp the concept of probability with several variables.
4. Assign **Lesson 128-1** as an independent assignment.

He has shown you, O man, what is good. And what does the Lord require of you?
To act justly and to love mercy and to walk humbly with your God.
Micah 6:8

Lesson 129

Concepts:

Word problems with ratios, probability, ratio & percent, converting mixed numbers to improper fractions, converting improper fractions to mixed numbers, measuring triangles, addition with missing data.

Objectives:

1. The student will be able to solve word problems that contain ratios.
2. The student will be able to find the probability that an event or events will occur.
3. The student will be able to calculate ratio and percent.
4. The student will be able to convert an improper fraction to a mixed fraction and a mixed fraction to an improper fraction.
5. The student will be able to measure given angles of a triangle.
6. The student will be able to complete addition problems that contain missing data.

Teaching Tips:

The students should have no difficulty applying this concept.

Materials, Supplies, and Equipment:

Activities:

1. Read **Lesson 129 Explanation** orally.
2. Discuss the similarities between finding equal ratios and finding equivalent fractions. Equal ratios are equivalent fractions.
3. Assign **Lesson 129-1** as independent work.

> *Surely this is our God; we trusted in Him, and he saved us. This is the Lord,*
> *we trusted in Him; let us rejoice and be glad in His salvation.*
> **Isaiah 25:9**

© MCMXCIX, Alpha Omega Publications, Inc.

Lesson 130

Concepts:

Finding Patterns, word problems with ratios, probability, converting mixed numbers to improper fractions, converting improper fractions to mixed numbers, measuring triangles, subtraction with missing data.

Objectives:

1. The student will be able to find a pattern.
2. The student will be able to complete word problems that contain ratios.
3. The student will be able to find the probability that an event or events will occur.
4. The student will be able to convert an improper fraction to a mixed fraction and a mixed fraction to an improper fraction.
5. The student will be able to measure given angles of a triangle.
6. The student will be able to complete subtraction problems that contain missing data.

Teaching Tips:

Any pattern work you can use as supplemental materials will be an asset. This might be a good time to integrate math and art by drawing tessellations.

Materials, Supplies, and Equipment:

Activities:

1. Read **Lesson 130 Explanation** orally.
2. Discuss different patterns that may be found in math such as the examples shown. Challenge the students to come up with other mathematical patterns. Have them share these with the class.
3. Assign **Lesson 131-1** as independent work.
4. If time allows, have the students create a tessellation picture as an art project.

... righteousness from God comes through faith in Jesus Christ to all who believe.
Romans 2:22

Lesson 131

Concepts:

Percents, quadrilaterals, factor trees, decimal multiplication, multiplication of fractions, using a protractor, using a compass to draw a circle.

Objectives:

1. The student will be able to define the different ways to use percent.
2. The student will be able to identify quadrilaterals.
3. The student will be able to complete factor trees.
4. The student will be able to multiply a decimal by a whole number.
5. The student will be able to multiply two fractions.
6. The student will be able to use a protractor to measure a given angle.
7. The student will be able to use a compass to draw a prescribed circle.

Teaching Tips:

It is best to use visuals or manipulatives to demonstrate the concept of percentages. A place value block of 100 is the best model to use with children.

Materials, Supplies, and Equipment:

1. 100 place value squares (for the students)
2. Large place value square (for instruction)
3. Individual paper place value squares for each student
4. Dry erase or overhead markers

Activities:

1. Prior to the lesson, have a place value card/square (which contains 100 individual squares) made for each student. Also have a large instructional place value card/square made for yourself. These should be laminated so that the student can use an erasable pen on them without damaging them. Pass these out to the students along with the erasable markers. Keep the instructional card for yourself.
2. Show the following example on the instructional card: Ask the students how much of the card is shaded. Begin by asking them to count the number of shaded squares. Since 82 of the squares are shaded and there are 100 squares present, ask the students to write a fraction that shows the shaded region (82/100). Changing to a decimal, we see that 0.82 of the whole square is shaded. Each small square on the card represents 1% of the whole card. Since 82 small squares are shaded, 82% of the card is shaded.

3. Have the students create and work several other examples.
   Below are a few more to work with them:

   0.14   0.37   0.74   0.96   1.00

4. The students may need to work with other shapes and objects to understand that all of something is 100%.
5. Assign **Lesson 131-1** as independent work.

Today, if you hear His voice, do not harden your hearts.
Psalm 95: 7b-8a

Lesson 132

Concepts:

Percent of a number, percents, quadrilaterals, prime & composite, multiplication of decimals, multiplication of mixed numbers, using a protractor.

Objectives:

1. The student will be able to find a given percent of a number.
2. The student will be able to define or demonstrate the different ways to use percent.
3. The student will be able to identify quadrilaterals.
4. The student will be able to identify prime and composite numbers.
5. The student will be able to multiply a decimal by a whole number.
6. The student will be able to multiply two mixed numbers.
7. The student will be able to use a protractor to measure a given angle.

Teaching Tips:

Bring in old catalogs or newspaper advertisements and let the students find sale items. Show them how to determine the amount of their savings.

Materials, Supplies, and Equipment:

1. Newspapers and catalogues
2. Calculator, if necessary.
3. *Worksheet 69*

Activities:

1. Read **Lesson 132 Explanation** with the students.
2. Point out to the students that we use this concept every day when shopping for bargains.
3. Have the student work in pairs to develop a sales brochure for a local store deducting 15% off of the products. The students need to use the newspapers and catalogues as guides to realistic pricing. They may also use these to clip out pictures for their brochure.
4. Taking it further: Have the students bring in sales receipts form stores. Ask them to determine how much money a senior citizen would save on the total bill, before taxes, if they received a 7% discount.
5. The student will be able to complete **Lesson 132-1** as independent work.

Come, let us bow down in worship, let us kneel before the Lord our Maker.
Psalm 95:6

Lesson 133

Concepts:

Percents & decimals, percent of a number, percents, angle measurement, exponents, multiplication of decimals, cross out simplification.

Objectives:

1. The student will be able to convert from a decimal to a percent and from a percent to a decimal.
2. The student will be able to find a given percent of a number.
3. The student will be able to demonstrate the different ways to use percent.
4. The student will be able to find the measurement of a given angle.
5. The student will be able to calculate the value of a given exponential number.
6. The student will be able to multiply by two decimal numbers.
7. The student will be able to simplify fractions using the cross simplification.

Teaching Tips:

Review Lesson 131 & 132 before beginning this lesson if you feel that the students are not grasping the relationship between percents, decimals, and fractions. Make sure you plainly show this relationship with each lesson on decimals or percents.

Materials, Supplies, and Equipment:

1. "Percent/Decimal Bingo"
2. M & M® candies
3. *Worksheet 70*

Activities:

1. Read **Lesson 133 Explanation** with the students.
2. Prior to the class, have the students turn in their place value cards to you. Use each card to create individual "BINGO" cards and a class "Percent/Decimal Bingo Game." Write various decimal and percent numbers on each student card. Keep tract of the numbers you use for your master list. In class, return the new bingo cards and play a Bingo game. You will be the "caller" using your master list as a guide. For example: If your master list contains the number 56% as being one written on a student card, you would call out 0.56. The student should recognize 56% as being the percentage equivalent to 0.56 and therefore mark his/her card with a M&M® . The first student to get "BINGO" wins.
3. The student will complete **Lesson 133-1** as independent work.

> *Yet the Lord longs to be gracious to you; He rises to show you compassion.*
> *For the Lord is a God of justice. Blessed are all who wait for Him.*
> **Isaiah 30:18**

© MCMXCIX, Alpha Omega Publications, Inc.

Lesson 134

Concepts:
Percents & fractions, percents & decimals, percent of a number, percents, measuring angles, exponents, division of a whole number by a fraction.

Objectives:
1. The student will be able to convert percents to fractions to percents.
2. The student will be able to convert from a decimal to a percent and from a percent to a decimal.
3. The student will be able to find a given percent of a number.
4. The student will be able to demonstrate the different ways to use percent.
5. The student will be able to find the measurement of a given angle.
6. The student will be able to calculate the value of a given exponential number.
7. The student will be able to divide a whole number by a fraction.

Teaching Tips:

Materials, Supplies, and Equipment:
1. *Worksheet 71*

Activities:
1. Read **Lesson 134 Explanation** with the students.
2. Play a game with the students at the chalkboard to reinforce these concepts.
   a. Divide the class into two equal teams.
   b. Call one person from each team to the board. Give them a decimal and have them write the equivalent percent on the board, or give them a percent have the write an equivalent decimal on the board.
   c. Each team with a correct answer gets one point.
   d. The team with the correct answer first gets one point. This means that each time has an opportunity to receive two points during one turn; one for answering first, one for answering correctly.
   e. Continue play until one team gets 10 points. They will be the winner.
3. The students will be able to complete **Lesson 134-1** as independent work.

How great are His signs, how mighty His wonders! His kingdom is an eternal kingdom; His dominion endures form generation to generation.
Daniel 4:3

Lesson 135

Concepts:
 Conversion of fractions, decimals, and percents, percents & fractions, percents & decimals, percents, square roots, division of decimals & whole numbers, division of fractions.

Objectives:
 1. The student will be able to complete a table that converts fractions, decimals, and percents to their equivalent forms.
 2. The student will be able to convert a fraction to a percent and a percent to a fraction.
 3. The student will be able to convert a percent to a decimal and a decimal to a percent.
 4. The student will be able to find a given percent of a number.
 5. The student will be able to find the square root of a given number.
 6. The student will be able to divide a decimal by a whole number.
 7. The student will be able to divide two fractions.

Teaching Tips:

Materials, Supplies, and Equipment:

Activities:
 1. Read **Lesson 135 Explanation** with the students.
 2. The students will be able to complete **Lesson 135-1** independently.

There is a way that seems right to a man, but its end is the way of death.
Proverbs 14:12

Lesson 136

Concepts:
Finding 1% of a number, conversion of fractions, decimals, and percents, percents & fractions, percents & decimals, numeration through trillions, square roots, division of decimals.

Objectives:
1. The student will be able to find 1% of a given number.
2. The student will be able to complete a table that converts fractions, decimals, and percents to their equivalent forms.
3. The student will be able to convert a fraction to a percent and a percent to a fraction.
4. The student will be able to convert a percent to a decimal and a decimal to a percent.
5. The student will be able to write a standard number through the trillions' place in expanded form.
6. The student will be able to find the square root of a given number.
7. The student will be able to divide a decimal number by another decimal number.

Teaching Tips:

Materials, Supplies, and Equipment:
1. *Worksheet 72*

Activities:
1. Read **Lesson 136 Explanation** with the students.
2. Work the sample problems with them.
3. Assign **Lesson 136-1** as independent work.

> *Fathers, ... bring them up in the training and admonition of the Lord.*
> **Ephesians 6:4**

Lesson 137

Concepts:

Finding 10% of a number, finding 1% of a number, conversion of fractions, decimals, and percents, numeration through trillions, scientific notation, changing fractions to decimals.

Objectives:

1. The student will be able to find 10% of a given number.
2. The student will be able to find 1% of a given number.
3. The student will be able to complete a table that converts fractions, decimals, and percents to their equivalent forms.
4. The student will be able to convert a fraction to a percent and a percent to a fraction.
5. The student will be able to convert a Roman numeral into standard form.
6. The student will be able to convert numbers into scientific notation.
7. The student will be able to change a fraction to a decimal.

Teaching Tips:

The students not have any difficulty with finding a percent of a number by this time.

Materials, Supplies, and Equipment:

1. *Worksheet 72*

Activities:

1. Read **Lesson 137 Explanation** with the students.
2. Assign **Lesson 137-1** as independent work.

> *We who are alive and remain shall be caught up together with them*
> *in the clouds to meet the Lord.*
> **1 Thessalonians 4:17**

© MCMXCIX, Alpha Omega Publications, Inc.

Lesson 138

Concepts:

Sales tax, finding 10% of a number, finding 1% of a number, conversion of fractions, decimals, and percents, numeration – decimals, scientific notation, changing fractions to decimals.

Objectives:

1. The student will be able to calculate sales tax on given transactions.
2. The student will be able to find 10% of a given number.
3. The student will be able to find 1% of a given number.
4. The student will be able to complete a table that converts fractions, decimals, and percents to their equivalent forms.
5. The student will be able to identify decimal numbers.
6. The student will be able to convert numbers into scientific notation.
7. The student will be able to change a fraction to a decimal.

Teaching Tips:

Materials, Supplies, and Equipment:

1. Sales receipts from various purchases
2. Catalogues or sale fliers from local newspapers
3. *Worksheet 73*

Activities:

1. Have each student go pretend "shopping" through the catalogues and sale fliers/newspapers. Tell them they may purchase 3 items of their choosing from these local fliers. Once the students have picked out their items, have them total up the amount of "money" spent.
2. Pass out the real sales receipts to each student. Discuss the fact that each state/county charges a sales tax on every purchase made within that county/state.
3. Read **Lesson 138 Explanation** with the students.
4. At this time have the students go back and calculate a 6% sales tax onto their "shopping total."
5. Assign **Lesson 138-1** as independent work.

Whoever drinks of the water that I shall give him will never thirst. But the water that I shall give him will become in him a fountain.
John 4:14

Lesson 139

Concepts:

Discounts, sales tax, finding 10% of a number, finding 1% of a number, comparing & ordering whole numbers, Base 2, division of fractions by whole numbers.

Objectives:

1. The student will be able to calculate specified discounts on a given monetary amount.
2. The student will be able to calculate sales tax on given transactions.
3. The student will be able to find 10% of a given number.
4. The student will be able to find 1% of a given number.
5. The student will be able to compare and order whole numbers.
6. The student will be able to convert base 10 numbers into base 2 numbers.
7. The student will be able to divide a fraction by a whole number.

Teaching Tips:

Materials, Supplies, and Equipment:

1. Sale papers and fliers from local newspapers
2. *Worksheet 74*

Activities:

1. Have the students look through the local sale papers. Have them find the sales which boast a "percentage off" sale. Ask them how to calculate how much money is being saved when something is a percentage off.
2. Read **Lesson 139 Explanation** with the students.
3. Go back to the newspapers and find several examples of percentage off sales. Calculate the amount of money saved on several of these ads.
4. Assign **Lesson 139-1** as independent work.

> *To be in His presence! A glorious thought*
> *So awesome I cannot conceive;*
> *I'll bow down and worship the Lord on His throne*
> *And add to the praise He'll receive.*
> **Sper**

Lesson 140

Concepts:
Problem solving – organized lists, discounts, sales tax, finding 10% of a number, six-digit addition, Base 2, division of mixed numbers.

Objectives:
1. The student will be able to problem solve by making an organized list.
2. The student will be able to calculate specific discounts on a given monetary amount.
3. The student will be able to calculate sales tax on given transactions.
4. The student will be able to find 10% of a number.
5. The student will be able to complete addition problems that contain up to six digits.
6. The student will be able to convert base 10 numbers to base 2.
7. The student will be able to divide two mixed numbers.

Teaching Tips:

Materials, Supplies, and Equipment:
1. Blue & red pens (one per student)
2. Pencils (one per student)
3. Colored paper (yellow, green, & white), one set per student

Activities:
1. Give each student a blue pen, a red pen, and a pencil. Also give them a sheet of white paper, a sheet of green paper, and a sheet of yellow paper. Ask them how many different combinations of pen color and paper color can be made? Allow them some time to work out the problem. Once they have found the answer discuss the different processes each student used to arrive at a correct answer.
2. Read **Lesson 140 Explanation** with the students.
3. Go back and complete Activity #1 by making an organized list.
4. Assign **Lesson 140-1** as independent work.

Christ Jesus came into the world to save sinners, of whom I am chief.
1 Timothy 1:15

Lesson 141

Concepts:
Integers, fractions-decimals-percents, order of operations, perimeter and area, measuring with a protractor, equivalent fractions, coordinate graphs

Objectives:
1. The student will be able to identify negative and positive integers.
2. The student will be able to find equivalent fractions, decimals, and percents.
3. The student will be able to place parentheses in a problem to make a mathematical sentence true.
4. The student will be able to find the area and perimeter of a rectangle.
5. The student will be able to measure angles in a circle with a protractor.
6. The student will be able to find a missing number to make two fractions equivalent.
7. The student will be able to plot points on a coordinate graph.

Teaching Tips:
Give students the opportunity to see examples of number lines that have negative and positive values like, Celsius thermometers, Sea Level Graphs, etc.

Materials, Supplies, and Equipment:

Activities:
1. Tell the students that you are going to discuss positive and negative numbers. Ask the students to think of examples where we might use negative numbers to communicate ideas. (They might include below sea level, below zero Celsius, losing weight, an overdrawn checking account, a yardage loss in football, etc.)
2. Read **Lesson 141 Explanation** together. Have the students find the following integers on the number line: -4, 0, +4, -1, +1. Have the students extent the number line and include –5, -6, -7, +5, +6 and +7.
3. Assign **Lesson 141-1** for independent work. The students should have no difficulty with this assignment.

Reinforced with faith, the weakest mortal is mightier than disaster.
Helen Keller

Lesson 142

Concepts:
Opposites, number lines, area and perimeter, equivalent fractions, fractions-decimals percents, coordinate graphs

Objectives:
1. The student will be able to find the opposite of an integer.
2. The student will be able to identify positive and negative integers.
3. The student will be able to find the area and perimeter of a rectangle.
4. The student will be able to find a missing number to make two fractions equivalent
5. The student will be able to find equivalent fractions, decimals, and percents.
6. The student will be able to plot points on a coordinate graph.

Teaching Tips:

Materials, Supplies, and Equipment:

Activities:

1. Have the students list things that they can think of that are opposites. (Some examples might be: up and down, hot and cold, big and little, red and green, black and white, true and false etc.) Tell them that they are going to study opposite numbers. Ask them to tell you what the opposite of 6 is. (-6) Ask them to identify the opposite of –4. (+4).
2. Read **Lesson 142 Explanation** with the students.
3. Have the students extend the number line to include –5, -6, -7 and the opposites of these numbers: +5, +6, +7.
4. Assign **Lesson 142-1** as independent work.

For the message of the cross is foolishness to those who are perishing, but to us who are being saved it is the power of God. For it is written: I will destroy the wisdom of the wise; and intelligence of the intelligent I will frustrate.
1 Corinthians 1:18

Lesson 143

Concepts:

Compare integers, opposites, area and perimeter, 5-digit multiplication, area of parallelograms, construct a square, adding decimals

Objectives:

1. The student will be able to compare integers.
2. The student will be able to find the opposite of an integer.
3. The student will be able to draw 3 different rectangles that have the same perimeter.
4. The student will be able to multiply 5-digit numbers.
5. The student will be able to find the area of a parallelogram.
6. The student will be able to construct a square.
7. The student will be able to add three decimals and find the correct sum.

Teaching Tips:

Many students get confused when they compare negative numbers. We learn from early childhood that 5 is greater than 2. When students are asked to compare –5 and –2, they often apply their knowledge from the positive side of the number line and ascertain that –5 is bigger than –2. It is important to use a number line for reference when students begin working with integers.

Materials, Supplies, and Equipment:

Activities:

1. Read **Lesson 143 Explanation** together. Have the students list four numbers that are less than –10. (Some examples are: -11, -12, -13, -14 etc.) Have the students list four numbers that are greater than –7 and are negative numbers. (Some examples are: -6, -5, -4, -3, -2, -1.)
2. Assign **Lesson 143-1** for independent work.

Just for Fun:

Preparation: Get one piece of paper for each member of your class. Write a number on each piece of paper. (Half of the numbers should be positive half of the numbers should be negative.) Put a number on each student's back with a piece of masking tape so that the number hidden.

How the game works: One student taps another on the back and says the word, "greater" or the word "less." The students look at each other's number. If the person was right…their number was greater or less, they get to stay in the game. The other student must sit out of the game.

How to win: Play continues until one player is left.

For he is the living God and he endures forever; his kingdom will not be destroyed his dominion will never end.
Daniel 6: 26

© MCMXCIX, Alpha Omega Publications, Inc.

Lesson 144

Concepts:

Adding integers with like signs, compare integers, opposites, order integers, perimeter and area of parallelograms, construct a hexagon

Objectives:

1. The student will be able to add integers with like signs.
2. The student will be able to compare integers.
3. The student will be able to find the opposite of an integer.
4. The student will be able to group positive and negative integers and order them from largest to smallest.
5. The student will be able to find the area of a parallelogram.
6. The student will be able to construct a regular hexagon.

Teaching Tips:

Some students get confused which direction to move on the number line. Tell them when they add integers they should move in the direction they see on the integer. For instance:

⁻5 + ⁻3 = ⁻8, they would move to the left.
⁺5 + ⁺3 = ⁺8, they would move to the right.

Materials, Supplies, and Equipment:

1. *Worksheet 75*

Activities:

1. Read **Lesson 144 Explanation** together as a class. Make sure the students understand which direction to move on the number line when adding negative numbers versus positive numbers.
2. The student should complete **Lesson 144-1** independently.

Long is the road from conception to completion.
Moliere

Lesson 145

Concepts:
Adding integers with like and unlike signs, compare integers, divide fractions, divide with 4-digit divisors, area of a triangle, construct a square

Objectives:
1. The student will be able to add integers with unlike signs.
2. The student will be able to add integers with like signs.
3. The student will be able to compare integers.
4. The student will be able to divide fractions.
5. The student will be able to divide by a 4-digit divisor.
6. The student will be able to find the area of a triangle.
7. The student will be able to construct a square.

Teaching Tips:
Students grasp this idea quickly when they begin by working on the concrete level.

Materials, Supplies, and Equipment:
1. 14 red disks, 14 green disks (per student)

Activities:
1. Read **Lesson 145 Explanation** together as a class. Use the red and green disks to demonstrate addition of integers with unlike signs. Tell the students that the red disks are represent a negative number and the green disks represent a positive number.
   a. Write the following problem on the board: $^+4 + {}^-3 =$
   b. Place 3 red disks in a line representing $^-3$.
   c. Place 4 green disks in a line beside the other disks representing $^+4$.

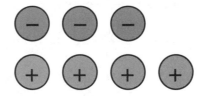

   d. It is easy to see that there is one extra green disk. We know $^+4 + {}^-3 = {}^+1$.

2. Follow the same procedure with a this problem: $^+1 + {}^-5 =$

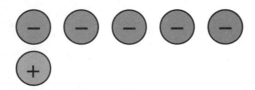

   It is easy to see that there are 4 extra red disks. We know $^+1 + {}^-5 = {}^-4$

3. Assign **Lesson 145-1** as independent work.

One can never consent to creep when one feels an impulse to soar.
Helen Keller

Lesson 146

Concepts:

Subtracting integers on a number line, word problems with integers, adding integers with like and unlike signs, compare integers, area of a triangle, construct a square

Objectives:

1. The student will be able to subtract integers on a number line.
2. The student will be able to solve word problems involving integers.
3. The student will be able to add integers with unlike signs.
4. The student will be able to compare integers.
5. The student will be able to find the area of a triangle.
6. The student will be able to construct a square.

Teaching Tips:

Some students find subtracting integers on a number line very difficult. If they are confused, go to the next lesson and introduce how to subtract integers by adding the opposite.

Materials, Supplies, and Equipment:

Activities:

1. Read **Lesson 146 Explanation** orally with the students. Work the following examples to make sure the students grasp the concept of subtracting integers.

   a. $0 - {}^-4 = {}^+4$

   b. ${}^-2 - {}^-4 = {}^+2$

2. Assign **Lesson 146-1**. Work closely with the students as they complete this assignment.

I am the Lord your God, who teaches you what is best for you,
who directs you in the way you should go.
Isaiah 48:17

Lesson 147

Concepts:

Subtracting integers by adding the opposite, adding integers with like and unlike signs, compare integers, area of a circle, subtracting decimals

Objectives:

1. The student will be able to subtract integers by adding the opposite.
2. The student will be able to subtract integers with unlike signs.
3. The student will be able to add integers with unlike signs.
4. The student will be able to order integers from least to greatest.
5. The student will be able to find the area of a circle.
6. The student will be able to subtract 5-digit numbers.
7. The student will be able to multiply numbers and complete a crossword puzzle.

Teaching Tips:

Students grasp this concept easily. It is a natural outgrowth of the graph work done in the last lesson.

Materials, Supplies, and Equipment:

1. *Worksheet 76*

Activities:

1. Review opposites with the students. Ask the students to give the opposite for the following numbers: -7 (+7), -3 (+3), +15 (-15), +102 (-102).
2. Read **Lesson 147 Explanation** orally.
3. Complete **Lesson 147-1** with the students. After completing this lesson, students should be convinced that you can subtract an integer by adding its opposite.
4. Assign **Lesson 147-2** for independent work.

I will never just live my life—I will invest my life.
Helen Keller

Lesson 148

Concepts:

Graphing ordered pairs in four quadrants, subtracting integers by adding the opposite, adding integers with like and unlike signs, area of a circle, giving change

Objectives:

1. The student will be able to graph ordered pairs in all four quadrants.
2. The student will be able to subtract integers by adding the opposite.
3. The student will be able to subtract integers with unlike signs.
4. The student will be able to find the area of a circle.
5. The student will be able to give appropriate change given the price of an item and the amount paid.

Teaching Tips:

Materials, Supplies, and Equipment:

1. *Worksheet 77*

Activities:

1. Read **Lesson 148 Explanation** together as a class. Have student plot the following coordinates to make sure they understand the concept. (0, 3), (3, 0), (4, -4), and (-4, 4).

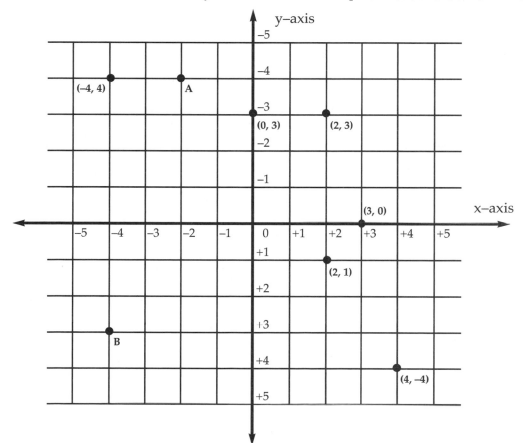

2. The students should complete **Lesson 148-1** as independent work.

Worry never robs tomorrow of its sorrow; it only saps today of its strength.
AJ Cronin

Lesson 149

Concepts:

Multiplying integers, subtracting integers by adding the opposite, finding the volume of cylinders, graphing ordered pairs in four quadrants, bisecting angles, finding the perpendicular bisector of a line

Objectives:

1. The student will be able to multiply integers.
2. The student will be able to subtract integers with unlike signs.
3. The student will be able to find the volume of a cylinder.
4. The student will be able to graph ordered pairs in all four quadrants.
5. The student will be able bisect an angle.
6. The student will be able to find the perpendicular bisector of a given line.

Teaching Tips:

Have the students copy the rules for multiplying integers and keep them in their notebooks. After several days of reviewing the rules they should be able to commit them to memory.

Materials, Supplies, and Equipment:

1. *Worksheet 78*

Activities:

1. Read **Lesson 149 Explanation** orally. Students should grasp this concept easily.
2. The students should complete **Lesson 149-1** as independent work.

> *But my righteousness will last forever, my salvation through all generations.*
> **Isaiah 51: 8b**

© MCMXCIX, Alpha Omega Publications, Inc.

Lesson 150

Concepts:

Dividing integers, multiplying integers, multiplying fractions, graphing ordered pairs in four quadrants, finding the volume of cylinders, dividing fractions

Objectives:

1. The student will be able to divide integers.
2. The student will be able to write three different multiplication problems using integers that would result in a positive answer, and three problems that would result in a negative answer.
3. The student will be able to simplify fractions and then multiply them.
4. The student will be able to graph ordered pairs in all four quadrants.
5. The student will be able to find the volume of a cylinder.
6. The student will be able to divide fractions.

Teaching Tips:

Review the rules for multiplying integers. Tell the students that the rules for dividing integers are exactly the same.

Materials, Supplies, and Equipment:

1. *Worksheet 79*

Activities:

1. Read **Lesson 150 Explanation**. Point out that the rules for multiplication of integers and the rules for division of integers are exactly the same.
2. The students should be able to complete **Lesson 150-1** independently.

> *You can't beat a person who never gives up.*
> **Babe Ruth**

Lesson 151

Concepts:
  Budgets, subtraction, prime numbers, multiply decimals, multiply fractions, area, and ratio

Objectives:
  1. The student will be able to use information given to fill in a monthly budget sheet.
  2. The student will be able to subtract two, five-digit numbers.
  3. The student will be able to find prime numbers and connect them.
  4. The student will be able to find the product of two decimals.
  5. The student will be able to find the product of two fractions.
  6. The student will be able to find the area of each geometric shape.
  7. The student will be able to divide each ratio to find an equal ratio.

Teaching Tips:
  Encourage the students to use a calculator for lesson 151-1.

Materials, Supplies, and Equipment:
  1. Calculator

Activities:
  1. Read **Lesson 151 Explanation** orally. Discuss why people budget their money. When children ask for candy or toys, they often don't understand why adults say they can't afford to buy the items when they have money in their wallets. This is a good time to discuss all of the weekly expenses and what will happen if all of the money is spent early in the pay period.
  2. Assign **Lesson 151-1**. Point out that it is very easy to misplace a decimal or add the wrong number when doing so many calculations at once. It is important that the student add these numbers with their calculators several times to make sure that their calculations are accurate.

But the person who truly loves God is the one who is open to God's knowledge.
1 Corinthians 8:3

Lesson 152

Concepts:
Writing checks, budgets, subtraction, multiply decimals, multiply fractions, surface area, proportions

Objectives:
1. The student will be able to write checks.
2. The student will be able to look at a yearly budget and answer questions correctly.
3. The student will be able to subtract two, five-digit numbers.
4. The student will be able to multiply two decimals.
5. The student will be able to multiply two mixed fractions.
6. The student will be able to find the surface area of three-dimensional shapes.
7. The student will be able to write a proportion and solve it.

Teaching Tips:
Encourage the students to use a calculator for lesson 152-1 and 152-2.

Materials, Supplies, and Equipment:
1. Calculator
2. *Worksheet 80*

Activities:
1. This is a good time to schedule a field trip to your local bank. If you call ahead, they will often give you a tour and explain basic banking practices. Brainstorm a list of questions before you go. Below are a few things you might want to ask.
    a. How old must you be to have a savings account? Checking?
    b. What interest rate do you pay for savings accounts, CDs, IRAs?
    c. Does the bank ever make mistakes?
    d. Does the bank reconcile their records every day?
    e. Do they ever find money that is counterfeit? How can they tell?
    f. What happens if someone writes a check for more than they have in their accounts?
    g. What is bankruptcy?
    h. How does a bank decide who gets a loan?
    i. How does a bank make sure no one can steal their money?
2. Read **Lesson 152 Explanation** together. Show the students some actual checks and real checkbook ledgers. Ask the students why it is so important that the checkbook ledger is accurate. **(You may think you have more money than you actually have and overdraw your account.)**
3. Ask the students why they think it is important to reconcile a checking account every month. **(Banks can make mistakes; you want to check their records. You may have made a mistake on your account. If you don't reconcile your account, you may think you have more money that you actually have and overdraw your account.)**
4. Assign **Lesson 152-1**. Point out that it is very easy to misplace a decimal or add the wrong number when doing so many calculations at once. It is important that the student add these numbers with their calculators several times to make sure that their calculations are accurate.

As the father has loved me, so have I loved you: Continue ye in my love.
John 15:9

Lesson 153

Concepts:

    Banking services, writing checks, budgets, exponential form, add fractions, convert fractions to decimals, divide a whole number by a fraction

Objectives:

1. The student will be able to answer questions about various banking services.
2. The student will be able to write checks.
3. The student will be able to list the five divisions of income in making a budget.
4. The student will be able to look at numbers written in exponential form and write them in standard form. The student will be able to look at numbers in standard form and write them in exponential form.
5. The student will be able to add fractions with common denominators.
6. The student will be able to convert each fraction to its decimal equivalent.
7. The student will be able to divide a whole number by a fraction.

Teaching Tips:

    Encourage the students to use a calculator for lesson 153-3.

Materials, Supplies, and Equipment:

1. Calculator

Activities:

1. Read **Lesson 153 Explanation** together. This is a good time to discuss why it is important to have a savings account. Not only is there the possibility that we might need the money for an emergency, often times we use a savings account to save for things we want to buy. Discuss why this is a much better method than buying items on credit.
2. Have the student call several banks and find out the interest rates for savings accounts, CDs and IRAs. Show the student how much difference 1% can make if you are saving large amounts of money.
3. The student should be able to complete **Lesson 153-1** independently.

No man hath seen God at any time, If we love one another, God dwelleth in us, and his love is perfected in us.
1 John 4:12

© MCMXCIX, Alpha Omega Publications, Inc.

Lesson 154

Concepts:

Simple interest, savings accounts, writing checks, checkbook ledger, budget finances, add and subtract fractions, change fractions to decimals, sales tax

Objectives:

1. The student will be able to find the simple interest charge and total loan amount for loans.
2. The student will be able to complete a savings account slip given specific information.
3. The student will be able to write a check.
4. The student will be able to record information in a checkbook ledger.
5. The student will be able to solve word problems about budgeting finances.
6. The student will be able to find the sum or difference of fractions.
7. The student will be able to change fractions into decimals.
8. The student will be able to determine sales tax.

Teaching Tips:

Encourage the students to use a calculator for lesson 154-1, 154-2 and 154-4.

Materials, Supplies, and Equipment:

1. Savings accounts slips from your local bank.
2. Calculator

Activities:

1. Read **Lesson 154 Explanation** together. Read the information entitled "Interest Earned" carefully. Explain to the students how important it is to be able to save money to make purchases rather than get a loan. The amount of money charged to lend money is very high – much higher than the amount you receive in savings.

2. If you can, show the students some savings account slips from their local bank. Allow them to fill out a real form. Ask them why it is important that all of the information is filled out clearly and accurately. **(If your account number is hard to read, the teller could put your money in someone else's account. If you add incorrectly, and the teller does not find the mistake, the wrong amount will be placed in your account.)** This is a good time to talk about how a bank reconciles their accounts every day. Sometimes they catch mistakes at the end of the day and have to contact their patrons to tell them that there was a mistake made with their account.

3. The student should be able to complete **Lesson 154-1** independently.

Now abideth faith, hope, love, these three; but the greatest of these is love.
1 Corinthians 13:13

Lesson 155

Concepts:
Computing interest, savings accounts, savings withdrawal, checkbook, subtraction, compare fractions, reading circle graphs

Objectives:
1. The student will be able to find the interest given a principle, rate, and length of time.
2. The student will be able to find simple interest and total loan amount given a loan amount and interest rate.
3. The student will be able to complete a savings account withdrawal slip.
4. The student will be able to complete a checkbook ledger.
5. The student will be able to find missing numbers while subtracting two, six-digit numbers.
6. The student will be able to compare fractions.
7. Given the total amount of income earned, the student will be able to convert percentages of income spent into actual dollar amounts.

Teaching Tips:
Encourage the students to use a calculator for lesson 155-1, 155-2, 155-3 and 155-4.

Materials, Supplies, and Equipment:
1. Calculator

Activities:
1. Read **Lesson 155 Explanation** together.
2. The student should be able to complete **Lesson 155-1** independently

Hatred stirs old quarrels, but love overlooks insults.
Proverbs 10:12

Lesson 156

Concepts:

Installment purchases, interest, compare interest rates, savings, binary, add or subtract fractions, divide mixed fractions.

Objectives:

1. The student will be able to complete a chart showing the monthly payments for an installment purchase.
2. Given the principle, interest rate, and length of time of the loan, the student will be able to find the amount of interest.
3. The student will be able to compare different interest rates and answer questions about how it affects the amount paid for a loan.
4. The student will be able to determine yearly savings given weekly income and percent of weekly savings.
5. The student will be able to complete a Binary Place Value Chart.
6. The student will be able to add or subtract fractions.
7. The student will be able to divide mixed fractions.

Teaching Tips:

Encourage the students to use a calculator for lesson 156-1, 156-2, 156-3 and 156-4.

Materials, Supplies, and Equipment:

1. Calculator

Activities:

1. Direct the students' attention to **Lesson 156 Explanation**. Read orally. This is a good time reinforce how expensive it is to buy something on credit. You are paying for both the item and for the money you were loaned.
2. Allow the student to complete **Lesson 156-1** independently.
   Complete **Lesson 156-3** with the student. Talk about why it is so important to get a low interest rate. If the student is interested, this is a good time to talk about why people refinance their houses when the interest rate drops substantially.

Things which the eye has not seen and the ear has not heard, and
which have not entered the heart of man,
all that God has prepared for those who love Him.
1 Corinthians 2:9

Lesson 157

Concepts:
Compare products, installment buying, interest earned, missing numbers, geometric terms, exponential form, multiplying decimals

Objectives:
1. The student will be able to determine which product is the least expensive.
2. The student will be able to complete an installment purchase table.
3. The student will be able to find the interest to be paid to a patron given the amount of their deposit, the interest rate and length of the term.
4. The student will be able to find a missing number given two equivalent fractions.
5. The student will be able to define geometric terms.
6. The student will be able to write a number written in exponential form in standard form.
7. The student will be able to multiply two decimals to find the product. Then they will put the products correctly in a crossword puzzle.

Teaching Tips:
Encourage the students to use a calculator for lesson 157-1, 157-2, 157-3 and 157-4.

Materials, Supplies, and Equipment:
1. Calculator

Activities:
1. Read **Lesson 157 Explanation** together. Explain how much money you can save being a wise consumer. This is a good time to show the students the ads in the newspaper for food, electronics, toys etc. See if they can find the same exact product listed for different prices. Talk about coupons and how they are used at the store to save money.
2. Ask the students to imagine that they were buying a new sound system. What are some things they could do to make sure that they were getting the most value for their money? **(Look in the newspaper for ads, call some stores and get price quotes, and go to several stores and get prices and ask questions.)**
3. Talk about impulse buying. Ask the students why it is not a good idea to see something expensive you want and just buy it. **(You may not have enough money to buy it, you may not want to buy it if you really thought about it, it might not be the best value for the money.)**
4. The students should be able to complete **Lesson 157-1** independently.

Thou art my hiding place; thou shalt preserve me from trouble;
thou shalt compass me about with songs of deliverance.
Psalm 32:7

Lesson 158

Concepts:

Average monthly expenses, compare products, installment buying, interest, mystery number, surface area, equivalent ratios

Objectives:

1. The student will be able to find average monthly expenses.
2. The student will be able to compare products and find the least expensive one.
3. The student will be able to complete an installment purchase table.
4. The student will be able to find the interest given the principle, the interest rate and length of the term.
5. The student will be able to use logical reasoning to find mystery numbers.
6. The student will be able to find the surface area of a box.
7. The student will be able to write two equivalent ratios.

Teaching Tips:

Encourage the students to use a calculator for lesson 158-1, 158-2, 158-3 and 158-4.

Materials, Supplies, and Equipment:

1. Calculator

Activities:

1. Read **Lesson 158 Explanation** together.
2. If possible, have the students track their expenses for a month. Have them write down every time they buy candy, food, toys etc. Have them total the amount of their expenses each week. Help them find out how much they spend on an average every week.
3. The student should be able to complete **Lesson 158-1** independently.

Do not say, "I will repay evil;" wait for the Lord, and He will save you.
Proverbs 20:22

Lesson 159

Concepts:

Type of operation, average monthly expenses, compare products, missing number, subtraction, add fractions, convert fractions to decimals

Objectives:

1. The student will be able to determine what operation to use given a word problem.
2. The student will be able to find average monthly expenses.
3. The student will be able to compare products and find the least expensive ones.
4. The student will be able to find the missing number in a fraction wheel.
5. The student will be able to find the difference given two six-digit numbers.
6. The student will be able to add fractions with common denominators.
7. The student will be able to convert a fraction into a decimal.

Teaching Tips:

Encourage the students to use a calculator for lesson 159-2 and 159-3.

Materials, Supplies, and Equipment:

1. Calculator

Activities:

1. Read **Lesson 159 Explanation** together.
2. Have the students complete **Lesson 159-1** independently.

Blessed is he that considereth the poor: the Lord will deliver him in times of trouble.
Psalm 41:1

Lesson 160

Concepts:

Traveler's checks, travel cards, gift cards, and money orders, type of operation, average monthly expenses, prime numbers, divide decimals, convert pints to gallons, divide larger decimals

Objectives:

1. The student will be able to answer questions about traveler's checks, travel cards, gift cards, and money orders.
2. The student will be able to determine what operation to use given a word problem.
3. The student will be able to find average monthly expenses.
4. The student will be able to find prime numbers and shade them.
5. The student will be able to divide a two-digit decimal by a decimal.
6. The student will be able to convert quarts to pints and gallons.
7. The student will be able to find divide a three-digit decimal by a decimal.

Teaching Tips:

Encourage the students to use a calculator for lesson 160-3.

Materials, Supplies, and Equipment:

1. Calculator

Activities:

1. Read **Lesson 160 Explanation**. Explain to the students how difficult it would be if you were in a foreign country and all of your money and credit cards were stolen.
2. Assign **Lesson 160-1** for independent work.

Take my yoke upon you, and learn of me; for I am meek and lowly in heart:
and ye shall find rest unto your souls.
Matthew 11:29

Answer Key

Lesson 1

1. 134,000,072,000,000
   23,120,085,500,009
   5,000,072,100,120
   5,000,390,500,000

2. 108   138   93   63   158   92

3. 21   12   7   39   4   17

4. Answers will vary but should follow these guidelines: Acute angles measure between 1 and 90, Obtuse angles should measure between 91 and 180, a Right angle should measure exactly 90.

   Acute Angle   Obtuse Angle
           Right Angle

5. $\dfrac{5}{6}$ $\dfrac{4}{10} = \dfrac{2}{5}$ $\dfrac{4}{6} = \dfrac{2}{3}$

         $2\dfrac{3}{4}$ $3\dfrac{2}{4} = 3\dfrac{1}{2}$

6. 11   210   126

Lesson 2

1. <u>3</u>.09 = three and nine hundredths
   <u>ones' place</u>

   10.<u>3</u>7 = ten and thirty-seven hundredths
   <u>tenths' place</u>

   0.001<u>8</u> = eighteen ten thousandths
   <u>ten thousandths' place</u>

   2.00<u>0</u>01 = two and one hundred thousandths
   <u>thousandths' place</u>

   <u>4</u>1.005 = forty-one and five ten thousandths
   <u>ten's place</u>

18.9<u>7</u>5 = eighteen and nine hundred seventy-five thousandths
<u>hundredths' place</u>

2. 15,140,607,000
   55,303,561,000,021
   6,000,500,000,400

3. 96   87   132

4. 66   19   6   18   45
   22   13   12   25
   PERSEVERE

5. $\dfrac{1}{10}$ – bank

   $\dfrac{3}{10}$ – fence

   $\dfrac{3}{5}$ – pie

   $\dfrac{3}{12}$ – puzzle

6. 4   43   30   72   49   11

Lesson 3

1. 200,000; 100,000; 4,500,000
   80,000,000; 10,000,000; 150,000,000
   8,000,000,000; 10,000,000,000; 179,000,000,000

2. 34.097   5.21   24.991   3.376
   23.40   46.950   62.55   1.72
   12.123   7.894   85.02

3. <
   >
   <
   <

4. 709   390   1,502   324
   1,685   179   1,228   152
   ETERNITY

5. quadrilateral   octagon   triangle
   hexagon   pentagon   nonagon

6. $\dfrac{3}{9}$ $\dfrac{2}{4}$ $\dfrac{16}{32}$ $\dfrac{8}{10}$

   $\dfrac{9}{27}$ $\dfrac{8}{24}$ $\dfrac{3}{6}$ $\dfrac{20}{25}$

Shape should spell JESUS.

Lesson 4

1. <   >   >
    <   >
    BE A SERVANT

2. 8,997,765,543,210

3. 8,000,000   5,000,000   14,000,000

    8,000,000,000   21,000,000,000
    71,000,000,000

    600,000   100,000   3,600,000

4. 34.80325   123.57345   0.47983
    5.64653   0.00313   80.00645
    986.21563   1.33333   465.80634
    15.23103   541.89415   0.89444
    0.00014   89.88134

5. $\begin{array}{r} 564 \\ +\,408 \\ \hline 962 \end{array}$ $\begin{array}{r} 451 \\ -\,346 \\ \hline 85 \end{array}$ $\begin{array}{r} 706 \\ +\,398 \\ \hline 1{,}144 \end{array}$

    $\underline{972}$ $\underline{105}$ $\underline{1{,}104}$

    $\begin{array}{r} 198 \\ -\,189 \\ \hline 19 \end{array}$

    $\underline{9}$

6. Answers will vary. The reduced form
    of each fraction is given:

    $\dfrac{1}{2}$ $\dfrac{1}{2}$ $\dfrac{1}{3}$ $\dfrac{5}{6}$ $\dfrac{1}{3}$

Lesson 5

1. f, t, f
    900 − 850 = 50

t, f, f
5,000 + 3,120 = 8,120

t, f, f
3,000 − 2,122 = 878

f, f, t
98 + 45 = 143

f, f, t
1,165 − 549 = 616

t, f, f
1,000 + 450 = 1,450

2. 125.832   125.031   125.030
    125.029   125.028   125.027
    125.00   124.9781   124.879
    124.87   124.777   124.6295
    124.5   124.499

Graphic should be a CROSS.

3. $\boxed{\begin{array}{l} 128{,}451{,}637{,}905 \\ 100{,}000{,}000{,}000 \end{array}}$
    $\underline{128{,}000{,}000{,}000}$

    $\boxed{\begin{array}{l} 32{,}564{,}889 \\ 32{,}000{,}000 \end{array}}$
    $\underline{33{,}000{,}000}$

    $\boxed{\begin{array}{l} 4{,}597{,}684 \\ 4{,}000{,}000 \end{array}}$
    $\underline{5{,}000{,}000}$

    $\boxed{\begin{array}{l} 12{,}806 \\ 10{,}000 \end{array}}$
    $\underline{12{,}800}$

4. 14.58993

5. 3,583   8,927   4,535   13,412   6,069

    2,779   2,480   1,061   1,466   3,967

6. $\dfrac{11}{12}$ $\dfrac{3}{4}$ $\dfrac{23}{32}$

    $\dfrac{2}{3}$ $\dfrac{1}{4}$ $\dfrac{1}{7}$

Lesson 6

1. 14   62   81   69
   25   9   48   127

2. 69   104   377
   915   125   480

3. Order:
   563,170,000; 500,496,321,784
   578,305,682,493; 587,509,873,220

   Rounded:
   563,200,000; 500,496,300,000
   578,305,700,000; 587,509,900,000

   Order:
   19,351,467,000; 9,046,300,803,000
   9,351,467,000,221; 9,937,000,000,000

   Rounded:
   19,351,500,000; 9,046,300,800,000
   9,351,467,000,000; 9,937,000,000,000

4.   8,219   4,880   2,154
   + 5,637   + 7,296   + 3,009
     13,856   12,176   5,163

     9,999   6,711
   + 7,748   + 1,252
     17,747   7,963

5.   8,219   7,296   2,154
   − 5,637   − 4,880   − 1,009
     2,582   2,416   1,145

     9,056   6,711
   − 7,748   − 1,534
     1,308   5,177

6. $\dfrac{3}{8}$ $\dfrac{2}{3}$ $\dfrac{8}{15}$ $\dfrac{2}{5}$

   $\dfrac{2}{3}$ $\dfrac{4}{7}$ $\dfrac{17}{25}$ $\dfrac{3}{5}$

Lesson 7

1. 9 – Commutative Property of Addition
   0 – Zero Property of Addition
   8 – Associative Property of Addition
   35 – Zero Property of Subtraction
   31 – Commutative Property of Addition
   54 – Zero Property of Subtraction

2. 1st - Work what is in parentheses.

   2nd - Work from left to right.

3. GODLINESS
   160 + 100 + 30 + 20 + 90 + 90 + 80 + 90
   + 90 = 750

   PROMISE
   0 + 60 + 100 + 50 + 90 + 90 + 80 = 470

   PHYSICAL
   0 + 10 + 140 + 90 + 90 + 70 + 150 + 20
   = 570

   TRAINING
   40 + 60 + 150 + 90 + 90 + 90 + 90 + 160
   = 770

   HOLY
   10 + 100 + 20 + 140 = 270

   Answers: Training, Godliness, Physical,
   Promise, Holy

4. 58   106   19
   155   271   25

5.   94,016   ?01,60?
   − 66,??4   − 2,819
     27,272   98,?89

     66,<u>7</u>44   101,608
                    98,<u>7</u>89

     9?,006   300,1??
   + 83,08?   + 56?,999
    180,088   ?63,142

     9<u>7</u>,006   300,1<u>4</u>3
     83,08<u>2</u>   562,<u>9</u>99
                   <u>8</u>63,142

6. $\dfrac{2}{3}$ $\boxed{<}$ $\dfrac{11}{12}$ $\dfrac{1}{2}$ $\boxed{>}$ $\dfrac{3}{8}$ $\dfrac{13}{16}$ $\boxed{<}$ $\dfrac{7}{8}$

   $\dfrac{5}{8}$ $\boxed{<}$ $\dfrac{3}{4}$ $\dfrac{2}{9}$ $\boxed{>}$ $\dfrac{1}{6}$

Order of larger fractions:

$\frac{11}{12}$ $\frac{7}{8}$ $\frac{3}{4}$ $\frac{1}{2}$ $\frac{2}{9}$

Lesson 8

1. 83,294   45,359   13,695
   644,385   610,033
   751,755   81,162

2. true (84 = 84)   false (93 ≠ 75)
   true (23 = 23)   false (62 ≠ 46)

3. 145   220   0
   218   88   190

4. Incorrect multiplication facts:
   3 x 15 = 35
   25 x 4 = 75
   18 x 2 = 35
   30 x 15 = 191
   45 x 3 = 67
   20 x 60 = 120
   98 x 3 = 249
   30 x 9 = 280
   Answer: Glory

5. Scalene   –

   Isosceles   –

   Equilateral –

   Right   –

   Answers:
   Student answers should contain the
   following information:

   Scalene triangles – all sides and angles
   have different measurements.

   Isosceles triangles have two sides and
   angles with the same measurements.

   Equilateral triangles have all sides and
   angles with the same measurements.

   A right triangle contains one 90 angle.

6. $\frac{1}{2}$ $\frac{2}{8}$ $\frac{3}{4}$ $\frac{1}{3}$

   Order:
   $\frac{3}{4}$ $\frac{1}{2}$ $\frac{1}{3}$ $\frac{2}{8}$

7. 9 – Commutative Property of Addition
   0 – Zero Property of Addition
   8 – Associative Property of Addition

   90 – Zero Property of Subtraction
   65 – Commutative Property of Addition
   198 – Zero Property of Subtraction

Lesson 9

1. | 366,721 | 567,343 |
    |---|---|
    | − 143,547 | − 313,185 |
    | 223,174 | 254,158 |

78,884	49,981
− 64,107	− 13,219
14,777	36,762

7,865	8,484
− 3,621	− 4,806
4,244	3,678

2. | 12,180 | |
    |---|---|
    | 31,182 | 5,891 |
    | + 7,009 | + 231 |
    | 50,371 | 6,122 |

783	
8,862	918,073
+ 10,057	+ 570,669
19,702	1,488,742

    $6,207.35 + $992.40 = $7,199.75

    93,221 + 78,033 = 171,254

3. 78 – Zero Property of Subtraction
   58 – Commutative Property of Addition
   1,252 – Zero Property of Subtraction

   91 – Commutative Property of Addition
   0 – Zero Property of Addition
   18 – Associative Property of Addition

4. 24   45   85

   25   59   64

5. 6   56   24   45   81   42

   63   36   0   24

6.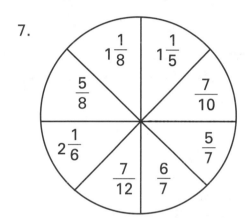

   Triangular Prism   Rectangular Pyramid   Cone

   Sphere   Rectangular Prism   Triangular Pyramid

7.

$$1\frac{1}{8} \quad 1\frac{1}{5}$$
$$\frac{5}{8} \quad \frac{7}{10}$$
$$2\frac{1}{6} \quad \frac{5}{7}$$
$$\frac{7}{12} \quad \frac{6}{7}$$

Lesson 10

1. <u>Order from lowest to highest:</u>
   1. New Castle City;   2. Mount Frissell
   3. Brasstown Bald,   4. Mount Rodgers
   5. Guadalupe Peak;   6. Mount Hood
   7. Humphries Peak;   8. Mount Elbert
   9. Mount Whitney

   $14{,}000 - 11{,}000 = 3{,}000$ ft

   $13{,}000 - 400 = 12{,}600$ ft

   Rodgers/Guadalupe =
   $9{,}000 - 6{,}000 = 3{,}000$
   Hood/Elbert =
   $14{,}000 - 11{,}000 = 3{,}000$
   The estimated difference is the same.

2. 106,941   867,537   379,930

   115,180   16,598   508,757

3. 5   6   6   8   9

   8   12   11   9   4

4. Answers will vary according to student response. Example answers are given.
   $4 + 5 = 9$ and $5 + 4 = 9$

   Subtraction is not commutative.

   $(3 + 5) + 2 = 10$ and $3 + (5 + 2) = 10$

   Subtraction is not associative.

   $4 + 0 = 4$

   $5 - 0 = 5$ and $6 - 6 = 0$

5.

   Rhombus   Parallelogram   Square

   Rectangle   Trapezoid

6. $\frac{3}{3} = 1$ whole; $\frac{9}{10}$; $\frac{2}{4} = \frac{1}{2}$; $\frac{9}{11}$

   $\frac{9}{12} = \frac{3}{4}$; $\frac{40}{100} = \frac{2}{5}$; $\frac{20}{25} = \frac{4}{5}$

   $\frac{6}{8} = \frac{3}{4}$

   $\frac{4}{6} = \frac{2}{3}$; $\frac{6}{9} = \frac{2}{3}$; $\frac{8}{10} = \frac{4}{5}$; $\frac{6}{7}$

   Answer: INTEGRITY

Lesson 11

1. $v = 9$ $m = 4$ $z = 4$ $v = 11$
   $c = 5$ $x = 2$ $r = 12$ $t = 2$
   $b = 9$ $c = 10$ $z = 11$ $k = 12$
   $x = 35$ $x = 81$ $x = 100$ $x = 39$
   $x = 49$ $x = 72$ $x = 63$ $x = 48$

2.
$$\begin{array}{r} 569{,}241 \\ -\ 531{,}955 \\ \hline 37{,}286 \end{array} \qquad \begin{array}{r} 900{,}801 \\ -\ 762{,}690 \\ \hline 138{,}111 \end{array}$$

$$\begin{array}{r} 306{,}082 \\ -\ 65{,}961 \\ \hline 240{,}121 \end{array} \qquad \begin{array}{r} 225{,}909 \\ -\ 157{,}753 \\ \hline 68{,}156 \end{array}$$

3.
$$\begin{array}{r} 909{,}270 \\ +\ 400{,}969 \\ \hline 1{,}310{,}239 \end{array} \qquad \begin{array}{r} 978{,}822 \\ +\ 568{,}097 \\ \hline 1{,}546{,}919 \end{array}$$

$$\begin{array}{r} 586{,}702 \\ +\ 601{,}588 \\ \hline 1{,}188{,}290 \end{array} \qquad \begin{array}{r} 656{,}342 \\ +\ 58{,}769 \\ \hline 715{,}111 \end{array}$$

4. straw = $4\frac{7}{8}$

   candy = $1\frac{1}{8}$

   medallion = $2\frac{5}{8}$

5. $\frac{6}{12} = \frac{1}{2}$ $\qquad \frac{10}{14} = \frac{5}{7}$ $\qquad \frac{5}{7}$

   $\frac{2}{24} = \frac{1}{12}$ $\qquad \frac{2}{11}$ $\qquad\qquad \frac{3}{10}$

6. teacher check

Lesson 12

1. 3   3   9   6

   65   10   24   54

2. $c = 7$ $x = 3$ $z = 3$ $k = 40$

   $x = 60$ $x = 56$ $x = 600$ $x = 54$

   $x = 28$ $x = 18$ $x = 204$ $x = 320$

3.

Across	Down
1. 59,230	1. 54,335
3. 35,584	2. 3,008
4. 8,637	5. 48
7. 678	6. 12,807

4. coin = $\frac{5}{8}$ inch

   eraser = $1\frac{3}{8}$ inch

   meatball = $1\frac{1}{8}$ inch

   paper clip = $1\frac{2}{8}$ inch

5. $\frac{4}{12} = \frac{1}{3}$ $\qquad \frac{2}{4} = \frac{1}{2}$ $\qquad \frac{3}{9} = \frac{1}{3}$

   $\frac{10}{12} = \frac{5}{6}$ $\qquad \frac{8}{11}$ $\qquad \frac{8}{10} = \frac{4}{5}$

6. 1. Zack $6.00; Randy $ 7.50
      Randy made $1.50 more than Zack.

   2. $780.00

   3. 240 cookies

   4. $5.75 x 75 = $431.25
      45.63 + $12.19 + $5.60 + $3.90 +
      $17.00 = $84.32
      $431.25 – $84.32 = $346.93 profit

Lesson 13

1. True
   False
   False
   True
   True
   False
   True

2. 2. $6 \boxed{+} 7 \boxed{+} 4 = 17$

   3. $12 \boxed{\div} 4 \boxed{+} 14 = 17$

   4. $36 \boxed{\div} 6 \boxed{-} 1 = 5$

   5. $45 \boxed{+} 9 \boxed{+} 6 \boxed{-} 10 = 50$

   6. $8 \boxed{+} 12 \boxed{+} 4 \boxed{\div} 2 = 12$
      or $8 \times 12 \div 4 \div 2 = 12$

3. $b = 6$ $c = 3$ $d = 4$ $k = 12$
   $x = 30$ $x = 24$ $x = 56$ $x = 12$

4.
```
   900              400
 + 400            + 600
 1,300  R         1,000  T

   700              700
 + 800            + 400
 1,500  S         1,100  E

   700              200
 + 100            + 500
   800  T           700  A

   200
 + 100
   300  B
```

Answer: BATTERS

5. 40 ounces   4 cups
   12 cups   32 cups
   32 pints   144 cups

6. $4\frac{1}{5}$;   7; $4\frac{1}{7}$; $28\frac{1}{2}$

   11; $4\frac{3}{9} = 4\frac{1}{3}$; $5\frac{1}{2}$; $8\frac{6}{9} = 8\frac{2}{3}$

   $1\frac{5}{25} = 1\frac{1}{5}$; $2\frac{18}{36} = 2\frac{1}{2}$;

   $6\frac{4}{14} = 6\frac{2}{7}$; $47\frac{3}{12} = 47\frac{1}{4}$

Lesson 14

1. 4,865   1,516   2,709   68,728   55,728
   2,424   3,426   5,128

2. 15   173
   43   16
   43   178
   234   81

3. $c = 9$ $x = 8$ $r = 9$ $t = 8$
   $b = 35$ $x = 100$ $z = 30$ $k = 25$
   $x = 65$ $x = 153$ $x = 700$ $x = 405$
   $x = 105$ $x = 279$ $x = 126$ $x = 336$

4. 8 cups   16 cups
   8 cups   48 cups
   64 cups   160 cups

5. $8\frac{4}{7}$ 9   13 $12\frac{2}{4} = 12\frac{1}{2}$

   $40\frac{3}{4}$ $70\frac{2}{3}$ 17   45

6.
```
  24,000           5,000
+ 12,000         + 1,000
  36,000           6,000

  12,000          68,000
+  6,000         + 2,000
  18,000          70,000

  45,000          15,000
+  6,000         + 2,000
  51,000          17,000

  22,000          57,000
+  5,000         + 11,000
  27,000          68,000

   4,000          17,000        100,000
+  1,000         + 3,000        +  6,000
   5,000          20,000        106,000
```

Answer: A television

7. 156

Lesson 15

1.
```
     68              92              49
   x 11            x  12           x  28
    748            1,104           1,372

    212             131             313
  x  62           x  27           x 120
 13,144           3,537          37,560

    264             305             413
  x 108           x 411           x 204
 28,512         125,355          84,252

    244
  x 321
 78,324
```

2. $\frac{41}{5}$ $\frac{74}{9}$ $\frac{31}{8}$ $\frac{67}{6}$

   $\frac{116}{7}$ $\frac{31}{2}$ $\frac{52}{3}$ $\frac{51}{4}$

3. $\frac{1}{3}$ 1.08   1.40 $1\frac{1}{2}$

   $1\frac{3}{5}$ 1.75 $1\frac{8}{10}$ 1.90

   2   2.01   2.1   2.3

   $2\frac{1}{2}$ 2.75   3.7

4. 168   9
   21,120   5,280
   9   2
   54   72

5. 2,360   4,792   6,138
   796   3,048   2,547

6. 108   925
   64   38
   7   24

7. 1. $\overline{AC}$
   2. $\overline{BA}$, $\overline{BC}$, or $\overline{BK}$
   3. 3 inches

Lesson 16

1.

50	80	100
x 20	x 20	x 50
1,000	1,600	5, 000

600	900	500
x 200	x 800	x 700
120,000	720,000	350,000

300
x 800
240,000

2.

a = 2	b = 5	c = 6
d = 7	f = 7	h = 6
e = 6	g = 1	i = 6

3. 3   1
   6   2
   30   10
   1,760   5,280   63,360
   3,520   10,560   126,720

4. $4\frac{3}{5}$ $9\frac{7}{8}$ $12\frac{1}{6}$ $4\frac{8}{9}$

   $16\frac{8}{55}$ $18\frac{1}{2}$ $35\frac{1}{3}$ $1\frac{8}{55}$

Answer: GOLDFISH

5. point V   line segment AB
   line XY   ray GH

6. Example:

2	3	4
3	4	2
4	2	3

7. 1. $15 \div 5 + 6 = 9$
   2. $61 + 9 + 22 = 92$
   3. $24 \div 6 - 1 = 3$
   4. $36 \times 6 - 16 = 200$

Lesson 17

1. $\begin{array}{r} 295 \\ 7\overline{)2,065} \end{array}$ $\begin{array}{r} 460 \text{ R5} \\ 7\overline{)3,225} \end{array}$ $\begin{array}{r} 421 \text{ R1} \\ 6\overline{)2,527} \end{array}$

   $8,132 \div 4 = 2,033$

   $\frac{1,566}{3} = 522$ $\frac{1}{8}$ of $5,400 = 675$

2.

80	80	100
x 70	x 80	x 100
5,600	6,400	10,000

1,000	900	600
x 800	x 900	x 600
800,000	810,000	360,000

3. Incorrect answers are:

69	132
x 10	x 43
6,900 (690)	5,688 (5,676)

Answer: SILKWORM

4. 25   80
    2   14,000
    120   1,392
    5   136,000

5. 210

6. $n = 224$; $n = 12$; $n = 9$; $n = 66$

7. Example:

    4   9   2

    3   5   7

    8   1   6

Lesson 18

1.
$$12\overline{)876} = 73 \qquad 45\overline{)725} = 16\text{ R}5$$

$$32\overline{)928} = 29 \qquad 18\overline{)846} = 47$$

$$41\overline{)1,150} = 28\text{ R}2 \qquad 54\overline{)3,892} = 72\text{ R}4$$

$$47\overline{)4,195} = 89\text{ R}12 \qquad 67\overline{)6,164} = 92$$

2. $\dfrac{2892}{6} = 482$; $17,592 \div 8 = 2,199$

$\dfrac{1}{7}$ of $48,104 = 6,872$; $6,354 \div 9 = 706$

$\dfrac{4,172}{4} = 1,043$; $\dfrac{1}{8}$ of $40,088 = 5,011$

3.
600	400
x 200	x 800
120,000	320,000

600	900
x 500	x 200
300,000	180,000

4.

						1		
1	0	4	6	4	7			2
	0			6		6	2	3	7
	4			2		0			9
	9	1	3	3	8	4			3
	8			0				

33,115	57	63
x 2	x 49	x 99
66,230	2,793	6,237

362	652	3,596
x 29	x 27	x 254
10,498	17,604	913,384

461
x 227
104,647

5. 9   192
    5   42,000
    200   1,392
    450   232,000

6. 66

7. $n = 296$ $n = 63$ $n = 35$ $n = 168$

Lesson 19

1.
$$72\overline{)634} = 8\text{ R}58 \qquad 78\overline{)628} = 8\text{ R}4$$

$$24\overline{)1,761} = 73\text{ R}9 \qquad 54\overline{)1,592} = 29\text{ R}26$$

$$89\overline{)2,416} = 27\text{ R}13 \qquad 64\overline{)1,832} = 28\text{ R}40$$

$$14\overline{)9,867} = 704\text{ R}11 \qquad 23\overline{)1,590} = 69\text{ R}3$$

2. $\dfrac{5394}{6} = 899$ $12,523 \div 7 = 1,789$

$\frac{1}{3}$ of 28,686 = 9,562   5,193 ÷ 9 = 577

$\frac{2,118}{2}$ = 1,059 $\frac{1}{5}$ of 43,870 = 8,774

3.
```
      80              30
  x   90          x   70
   7,200           2,100

     900             300
  x  400          x  600
 360,000         180,000
```

4. Answers: Thermometer readings should match the indicated temperature.

5. 54   40   80   36   100
   50   180   320   56   150

6. Order of numbers will vary.

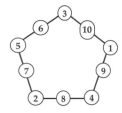

7. 10   9   7
   25   15   9
   76   8   79

Lesson 20

1. 40   34
   120   244

2. 70   70
   158   405

3.
```
        8 R67            8 R73
  74)659          98)857

        7 R20              62
  67)489          48)2,976
```

4.
```
      489            881 R3
  8)3,912        7)6,170

      603 R4
  6)3,622        28,555 ÷ 5 = 5,711
```

$\frac{1,546}{2}$ = 773 $\frac{1}{8}$ of 9,632 = 1,204

5. Answers: Thermometer readings should match the indicated temperature.

6. 37° C   –   body temperature
   0° C   –   water freezes
   -15° C   –   very cold winter day
   100° C   –   water boils
   20° C   –   room temperature

7. 51   194   42
   38   37   9

Lesson 21

1.
```
      1,602           1,242
  x   4,388       x   2,175
  7,029,576       2,701,350

      5,080           2,314
  x   3,324       x   1,432
 16,885,920       3,313,648
```

2. Answers will vary. Check to make sure that each requested number is in the appropriate place.

3. 352.5 = 353   205.25 = 205

   627.4 = 627   1,079.75 = 1,080

4.
```
        5 R9            6 R6            8 R3
  28)149         37)228         53)427

        5 R10           5 R8            9 R4
  82)420         62)318         19)175
```

5. 12, 15, 18   9, 11, 13

   26, 31, 28, 33   82, 77, 78, 73

6. <u>John:</u>
   Highlighter package – $5.95
   WWJD bracelet – $3.00
   Silver cross – $7.95

© MCMXCIX, Alpha Omega Publications, Inc.

$6.00 + $3.00 + $8.00 = $17.00
$20.00 – $17.00 = $3.00 left over

Sally:
Bible cover – $12.95
Computer game – $15.95
$13.00 + $16.00 = $29.00

Tom:
Music CD – $16.00 or Computer Game – $15.95
Devotional book – $11.95
$16.00 + $12.00 = $28.00

Cathy:
12 silver crosses at $7.95 each
$8.00 x 12 = $96.00

7. 526.3 = 526   3,225.5 = 3,226
   8.4 = 8   25.6 = 26
   42.8 = 43

Lesson 22

1.
```
      45,871                23,065
   x  11,010             x  15,322
  505,039,710           353,401,930

      36,413                 6,805
   x  54,223             x   1,205
 1,974,422,099           8,200,025

       5,143
   x   2,236
   11,499,748
```

2. Answers: 1,342,213; 4,756,891;
   120,000,000,000,000; 45,667,208

3. $15.00 x 2 = $30.00
   $15.00 x 50 = $750.00
   $2.00 + ($5.00 x 3) + $5.00 = $22.00
   Answers will vary.

4. 83   181   142   153   71   64

5. 1,872   3,750   744
   6,970   508   39,423   42,777
   2,940   5,644   8,900
   Answer: BE THANKFUL

6.
```
      45,803                 5,667
   x  13,000             x   4,511
  595,439,000           25,563,837

      12,891                 1,323
   x  18,459             x   1,006
  237,954,969            1,330,938

       7,002
   x   4,287
   30,017,574
```

Lesson 23

1. 4,000   1,500,000   63,000   4,800,000
   240,000   160,000   2,000   4,000

2. 6,987,543,211,100
   10,201,359
   1,752,000
   3,012,224,667,899
   264,410,000

3. 3,100   7,500   52,000
   44,000   22,000   4,200
   1,900   89,000   75,000
   Answer: SACRIFICE

4. 70   87   204
   168   159   54

5. 414   1,515

Lesson 24

1.
```
        8 R1                    9 R35
  532 )4,257            235 )2,150

       86 R60                  83 R170
  115 )9,950            450 )37,520
```

2. 35 x 5 = 175   54 x 5 = 270
   1,567 x 9 = 14,103   329 x 8 = 2,632

3. 8,614 x 9,134 = 78,680,276
   5,562 x 6,225 = 34,623,450
   19,303 x 11,002 = 212,371,606
   21,453 x 21,771 = 467,053,263

Horizons Math 6 Answer Key

4. 9831, 9813, 8931 or 8913
    152
    7456, 7465, 6754 or 6574
    873

5. 56; 98; 12; 99; 10   55
    9; 21; 83; 15   32
    33; 121; 1,111;   421.6
    1,295; 3,065; 295, 59; 21   947

6. Across   Down
    1. 8,200   2. 2,900
    3. 506,000   4. 43,000
    4. 497,000   5. 6,100
    6. 129,000   7. 7,000

Lesson 25

1.
$$1,458 \overline{)4,374}^{\;3}$$
$$8,321 \overline{)124,817}^{\;15\ R2}$$

$$7,803 \overline{)897,349}^{\;115\ R4}$$
$$3,267 \overline{)182,952}^{\;56}$$

$$159 \overline{)3,660}^{\;23\ R3}$$
$$448 \overline{)49,728}^{\;111}$$

$$692 \overline{)33,910}^{\;49\ R2}$$

2.
$$\begin{array}{r} 20 \\ \times\ 20 \\ \hline 400 \end{array}\qquad \begin{array}{r} 150 \\ \times\ 120 \\ \hline 18,000 \end{array}$$

$$\begin{array}{r} 280 \\ \times\ 550 \\ \hline 154,000 \end{array}\qquad \begin{array}{r} 9,400 \\ \times\ 260 \\ \hline 2,444,000 \end{array}$$

$$\begin{array}{r} 82,00 \\ \times\ 320 \\ \hline 26,240,000 \end{array}\qquad \begin{array}{r} 2,400 \\ \times\ 1,200 \\ \hline 2,880,000 \end{array}$$

$$\begin{array}{r} 46,000 \\ \times\ 1,200 \\ \hline 55,200,000 \end{array}\qquad \begin{array}{r} 70 \\ \times\ 30 \\ \hline 2,100 \end{array}$$

$$\begin{array}{r} 70 \\ \times\ 10 \\ \hline 700 \end{array}$$

Answer: INTEGRITY

3.
$$\begin{array}{r} 59,100 \\ \times\ 36,360 \\ \hline 2,148,876,000 \end{array}\qquad \begin{array}{r} 46,521 \\ \times\ 38,810 \\ \hline 1,805,480,010 \end{array}$$

$$\begin{array}{r} 50,459 \\ \times\ 47,841 \\ \hline 2,414,009,019 \end{array}\qquad \begin{array}{r} 14,784 \\ \times\ 20,826 \\ \hline 307,891,584 \end{array}$$

4. 18   24.5 = 25   43
    16   148.75 = 149   89.5 = 90

5. 1,256   1,871   6,341   4,554

6. B. Kathy is not in Joseph's class.
    B. There is a meeting today.
    C. No conclusion can be drawn from the information given.

Lesson 26

1.
$$11 \overline{)7,243}^{\;200}$$
$$12 \overline{)4,596}^{\;500}$$
too low   too high
658 R5   383

$$23 \overline{)2,111}^{\;70}$$
$$5 \overline{)829}^{\;400}$$
too low   too high
91 R18   165 R4

2.
$$125 \overline{)5,662}^{\;45\ R37}$$
$$543 \overline{)8,903}^{\;16\ R215}$$

$$1,234 \overline{)6,903}^{\;5\ R733}$$
$$7,601 \overline{)10,546}^{\;1\ R2,945}$$

$$437 \overline{)12,870}^{\;29\ R197}$$
$$1,033 \overline{)56,341}^{\;54\ R559}$$

$$101 \overline{)529}^{\;5\ R24}$$

GLORIFY

3. Nearest ten.
    12,460   22,310   45,720

    Nearest hundred.
    354,800   97,400   156,000

    Nearest thousand.
    1,708,000   498,000   2,281,000

4. 1,247   34,768   701
   38,166   78,993   396,059

5.   27[4]   746   [6]09
    + 738   + [4]24   + 893
    [1],012   1,1[70]   1,50[2]

      [7]48   490   987
    + 147   + [7]55   + 2[8]1
     89[5]   1,24[5]   1,26[8]

6. Two largest numbers:
   9,789 and 9,807

   Two smallest numbers:
   201 and 191

   Shape: LIPS

Lesson 27

1. 150 ÷ 3 = 50   560 ÷ 7 = 80
   2,400 ÷ 6 = 400   4,900 ÷ 7 = 700

2.   40   50
    15)601   21)843

    correct   too high
    40 R1   40 R3

          10   5
    55)1,021   89)182
    too low   too high
    18 R31   2 R4

3.   22 R57   16 R144
    371)8,219   296)4,880

              1 R855   1 R1,040
    2,154)3,009   5,671)6,711

4. 6,326   18,914   1,114
   12,106   190,847   55,775

5. Drawings will vary some.

   15 ft. + 15 ft. + 30 ft. + 30 ft. = 90 ft.
   or (15 ft x 2) + (30 ft. x 2) = 90 ft.

   (12 in x 2) + (25 in x 2) = 74 in
   or 12 in + 12 in + 25 in + 25 in = 74 in.

10 m x 4 = 40 m

(8 m x 2) + (6 m x 4)= 40 m
or 8 + 8 + 6 + 6 + 6 + 6 = 40 m

6. JESUS   2.3 + 0.2 + 0.7 + 0.5 + 0.7
                  = 4.4

   ABRAHAM   0.3 + 1.7 + 0.6 + 0.3 + 0.8
                  + 0.3 + 1.3 = 5.3

   PAUL   1.4 + 0.3 + 0.5 + 1.0 = 3.2

   WISDOM   2.0 + 1.2 + 0.7 + 0.9 + 0
                  + 1.3 = 6.1

   OBEDIENCE   0 + 1.7 + 0.2 + 0.9 + 1.2
                  + 0.2 + 0.4 + 1.1 + 0.2
                  = 5.9

   DISCIPLINE   0.9 + 1.2 = 0.7 + 1.1 + 1.2
                  + 1.4 + 1.0 + 1.2 + 0.4
                  + 0.2 = 9.3

7. 34.002 + 52.65 - 24.1 = 63.552
   86.403 + 164.023 - 104.806 = 145.62
   4.03 + 5,000 + .03 - 1,015 = 3,989.06
   158.214 + 7.4 - 78.06 = 87.554

Lesson 28

1. 12 stacks
   6 trays
   12 pencils
   40 hours per week
   $110.00

2.   50   30
    5)250   9)270

        50   90
    8)400   5)450

        800
    9)7,200

© MCMXCIX, Alpha Omega Publications, Inc.

3.
$$11 \overline{)9{,}143} \quad 200$$
too low
831 R2

$$15 \overline{)4{,}596} \quad 500$$
too high
306 R6

$$29 \overline{)3.001} \quad 70$$
too low
103 R14

$$5 \overline{)909} \quad 400$$
too high
181 R4

4.
$$1{,}257 \overline{)11{,}256} \quad 8 \text{ R}1200$$

$$2{,}584 \overline{)45{,}645} \quad 17 \text{ R}1{,}717$$

$$3{,}002 \overline{)6{,}124} \quad 2 \text{ R}120$$

$$2{,}546 \overline{)7{,}639} \quad 3 \text{ R}1$$

$$5{,}671 \overline{)5{,}672} \quad 1 \text{ R}1$$

5. 61,153   57,691   415
   8,027   11,931   850

6. 346 yds
   7 ft
   1405 meters
   30 ft

Lesson 29

1. $1.26 –   1 dollar, 1 quarter, 1 penny

   $1.71 –   1 dollar, 2 quarters, 2 dimes
              1 penny

   $8.64 –   1 five, 3 ones, 2 quarters
              1 dime, 4 pennies

   $17.85 –   1 ten, 1 five, 2 ones
              3 quarters, 1 dime

   $12.81 –   1 ten, 2 ones, 3 quarters
              1 nickel, 1 penny

   $54.50 –   1 fifty, 4 ones, 2 quarters

2. 75 MPH
   10 lines per second
   12 box = 47 with 8 left over

8 box = 71 with 4 left over
4 more will be left over if the bigger box is used

10 pack about $1.80 each.
20 pack about $1.95 each.
The 10 pack for $17.99 is a better deal.

3. 3   5   3   4
   8   5   4   6

4. 1   31   2   5
   36   153   18   105

5. Clockwise from the top:
$$\frac{3}{6} = \frac{1}{2}; \quad \frac{2}{6} = \frac{1}{3}; \quad \frac{5}{6}; \quad \frac{6}{6} = 1; \quad \frac{1}{6}$$

$$\frac{6}{14} = \frac{3}{7}; \quad \frac{4}{14} = \frac{2}{7}; \quad \frac{2}{14} = \frac{1}{7}$$

$$\frac{10}{14} = \frac{5}{7}; \quad \frac{14}{14} = 1$$

6. 15 ft. x 21 ft. = 315 ft²
   25 m x 25 m = 625 m²
   10 ft. x 18 ft. = 180 ft²
   12 ft x 24 ft = 288 ft²

7. too high; 2 R202   too low; 5 R82
   too low; 48 R469   too high; 9 R939

Lesson 30

1. 1. $3.25 + $0.60 + $0.95 = $4.80
   2. $1.00 + $1.50 + $0.75 + $0.75 = $4.00
   3. Dawson - $4.95
      Alex - $2.95 + $1.00 + $0.95 = $4.90
      Dawson spent $0.05 more.
   4. $3.00 + $0.60 + $0.60 = $4.20
      $4.20 ÷ 2 = $2.10
   5. The only 2 sandwiches which will total $5.95 are the Egg Salad and the Turkey.
   6. cheesecake with a topping

2. 48   3   21   5
   5   87   95   9

© MCMXCIX, Alpha Omega Publications, Inc.

3. 8; 10; 12   17; 21; 25
   80; 85; 75   92; 98; 105

4.

$$\overrightarrow{\text{M} \quad \text{N}}$$

$$p \quad \overleftrightarrow{}$$

$$\overline{\text{A} \qquad \text{B}}$$

A plane is a flat surface that continues infinitely in all directions.

5. 30 seconds   – $\frac{1}{2}$ minute

   $5\frac{1}{2}$ days   –   132 hours

   60 minutes   –   1 hour

   12 hours   – $\frac{1}{2}$ day

   24 hours   –   1,440 minutes

6. $\frac{5}{16}$ $\frac{40}{100} = \frac{2}{5}$

   $\frac{66}{78} = \frac{11}{13}$ $\frac{100}{100}$ = 1 whole

   $\frac{56}{58} = \frac{28}{29}$ $\frac{13}{33}$

7. 225 m²   311 m²
   50 ft²   750 ft²

Lesson 31

1. 1. Point K
   2. Line AB
   3. Line Segment PQ
   4. Ray XY
   5. Line x
   6. Line Segment LM
   7. Plane Z

1. $p \parallel q$
2. k intersects l
3. $d \perp c$

2. 52,020   59,488
   138,182   1,117,862
   795,108   632,270   321,884   391,475

3. 1. New York, North Dakota, 17,403,141 difference in population
   2. Arizona, Maryland 103,867 sq. miles difference in land area
   3. 1,384,483 greater population
   4. 12,993 ft.
   5. 146 ft.

4. $v = 7$ $m = 8$ $c = 8$ $x = 9$
   $b = 5$ $c = 12$ $x = 35$ $x = 28$
   $x = 14$ $x = 8$ $x = 12$ $x = 40$

5. Even numbers: 22, 28, 30, 32, 36, 38 44, 50, 56, 60

   Odd numbers: 3, 5, 7, 11, 15, 17

6. 20   20   20   20
   30   30

Lesson 32

1. 1. acute   5. right
   2. obtuse   6. acute
   3. right   7. obtuse
   4. acute   8. right

   1. 35°
   2. 90°
   3. 120°

2.

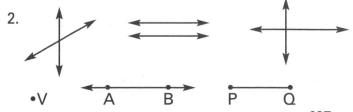

•V   A   B   P   Q

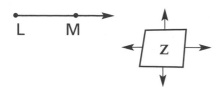

3. 45   13   150

   3   108   16

  72   23   98

4. Unshaded boxes:

   132.6 H;   0.003 O   3.9221 N

   4.55 E   12.2 Y   99.380 C

   5.0003 O 6.2 M   18.3 B

   Answer: honeycomb

5. 1. California, Mount Whitney 14,494 ft.

   2. Florida, Walton County 345 ft.

   3. Georgia, 4,784 ft. higher, 9649 ft.

   4. Georgia, Florida, Delaware,
      Connecticut, Arkansas, and Alabama

6. Any order:

   14 ⊕ 7 ⊕ 11 = 32

   14 ⊕ 7 ⊖ 11 = 10

   14 ⊖ 7 ⊕ 11 = 18

Lesson 33

1. yes   no   yes   yes   yes

triangle	3	3	0
quadrilateral	4	4	2
pentagon	5	5	5
hexagon	6	6	9
octagon	8	8	20
decagon	10	10	35

2.   Answers will vary

      Answers will vary

      90°

      180°

3. 1. *m* ‖ *a*

   2. point G

   3. m ⊥ b;   a ⊥ b

   4. p intersects a, m, or b
      b intersects a, m, or p

   5. yes

4. Correct answers:

   1,437,169   28,596   3,657

   2,119,854   141,664   99,140

   Answer: Daniel

5. 94   132   96   139   114   121

6. $4.79 change due
   4 ones, 3 quarters, 4 pennies

   $18.85 change due
   1 ten dollar bill, 1 five dollar bill
   three ones, 3 quarters, 1 dime

   $0.31 change due
   1 quarter, 1 nickel, 1 penny

   $0.86 change due
   3 quarters, 1 dime, 1 penny

   $7.25 change due
   1 five dollar bill, 2 ones, 1 quarter

Lesson 34

1. 1. ∠D, ∠C, ∠F, ∠E

   2. C̄D̄ and ĒF̄; C̄Ē and D̄F̄

   3. parallelogram, rectangle

2. 1. ∠AXB, ∠AXC, ∠BXC, ∠CXD

   2. ∠BXD

   3. ∠AXD

   4. ∠X or ∠BXA

   5. ∠BXA Because ∠X refers to many
      other angles.

3. point   –   a.

    parallel   –   d.

    line   –   b.

    line segment   –   e.

    ray   –   f.

    intersecting lines   –   h.

    perpendicular lines –   g.

    plane   –   c.

4. triangle   –   3 sides

    octagon   –   8 sides

    decagon   –   10 sides

    quadrilateral   –   4 sides

    hexagon   –   6 sides

    pentagon   –   5 sides

5. 286 N;   355 E;   450 B;   49 U

   391 C;   210 H;   333 A   47 D

   286 N;   355 E;   130 Z   130 Z

   333 A;   388 R

   Answer: NEBUCHADNEZZAR

6. 77   62   46

   291   107   179

Lesson 35

1. Answer: The following figures should be circled: E and G; C and F; B and J; and D and I.

2. 1. Polygon, Quadrilateral
   Parallelogram, Rectangle

   2. Polygon, Quadrilateral
   Parallelogram, Square, Rectangle
   Rhombus

   3. Polygon, Quadrilateral, Trapezoid

   4. Polygon, Quadrilateral
   Parallelogram, Rhombus

3. 1.   –   C.

   2.   –   D.

   3.   –   G.

   4.   –   B.

   5.   –   A.

   6.   –   F.

   7.   –   H.

   8.   –   E.

4. 105; obtuse

   30; acute

5. 1. $332.80

   2. Backpack, stove, hydration system;
   Sleeping bag, stove, hydration
   system

   3. 62.5 = 63 hours

   4. 3 ones, 3 quarters, 1 dime, 1 penny

6. N = 214

   K = 31

   X = 125

   V = 3,528

Lesson 36

1. $\triangle$ABC; isosceles

   $\triangle$KLM; scalene

   $\triangle$QRS; equilateral

2. teacher check

3.

square   rhombus   scalene or rt. triangle

rectangle   equil triangle   octagon

 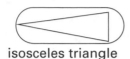
hexagon   isosceles triangle

4. 3   4   4   8
    3   4   4   8
    0   2   2   20

5. 224   385   134   432

$\frac{16}{20} = \frac{4}{5}$ $\frac{15}{30} = \frac{1}{2}$ $\frac{3}{4}$ $\frac{2}{2}$ or 1

6. 1. $34.00
    2. $6.50
    3. candy or a small popcorn
    4. No
    5. Yes
       Candy
       Medium or small popcorn

Lesson 37

1. 110°   75°
    60°   130°

2. <u>Congruent Segments</u> – Two segments that have the same length are congruent to each other.

    <u>Congruent Angles</u> – Two angles that have the same measure are congruent to each other.

    <u>Congruent Polygons</u> – Two polygons that have congruent matching angles and congruent matching sides are congruent to each other.

    <u>Regular Polygon</u> – A regular polygon has all sides the same length and all angles the same measure.

<u>Line of Symmetry</u> – If a figure can be folded so that the two parts are congruent, the fold line is the line of symmetry.

3. Answers will vary.

4. c = 9   x = 12   z = 52
    w = 180   t = 9

5.

145	156	88	122	149	442	50	110	140
99	389	92	645	111	519	70	165	91
51	781	77	201	101	987	90	150	79
62	312	90	79	84	694	140	61	94

Number: 100

6. century
    bicentennial
    decade
    AD
    millennium
    BC

Lesson 38

1. 1. $\overline{XZ}$ and $\overline{LN}$
    2. $\overline{OP}$
    3. $\overline{MN}$, $\overline{ML}$, $\overline{MZ}$, $\overline{MX}$, $\overline{MV}$
    4. $\angle LMV$
    5. 6 mm

2. 64°   52°   40°
    60°
    90°
    50°

3. isosceles   equilateral   (scalene)
    (isosceles)   (scalene)

4. dodecagon   Y
    decagon   O
    nonagon   U
    octagon   G
    heptagon   O

hexagon T
pentagon I
quadrilateral T
triangle !
YOU GOT IT!

5. A regular polygon has all sides the same length and all angles the same measure.

6. x = 4   x = 12   n = 33
   t = 28   x = 7   v = 2

7. 19th
   15th
   20th
   14th
   23rd

Lesson 39

1. 5 faces, 9 edges, 6 vertices
   4 faces, 6 edges, 4 vertices
   6 faces, 12 edges, 8 vertices
   rectangular prism   hexagonal prism
   cylinder   octagonal prism

2. 1. 22 mm
   2. 88 mm
   3. ∠FEK, ∠DEK
   4. $\overline{QR}$

3. equilateral – blue:

isosceles – red:

scalene – yellow:

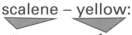

hexagons – black:

4. ∠A = 45°   ∠B = 45°   ∠C = 65°
   ∠D = 71°   ∠E = 71°   ∠F = 55°

5. x = 98   d = 30   r = 7   n = 4
   n = 81   e = 55   k = 75   n = 8

6. 969
   17

Lesson 40

1. Example:

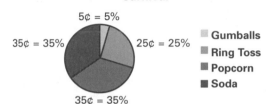

2. 1. cube   —   h.
   2. sphere   —   g.
   3. rectangular pyramid   —   e.
   4. rectangular prism   —   b.
   5. triangular pyramid   —   c.
   6. triangular prism   —   f.
   7. cone   —   d.
   8. cylinder   —   a.

3. Example:

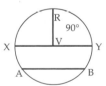

4. x = 234   v = 209   r = 284   z = 7
   n = 120   n = 9   h = 96   n = 6

5. ∠A = 90°   ∠B = 69°   ∠C = 45°
   ∠D = 45°   ∠E = 60°

6. <u>53, 87, 142</u> (Add 2 numbers together to find their sum. Add 2 to that sum.)

   <u>13, 21, 34</u> (Every number is the sum of the two numbers preceding it.)

   <u>16, 19, 22</u> (Add 3)

Lesson 41

1. Shaded numbers are correct answers.

X	1	2	3	4	5	6	7	8	9	10	11	12
1	1	2	3	4	5	6	7	8	9	10	11	12
2	2	4	6	8	10	12	15	16	18	20	22	24
3	3	6	9	12	15	16	23	26	27	30	33	36
4	4	8	12	16	20	24	27	32	36	40	44	48
5	5	10	15	20	25	30	30	40	45	50	55	60
6	6	12	18	24	30	36	42	48	54	60	66	72
7	7	14	22	28	35	42	49	56	63	60	77	84
8	8	15	26	33	40	48	56	64	70	75	89	106
9	9	18	25	36	45	54	63	72	81	80	99	108
10	10	20	20	40	50	60	70	80	90	110	110	120
11	11	22	33	44	55	66	77	88	99	110	121	132
12	12	24	36	48	60	72	84	96	108	120	132	144

2. 1. 5
    2. 20
    3. 15
    4. 10

3. Rectangular pyramid   5   8   5
    Cube   6   12   8
    Triangular pyramid   4   6   4
    Hexagonal prism   8   18   12

4. teacher check

5. Answers will vary. Example answers
    are as follows:
    $4 + 5 = 9$, $5 + 4 = 9$
    $(2 + 3) + 6 = 2 + (3 + 6)$
    $10 + 0 = 10$, $0 + 10 = 10$
    $5 - 0 = 5$ and $5 - 5 = 0$

6. $3 + (6 \times 5) = 33$
    $30 + (9 \times 3) = 57$
    $(2 \times 5) + (16 \div 4) = 14$
    $(24 \div 4) \times 3 = 18$
    $7 \times (9 - 6) = 21$
    $(3 \times 9) + (3 \times 4) = 39$
    $200 \div (2 \times 20) = 5$
    $100 - (75 \div 3) = 75$

7. 1 fifty, 1 twenty, 1 ten, 1 five, 3 ones,
    1 quarter, 2 dimes = $88.45

    1 hundred, 1 twenty, 1 five, 1 one,
    1 quarter, 1 penny = $126.26

    1 twenty, 1 one, 2 quarters, 2 dimes,
    1 penny = $21.71

    1 five hundred, 1 one hundred, 1 fifty,
    1 twenty, 1 five, 3 ones, 2 quarters,
    1 dime, 4 pennies = $678.64

    2 one hundreds, 1 fifty, 1 twenty, 1 ten,
    4 ones, 3 quarters, 1 dime = $284.85

    2 ones, 3 quarters, 1 nickel, 1 penny
    = $2.81

    1 five hundred, 2 one hundreds, 1 fifty,
    4 ones, 2 quarters = $754.50

Lesson 42

1. $2 \times 3 = 6$ $1 \times 6 = 6$

    $1 \times 7 = 7$

    $3 \times 4 = 12$ $2 \times 6 = 12$

     $1 \times 12 = 12$

    $1 \times 14 = 14$

    $2 \times 7 = 14$

    $1 \times 9 = 9$ $3 \times 3 = 9$

    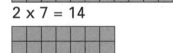

    7 is the only prime number shown.
    composite numbers: 6, 12, 14, & 9

2. Tithe – 36°
    Savings – 36°
    Toys – 90°
    Entertainment – 108°
    Food – 90°

2. (cont.)

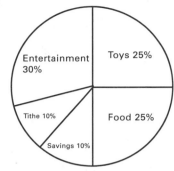

1. cont.

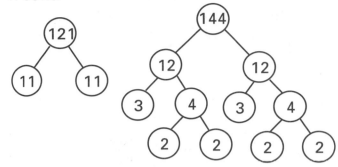

3. <u>multiples of 5</u>: 5, 10, 15, 20, 25, 30, 35
40, 45, 50, 55, 60, 65, 70, 75, 80, 85, 90
95, 100

<u>multiples of 7</u>: 7, 14, 21, 28, 35, 42, 49
56, 63, 70, 77, 84, 91, 98

<u>multiples of 6</u>: 6, 12, 18, 24, 30, 36, 42
48, 54, 60, 66, 72, 78, 84, 90, 96

<u>multiples of 11</u>: 11, 22, 33, 44, 55, 66
77, 88, 99

4. 119,260   1,129,693   67,353
674,027   4,349

5. 1. pigs
2. debt
3. God
4. sin
5 & 6. holy, glory

3,752 x 7,913 = 29,689,576
5,311 x 3,752 = 19,926,872
5,311 x 5,311 = 28,206,721

6. 25   14   1
50   60   1,530

Lesson 43

1.

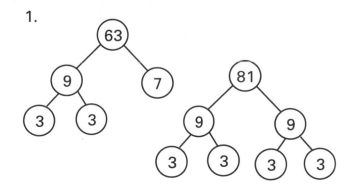

2. <u>multiples of 7</u>: 7, 14, 49

3. Triangular prism
Pentagonal prism
Rectangular prism
Triangular pyramid
Pentagonal pyramid
Rectangular pyramid

4. 37   20   181
59   8   96

5. ($4.02. Answer is correct)

(Incorrect. 1 ten, 3 one dollar bills
1 quarter, 2 pennies = $13.27)

($2.11. Answer is correct)

($13.58. Answer is correct)

(Incorrect. 2 twenties, 2 pennies
= $40.02)

(Incorrect. 1 five, 1 quarter, 2 dimes
= $5.45)

6. Answers will vary.
Example answers are given.

When the grouping of the numbers is
changed, the answer is the same.
(5 + 2) + 1 = 8, 5 + (2 + 1) = 8

When one addend is zero, the sum is
the other number. 8 + 0 = 8

The difference between any number
and zero is that number. 5 − 0 = 5

© MCMXCIX, Alpha Omega Publications, Inc.

Subtraction "undoes" addition and
addition "undoes" subtraction.
11 – 7 = 4, so 7 + 4 = 11

Lesson 44

1.

10^2	10 x 10	100	2	2
10^3	10 x 10 x 10	1,000	3	3
10^4	10 x 10 x 10 x 10	10,000	4	4
10^5	10 x 10 x 10 x 10 x 10	100,000	5	5
10^6	10 x 10 x 10 x 10 x 10 x 10	1,000,000	6	6

2.

22	7	30	31	41	35	23	29	83	4	53	7	2	55	53	46	27	18	11	3	7
56	13	39	17	31	65	29	73	12	15	18	36	19	8	73	54	16	16	58	24	5
98	11	27	13	4	14	2	10	6	25	90	40	23	12	19	96	7	14	92	75	23
14	2	16	7	6	86	7	22	8	27	92	44	53	28	29	22	18	12	42	25	19
63	11	42	3	11	52	5	54	28	10	13	41	17	33	37	10	11	10	2	5	17
77	23	99	2	45	70	11	12	65	84	24	72	2	44	47	85	28	8	60	14	29
5	19	16	43	13	46	13	48	30	16	50	70	47	55	43	94	38	6	80	46	43
43	37	12	37	2	8	19	9	69	72	31	37	43	66	13	76	48	4	11	13	17

Jeremiah 31:3

3.

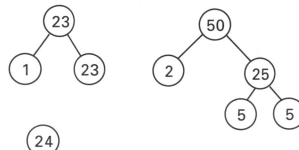

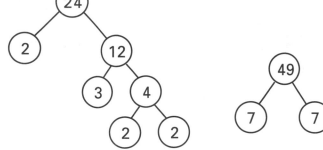

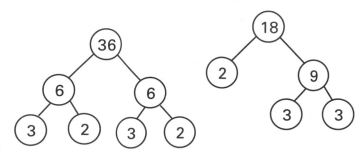

4. 481,559   1,424,053   758,585
   895,910   1,320,866

5. 18
   21
   24
   27
   30

   40
   48
   56
   64
   72
   80

   35
   42
   49
   56
   63
   70

   10
   12
   14
   16
   18
   20

6. 2,451 x 6,703 = 16,429,053
   5,500 x 7,012 = 38,566,000
   3,469 x 4,117 = 14,281,873
   3,469 x 2,451 = 8,502,519

Lesson 45

1.

196	14	14 x 14 = 196 or 14^2
529	23	23 x 23 = 529 or 23^2
25	5	5 x 5 = 25 or 5^2
225	15	15 x 15 = 225 or 15^2
16	4	4 x 4 = 16 or 4^2

2.

10^3	10 x 10 x 10	1,000	3	3
7^4	7 x 7 x 7 x 7	2,401	4	N/A
10^5	10 x 10 x 10 x 10 x 10	100,000	5	5
9^6	9 x 9 x 9 x 9 x 9 x 9	531,441	6	N/A

3. Answers:
   2, 3, 5, 7, 11, 13, 17, 19, 23, 29
   31, 37, 41, 43, 47

4.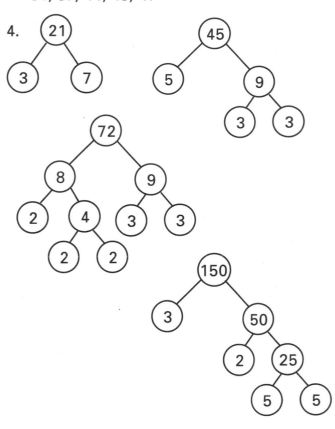

5. 92,901   165,352   186,301   205,996

6. They will all meet up at 11:00 AM.
   The charts below show each walking
   schedule.

	Sabrina	Lois	Kathy
Lap 1	8:09	8:10	8:12
Lap 2	8:18	8:20	8:24
Lap 3	8:27	8:30	8:36
Lap 4	8:36	8:40	8:48
Lap 5	8:45	8:50	9:00
Lap 6	8:54	9:00	9:12
Lap 7	9:03	9:10	9:24
Lap 8	9:12	9:20	9:36
Lap 9	9:21	9:30	9:48
Lap 10	9:30	9:40	10:00
Lap 11	9:39	9:50	10:12
Lap 12	9:48	10:00	10:24
Lap 13	9:57	10:10	10:36
Lap 14	10:06	10:20	10:48
Lap 15	10:15	10:30	(11:00)
Lap 16	10:24	10:40	
Lap 17	10:33	10:50	
Lap 18	10:42	(11:00)	
Lap 19	10:51		
Lap 20	(11:00)		

7. 215,868,890   500,983,879
   63,312,990   433,315,337

Lesson 46

1. 50: 1, 2, 5, 10, 25, 50
   60: 1, 2, 3, 4, 5, 6, 10, 12, 15, 20, 30, 60
   Common Factors: 1, 2, 5, 10

   13: 1, 13
   15: 1, 3, 5, 15
   Common Factors: 1

   42: 1, 2, 3, 6, 7, 14, 21, 42
   28: 1, 2, 4, 7, 14, 28
   GCF: 14

   16: 1, 2, 4, 8, 16
   24: 1, 2, 3, 4, 6, 8, 12, 24
   GCF: 8

   75: 1, 3, 5, 15, 25, 75
   100: 1, 2, 4, 5, 10, 20, 25, 50, 100
   GCF: 25

   125: 1, 5, 25, 125
   150: 1, 2, 3, 5, 6, 10, 25, 30, 50, 75, 150
   GCF: 25

2. 4
   19
   9
   15
   20
   25

3. Answers: 8^2, 15^5, 4^5, 9^3

4. Prime numbers: 11, 47, 2, 3, 5, 13, 7,
   17, 41, 19, 37, 23

5. 451,091   264,602   210,772
   48,689   166,809
   Answer: MERCY

6.
$$\begin{array}{r} 33,123 \\ \times\ 11,890 \\ \hline 393,832,470 \end{array} \qquad \begin{array}{r} 56,032 \\ \times\ 23,000 \\ \hline 1,288,736,000 \end{array}$$

$$\begin{array}{r} 49,799 \\ \times\ 20,589 \\ \hline 1,025,311,611 \end{array} \qquad \begin{array}{r} 46,023 \\ \times\ 90,812 \\ \hline 4,179,440,676 \end{array}$$

Horizons Math 6 Answer Key

Lesson 47

1. 3, 4 – 12
   6, 10 – 30
   3, 6 – 6
   5, 4 – 20
   4, 12 – 12
   7, 3 – 21

2. 9, 12   – 3
   25, 50   – 25
   40, 50   – 10
   25, 100   – 25
   16, 36   – 4
   500, 1,000 – 500

3. 25 = 5   400 = 20
   81 = 9   196 = 14
   49 = 7   324 = 18
   144 = 12   10,000 = 100

4.

8^3	8 x 8 x 8	512
5^4	5 x 5 x 5 x 5	625
3^2	3 x 3	9
22^3	22 x 22 x 22	10,648
2^9	2 x 2 x 2 x 2 x 2 x 2 x 2 x 2 x 2	512

5. Corrected problems:

$$231 \overline{)4,293} \quad 18 \text{ R}135$$

$$703 \overline{)5,691} \quad 8 \text{ R}67$$

$$642 \overline{)11,251} \quad 17 \text{ R}337$$

$$355 \overline{)4,876} \quad 13 \text{ R}261$$

6. 170   1,020   1,190   180   950
   4,090   8,640   4,440

Lesson 48

1. 3250000   = 3.25×10^6
   4596000   = 4.596×10^6
   87591   = 8.7591×10^4
   157   = 1.57×10^2
   0.0245   = 2.45×10^{-2}
   23.5 million = 2.35×10^7

2. 45, 30 – 90
   20, 100 – 100
   5, 16   – 80
   32, 16 – 32
   5, 8   – 40
   23, 69 – 69
   45, 3   – 45
   8, 6   – 24

3. 8, 28   – 4
   40, 24 – 8
   48, 16 – 16
   20, 16 – 4
   18, 21 – 3
   11, 17 – 1

4. 24 = 576   15 = 225
   36 = 1,296   60 = 3,600
   12 = 144   45 = 2,025

5. 369 R20   241 R660
   457 R111   5,463 R57

6. 900   1,200   500   1,400
     L   O   V   E

    400   1,000   1,400
     T   H   E

    900   1,200   700   600
     L   O   R   D

   LOVE THE LORD

7. 128   56   55   101   184

Lesson 49

1. 11 = 1011_2
   19 = 10011_2
   12 = 1100_2
   15 = 1111_2
   21 = 10101_2

2. 4,560,000 = 4.56×10^6
   0.999 = 9.99×10^{-1}
   468 million = 4.68×10^8
   98.8 = 9.88×10^1

2. (cont.)

$0.00067 = 6.7 \times 10^{-4}$

$865,000 = 8.65 \times 10^5$

3. 6, 3   – 6
    8, 4   – 8
    10, 100   – 100
    3, 8   – 24
    5, 10   – 10
    30, 90   – 90

4. 9, 18   – 9
    15, 20   – 5
    36, 40   – 4
    25, 30   – 5
    32, 36   – 4
    75, 150 – 75

5. 23 R290   16 R1,450
    33 R3   14 R1,504

6. $4\frac{13}{15}$ $3\frac{4}{5}$ $25\frac{8}{35}$ $2\frac{31}{47}$

    $2\frac{8}{11}$ $15\frac{1}{3}$ $3\frac{5}{27}$ $2\frac{21}{23}$

Lesson 50

1. The finished product will show the information listed below. The symbol chosen by the student might vary, but most will draw a desk or chair of some sort.

    Example:

Meeting Hall	(10 chairs drawn)
Kindergarten Class	(5 chairs drawn)
Grade 1 class	(5 chairs drawn)
Grade 2 class	(5 chairs drawn)
Grade 3 class	(5 chairs drawn)
Grade 4 class	(5 chairs drawn)
Grade 5 class	(5 chairs drawn)
Grade 6 class	(5 chairs drawn)
Office	(2 chairs drawn)

(drawing of 1 chair) = 5 chairs

2.

(64) 2^6	(32) 2^5	(16) 2^4	(8) 2^3	(4) 2^2	(2) 2^1	(1) 2^0	=	
		1	1	1	0	0	=	28
			1	0	1	0	=	10
	1	0	0	1	1	0	=	38
				1	1	1	=	7
1	1	1	1	0	1	1	=	123
1	0	1	0	1	1	=	43

3.

Standard Form	Scientific Notation
100,000	10×10^4
5,880,000,000,000	5.88×10^{12}
37,000,000	3.7×10^7
0.00000073	7.3×10^{-7}
10,000	10×10^3
236,000,000	2.36×10^8
65,880,000,000,000,000,000,000	6.588×10^{22}
0.000098	9.8×10^{-5}

4. 10: 2×5
    20: $2 \times 2 \times 5$ $2 \times 2 \times 5 = 20$
                              or $2^2 \times 5 = 20$

    25: 5×5
    35: 5×7 $5 \times 5 \times 7 = 175$
                      or $5^2 \times 7 = 175$

    100: $2 \times 2 \times 5 \times 5$
    25: 5×5 $2 \times 2 \times 5 \times 5 = 100$
                      or $2^2 \times 5^2 = 100$

    60: $2 \times 2 \times 3 \times 5$
    45: $3 \times 3 \times 5$ $2 \times 2 \times 3 \times 3 \times 5 = 180$
                          or $2^2 \times 3^2 \times 5 = 180$

    2: 2
    5   5 $2 \times 5 = 10$

    2: 2
    50: $2 \times 5 \times 5$ $2 \times 5 \times 5 = 50$
                          or $2 \times 5^2 = 50$

5. 2 R3,588   3 R1,609
    30 R1,082   25 R1,607
    ROCK

6. 4,000   10,000   8,000
    10,000   8,000   8,000

7. $89\frac{2}{3}$ $6\frac{1}{3}$ $14\frac{1}{3}$ $3\frac{3}{4}$

    $100\frac{1}{3}$ $2\frac{5}{17}$ $4\frac{1}{2}$ $16\frac{7}{13}$

Lesson 51

1.

8,923.004
Read: 8,923 and 4 thousandths
Written: Eight thousand, nine hundred twenty-three and four thousandths
Expanded form: $8,000 + 900 + 20 + 3 + 0.004 = 8,923.004$

183.304
Read: 183 and 304 thousandths
Written: One hundred eighty-three and three hundred four thousandths
Expanded form: $100 + 80 + 3 + 0.3 + 0.004 = 183.304$

459.394
Read: 459 and 394 thousandths
Written: Four hundred fifty-nine and three hundred ninety-four thousandths
Expanded form: $400 + 50 + 9 + 0.3 + 0.09 + 0.004 = 459.394$

3.00009
Read: 3 and 9 hundred thousandths
Written: Three and nine hundred thousandths
Expanded form: $3 + .00009 = 3.00009$

25.89123
Read: 25 and 89123 hundred thousandths
Written: Twenty-five and eighty nine thousand, one hundred twenty-three hundred thousandths
Expanded form: $20 + 5 + 0.8 + 0.09 + 0.001 + 0.0002 + 0.00003 = 25.89123$

67.89
Read: 67 and 89 hundredths
Written: Sixty-seven and eighty-nine hundredths
Expanded form: $60 + 7 + 0.8 + 0.09 = 67.89$

2. The finished product will show the information listed.

Example:

Number of Airline Tickets Sold During One Week

Monday	(23 symbols drawn)
Tuesday	($18 \frac{1}{2}$ symbols drawn)
Wednesday	($21 \frac{1}{2}$ symbols drawn)
Thursday	(18 symbols drawn)
Friday	(30 symbols drawn)

3.

2^4	2^3	2^2	2^1	1	
	1	0	1	1	$= 8 + 0 + 2 + 1 = 11$
		1	1	1	$= 4 + 2 + 1 = 7$
	1	0	0	1	$= 8 + 0 + 0 + 1 = 9$
			1	1	$= 2 + 1 = 3$
1	0	1	1	0	$= 16 + 4 + 2 = 22$
1	1	1	1	1	$= 16 + 8 + 4 + 2 + 1 = 31$

4.
0.02978	–	2.978×10^{-2}
2,978,000,000	–	2.978×10^{9}
2,978,000,000,000	–	2.978×10^{12}
0.002978	–	2.978×10^{-3}
29,780	–	2.978×10^{4}
297,800,000	–	2.978×10^{8}

5. Parallelogram Rhombus Trapezoid
Octagon   Pentagon Hexagon

6. 300 70 20 210 150 250

7. 1 dollar, 1 quarter, 1 penny = ($1.26)

1 dollar, 2 quarters, 2 dimes, 1 penny = ($1.71)

3 dollars, 2 quarters, 1 dime, 4 pennies = ($3.64)

1 five, 2 ones, 3 quarters, 1 dime = ($7.85)

1 hundred, 2 ones, 3 quarters, 1 nickel 1 penny = ($102.81)

© MCMXCIX, Alpha Omega Publications, Inc.

Lesson 52

1.
0.4590	31.147	0.040	7.001
0.4594	31.148	0.047	7.019
0.4612	31.150	0.074	7.109
0.4650	32.151	0.704	7.190

2. Answers will vary.

3. The finished product will show the information listed.

   Example:

   Time Spent Watching TV Each Day

30 minutes	(1 TV set drawn)
60 minutes	(3 TV sets drawn)
120 minutes	(5 TV sets drawn)
180 minutes	(9 TV sets drawn)

4.
2^4	2^3	2^2	2^1	1	
1	1	0	1	1	= 27
			1	1	1 = 7
1	1	0	0	1	= 25
			1	0	= 2
1	0	1	1	1	= 23
1	1	1	1	1	= 31

5.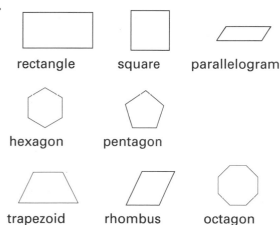

   rectangle   square   parallelogram

   hexagon   pentagon

   trapezoid   rhombus   octagon

6. Answers will vary.

Lesson 53

1. 6.322   23.67   42.04
   38.253   383.303

2. The finished product will show the information listed below.

   Example:

   Lima Bean Growth

Week 1	(1/2 a lima bean seed drawn)
Week 2	(1 lima bean seed drawn)
Week 3	(1/2 a lima bean seed drawn)
Week 4	(1 1/4 lima bean seeds drawn)
Week 5	(1 lima bean seed drawn)

3. 100°   45°
   60°   20°

4. 0.02039 $<$ 0.02309

   56.807 $<$ 57.807

   1,765.2654 $>$ 1.765.2546

   0.231 $<$ 1.231

   19.1 $=$ 19.100

   6.954 $>$ 6.594

5. Corrected problems:
49,952 – 23,465 = 26,490	– 26,480
5,234 – 653 = 4,590	– 4,580
7,998 – 3,939 = 4,100	– 4,060
2,232 – 1,519 = 730	– 710

6. 3 marbles
   5 marbles

Lesson 54

1. 5.042   3.017   150.61
   29.001   1.602   517.12

2. 4.1   25.5   12.959   8.736
   1.405   228.33   988.60   898.43
   Answer: HOLINESS

3. The _7_ is in the hundreds place.
   The _4_ is in the thousandths' place.
   The _6_ is in the ones' place.

3. (cont.)

The _2_ is in the hundred thousandths' place.

The _9_ is in the hundredths' place.

The _3_ is in the thousands' place.

4. 40°   20°
   45°   18°

5. 1,000   0   1,000
   3,000   0   1,000

6. 1,234,567

Lesson 55

1. 26   218   12   39
   0.3   232.5   135.2   2.1

2. 236.695   480.46   391.02
   539.23   728.03

3. 71.52;   80.03;   103.92;   84.64;   918.7
   7.689;   173.08;   11,054.04;   48.552;   8.1948

   Answer: Dedication

4. $\dfrac{34}{4}$ = $8\dfrac{1}{2}$

   $\dfrac{26}{7}$ = $3\dfrac{5}{7}$

   $\dfrac{16}{3}$ = $5\dfrac{1}{3}$

   $3\dfrac{18}{5}$ = $6\dfrac{3}{5}$

   $5\dfrac{47}{8}$ = $10\dfrac{7}{8}$

   $16\dfrac{61}{6}$ = $26\dfrac{1}{6}$

5. Across   Down
   1. TWENTY EIGHT   3. FOUR
   2. FIFTEEN   4. THIRTY SIX
   3. FIFTY SIX   5. EIGHT
                          6. NINE

6. Answers will vary. Examples are given.

Sum	4 + 5 = 9;	9 is the sum.
Difference	5 − 3 = 2;	2 is the difference.
Product	5 x 6 = 30;	30 is the product.
Quotient	12 ÷ 4 = 3;	3 is the quotient.
Divisor	12 ÷ 4 = 3;	4 is the divisor.
Dividend	12 ÷ 4 = 3;	12 is the dividend.
Addend	5 + 5 = 10;	both 5's are considered addends.
Multiplier	4 x 5 = 20;	4 is the multiplier.
Subtrahend	15 − 5 = 10;	5 is the subtrahend.
Minuend	15 − 5 = 10;	15 is the minuend.

Lesson 56

1. 1,361.2   721.8
   509   1,003
   5,356.3   1,161

2. $110 $10 $58 $0 $21

3. 7.191   1.38   2.174
   3.081   9.279   .113

4. $\dfrac{12}{27}$ − $\dfrac{4}{9}$

   $\dfrac{16}{24}$ − $\dfrac{2}{3}$

   $\dfrac{36}{54}$ − $\dfrac{2}{3}$

   $\dfrac{18}{30}$ − $\dfrac{3}{5}$

   $\dfrac{24}{60}$ − $\dfrac{2}{5}$

   $\dfrac{24}{40}$ − $\dfrac{3}{5}$

5. Across   Down
   1. 9,646 ÷ 7 = 1,378   1. 856 ÷ 8 = 107
   3. 915 ÷ 3 = 305   2. 140 ÷ 4 = 35
   5. 576 ÷ 6 = 96   4. 594 ÷ 3 = 198

6.

Divisor $5\overline{)25}$ Quotient
Dividend

$4 \times 5 = 20$
Multiplicand Multiplier Product

$4 + 4 = 8$
Addend Addend Sum

$10 - 6 = 4$
Minuend Subtrahend Difference

Lesson 57

1. CXI XIX CXXIV
   XIV X LVI
   XXX MXVII

2. 136.7431   553.2184
   94.737   675.9219

3. 5.2   4.0   3.1
   9.083 15.982 7.153
   3.21   6.36   7.42

4. $8.07
   36.5
   $30.33
   4.4 acres

5.

6.

4	5	9
3	2	5
7	7	14

9	8	17
3	6	9
12	14	26

6	15	21
11	2	13
17	17	34

Lesson 58

1. Range: 57   Range: 200
   Mean: 59   Mean: 200

   Range: 13   Range: 28
   Mean: 23   Mean: 30

2. 11.185
   33.617
   60.233
   26.3505

3. Answers to follow in maze:
   2.943
   6.501
   3.256
   7.339
   7.496
   3.245
   3.087
   6.802
   2.731
   6.548

4. $142.00
   $8.00
   40.2
   21.2

5. Magic Number: 15,000

5. (cont.)

400	300	800
900	500	100
200	700	600

Mystery Number: 1500

6. Answers will vary.

Lesson 59

1. 1, 5, 7, 7, 18, 22, 24
   Range: 23
   Mean: 12
   Mode: 7
   Median: 7

   10, 12, 16, 70, 70, 98
   Range: 88
   Mean: 46
   Mode: 70
   Median: 43 (16 + 70 = 86 ÷ 2 = 43)

   $3, $9, $9, $22, $52
   Range: 49
   Mean: 19
   Mode: 9
   Median: 9

   10 in., 14 in., 20 in., 56 in.
   Range: 46
   Mean: 25
   Mode: there is no mode.
   Median: 17 (14 + 20 = 34 2 = 17)

2. 2.9   71.3
   33.75   0.48
   41.63   55.70

3. 275.60   65.90   14.100
   4.340   8.730   30.290
   39.8620   508.1130   34.9140

4.

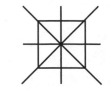

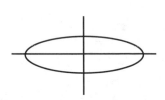

5. Answers will vary. Example answers are given. Sample answers:

   $\dfrac{30}{70}$ $\dfrac{7}{8}$ $\dfrac{1}{2}$

   $\dfrac{10}{90}$ $\dfrac{5}{8}$ $\dfrac{6}{20}$

6. $\dfrac{7}{63}$

   225

Lesson 60

1. not enough information
   $2.75

   (4 x 3) + 20 = 32
   32 x $1.25 = $40.00

   not enough information

2. 4, 5, 8, 17, 17, 22, 25
   Range: 21
   Mean: 14
   Mode: 17
   Median: 17

   10, 11, 12, 65, 65, 98
   Range: 88
   Mean: 43.5 = 44
   Mode: 65
   Median: 38.5 (12 + 65 = 77 ÷ 2 = 38.5)

2. (cont.)

    $3, $9, $9, $32, $72

    Range: 69

    Mean: 25

    Mode: 9

    Median: 9

    10 in., 14 in., 42 in., 58 in.

    Range: 48

    Mean: 31

    Mode: there is no mode.

    Median: 28 (14 + 42 = 56 2 = 28)

3. 61.8;   97.3;   6.1;   68.5;   11;   31.8

4. 2.39   7.99   1.189
    41.922   1,068.7   4,882.05

5.

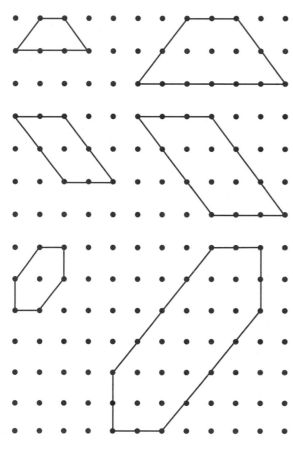

6.
$$\frac{25}{50}$$

$$\frac{10}{15}$$

$$\frac{20}{40} \qquad \frac{30}{45} \qquad \frac{4}{6}$$

$$\frac{44}{66}$$

$$\frac{9}{18}$$

$$\frac{5}{10}$$

Lesson 61

1. $\frac{5}{6}$ $\frac{9}{10}$ $\frac{4}{9}$ $\frac{1}{10}$ $\frac{2}{3}$ $\frac{2}{5}$

    $\frac{1}{8}$ $\frac{6}{89}$ $\frac{8}{9}$ $\frac{3}{13}$ $\frac{3}{4}$ $\frac{1}{4}$

    $\frac{3}{8}$ $\frac{1}{12}$ $\frac{19}{20}$ $\frac{1}{4}$ $\frac{3}{4}$ $\frac{7}{12}$

2. 634.81   224.83   125.4

3. Answer: The answer is the mirror image of the design drawn.

4. 6   6   9   8
    41   46   86   7

5. 18   18   18
    331   360   360

6. 1. 2.46   S
    2. 34.99   C
    3. 9.2   R
    4   12.945   E
    5. 5.99   W
    6. 5.0   D
    7   46   R
    8. 356.75   I
    9. 0.7   V
    10. 3.89   E
    11. 3   R
    Answer: Screwdriver

Horizons Math 6 Answer Key

Lesson 62

1. 1. $\dfrac{6}{7}$ M

   2. $\dfrac{1}{2}$ I

   3. $\dfrac{1}{4}$ L

   4. 1 K

   5. $\dfrac{11}{15}$ T

   6. $\dfrac{9}{10}$ R

   7. $\dfrac{5}{8}$ U

   8. $\dfrac{1}{10}$ C

   9. 1 K

   The answer is MILK TRUCK.

2. $\dfrac{1}{2}$ $\dfrac{2}{13}$ $\dfrac{1}{10}$ $\dfrac{7}{15}$ $\dfrac{3}{4}$ $\dfrac{1}{9}$

   $\dfrac{7}{11}$ $\dfrac{1}{4}$ $\dfrac{3}{5}$ $\dfrac{1}{100}$ $\dfrac{1}{4}$ 1

3. Mean   20
   Median   20
   Mode   There is no mode.

   Mean   80
   Median   88
   Mode   100

4. 12,140,791   T
   15,883,868   E
   8,228,572   B
   18,899,376   R
   9,015,844   A
   29,823,542   S
   9,642,444   T

   BATTERS

5. 11   45   1,127

6.
4.9	(7.0)	(6.9)	(7.4)	6.2	9.3
7.5	1.7	7.6	(6.8)	6.3	12.1
6.4	5.6	6.4	(7.1)	7.7	9.7
5.4	17.4	18.7	(6.9)	7.9	12.7
4.7	1.4	8.9	(6.5)	7.8	6.1
9.9	71.7	74.4	(7.3)	8.8	9.3

Lesson 63

1.
8, 16, 24, 32	8	8
8, 16, 24	24	24
5, 10, 15, 20	20	20
7, 14, 21	14	14
6, 12, 18	12	12
12, 24, 36	24	24

2. $\dfrac{7}{9}$ $\dfrac{17}{17}=1$ $\dfrac{4}{9}$

   $\dfrac{15}{30}=\dfrac{1}{2}$ $\dfrac{8}{32}=\dfrac{1}{4}$ $\dfrac{9}{48}=\dfrac{3}{16}$

   $\dfrac{2}{20}=\dfrac{1}{10}$ $\dfrac{10}{24}=\dfrac{5}{12}$ $\dfrac{4}{12}=\dfrac{1}{3}$

   $\dfrac{10}{32}=\dfrac{5}{16}$ $\dfrac{12}{17}$ $\dfrac{10}{22}=\dfrac{5}{11}$

3. $\dfrac{1}{3}$ $\dfrac{4}{9}$ $\dfrac{1}{2}$ $\dfrac{6}{7}$ $\dfrac{1}{3}$ $\dfrac{1}{2}$

4. Mean   20
   Median   19
   Mode   18

   Mean   85
   Median   88
   Mode   There is no mode.

5. 19,841,584   16,073,687
   13,638,051   14,795,166

6. 98
   222
   9

Lesson 64

1. $\frac{2}{9} < \frac{7}{9}$ $\frac{7}{14} < \frac{10}{14}$

$\frac{3}{4} > \frac{2}{4}$ $\frac{8}{43} < \frac{9}{43}$

$\frac{1}{3} = \frac{2}{6}$ $\frac{2}{7} > \frac{1}{4}$

$\frac{7}{8} > \frac{2}{3}$ $\frac{3}{5} > \frac{4}{7}$

$\frac{5}{9} > \frac{2}{5}$ $\frac{5}{8} > \frac{1}{2}$

$\frac{4}{9} < \frac{5}{7}$ $\frac{7}{9} > \frac{2}{3}$

2.   21   18   6
    30   8   24   15

3. 1 $\frac{10}{15} = \frac{2}{3}$ $\frac{9}{18} = \frac{1}{2}$

$\frac{1}{3}$ $\frac{11}{33} = \frac{1}{3}$ $\frac{15}{50} = \frac{3}{10}$

$\frac{17}{34} = \frac{1}{2}$ $\frac{7}{60}$ $\frac{16}{22} = \frac{8}{11}$

4. 142,221,131   215,779,720
    1,372,544,200   748,111,311

5. 1. Niger 186,000 sq. miles greater
    2. Kenya 210,000 sq. miles greater
    3. Niger
    4. Rwanda
    5. South Africa
    6. Nambia

6. 1. decade
    2. century
    3. millenium

Lesson 65

1. $\frac{9}{10}$ $\frac{11}{14}$ $\frac{3}{6} = \frac{1}{2}$ $\frac{14}{15}$

$\frac{5}{8}$ $\frac{5}{9}$ $\frac{1}{6}$ $\frac{3}{10}$

2. The shaded blocks spell the word YES.

3. $\frac{1}{3} = \frac{3}{9}$ $\frac{7}{14} < \frac{4}{7}$

$\frac{3}{4} > \frac{2}{12}$ $\frac{8}{9} < \frac{9}{10}$

4. 45   42   8   9
    10   12   24   15

5. $\frac{7}{8}$ $\frac{2}{12} = \frac{1}{6}$ $\frac{5}{5} = 1$

$\frac{10}{20} = \frac{1}{2}$ $\frac{15}{25} = \frac{3}{5}$ $\frac{4}{14} = \frac{2}{7}$

Boxes not shaded spell GOLDFISH.

6. 539,987,345,903,702 ten trillions
    987,439,000,000 millions
    887,409,873,329,000 hundred trillions
    935,873,873,011 ten millions
    793,000,000,000,000 trillions
    819,045,893,219 hundred billions
    709,574,847,938,000 ten billions
    398,765,389,218 billions

Lesson 66

1. $\frac{32}{5}$ $\frac{22}{7}$ $\frac{15}{4}$ $\frac{8}{6}$

$\frac{40}{9}$ $\frac{18}{2}$ $\frac{27}{2}$ $\frac{34}{3}$

2. $\frac{13}{21}$ $\frac{17}{30}$ $\frac{4}{9}$ $\frac{7}{12}$

$\frac{1}{8}$ $\frac{1}{9}$ $\frac{1}{6}$ $\frac{1}{2}$

$\frac{15}{22}$ $\frac{2}{5}$ $\frac{1}{2}$ $\frac{1}{2}$

$\frac{1}{3}$ $\frac{17}{30}$ $\frac{4}{9}$ $\frac{19}{30}$

The answer is HISS-TORY.

3. $\dfrac{1}{9} < \dfrac{2}{6}$ $\dfrac{2}{14} = \dfrac{1}{7}$ $\dfrac{3}{4} > \dfrac{7}{12}$

$\dfrac{8}{43} < \dfrac{9}{43}$ $\dfrac{3}{10} = \dfrac{6}{20}$ $\dfrac{2}{12} < \dfrac{3}{14}$

$\dfrac{4}{16} = \dfrac{1}{4}$ $\dfrac{3}{11} > \dfrac{4}{15}$

4. 63   72   22   20
   20   48   20   21

5.

1. 1 3 2,1 0 6,5 0 9,0 4 5,0 0 0
2. 1 1 3,1 4 3,9 1 2,1 0 0,0 0 0
3. 3 8 3,2 5 4,3 4 0,3 4 1,1 2 0
4. 6 0 2,3 6 2,4 0 2,0 6 3,1 0 0
5. 5 0 9,5 9 9,5 1 3,9 5 4,5 0 0
6. 3 1 6,3 9 7,6 8 6,6 0 5,0 0 0
7. 2 5 7,3 8 7,5 4 0,0 0 0,0 0 0
8. 6 7 9,2 0 8,0 0 0,0 0 0,0 0 0

The hidden number is 132

Lesson 67

1. $3\dfrac{3}{5}$;   5; $9\dfrac{2}{3}$

   $6\dfrac{1}{3}$; $6\dfrac{3}{4}$; $4\dfrac{3}{9} = 4\dfrac{1}{3}$

   12; $10\dfrac{3}{9} = 10\dfrac{1}{3}$;   3

   $3\dfrac{5}{30} = 3\dfrac{1}{6}$; $5\dfrac{8}{14} = 5\dfrac{4}{7}$; $4\dfrac{2}{12} = 4\dfrac{1}{6}$

2. $1\dfrac{7}{8}$ 2 $7\dfrac{1}{4}$ 8   2

   $13\dfrac{1}{9}$ 2   2   4   2

   The answer is CHILI.

3. $\dfrac{9}{12} = \dfrac{3}{4}$; $\dfrac{31}{57}$; $\dfrac{10}{18} = \dfrac{5}{9}$; $\dfrac{18}{30} = \dfrac{3}{5}$

   $\dfrac{53}{70}$; $\dfrac{53}{84}$; $\dfrac{103}{144}$; $\dfrac{14}{70} = \dfrac{1}{5}$

4. $\dfrac{3}{19}$ A

   $\dfrac{8}{10}$ P

   $\dfrac{5}{12}$ P

   $\dfrac{9}{11}$ L

   $\dfrac{6}{15}$ E

   The answer is APPLE.

5. 53 R23   154 R398   63 R265

Lesson 68

1. $10\dfrac{5}{6}$; $40\dfrac{7}{12}$; $34\dfrac{3}{8}$; $19\dfrac{1}{4}$; $6\dfrac{7}{10}$

   $4\dfrac{10}{21}$; $6\dfrac{66}{90} = 6\dfrac{11}{15}$; $5\dfrac{41}{56}$; $2\dfrac{5}{14}$

   $11\dfrac{29}{30}$

2. $4\dfrac{2}{9} = \dfrac{38}{9}$ $3\dfrac{1}{3} = \dfrac{10}{3}$ $7\dfrac{1}{7} = \dfrac{50}{7}$

   $7\dfrac{1}{4} = \dfrac{29}{4}$ $9\dfrac{1}{5} = \dfrac{46}{5}$ $6\dfrac{3}{9} = \dfrac{57}{9}$

   $3\dfrac{4}{5} = \dfrac{19}{5}$ $8\dfrac{3}{8} = \dfrac{67}{8}$ $8\dfrac{1}{9} = \dfrac{73}{9}$

   $6\dfrac{1}{2} = \dfrac{13}{2}$ $6\dfrac{3}{6} = \dfrac{39}{6}$ $4\dfrac{1}{4} = \dfrac{17}{4}$

   $8\dfrac{2}{11} = \dfrac{90}{11}$ $9\dfrac{3}{8} = \dfrac{75}{8}$ $3\dfrac{2}{5} = \dfrac{17}{5}$

   $9\dfrac{2}{3} = \dfrac{29}{3}$ $7\dfrac{3}{7} = \dfrac{52}{7}$ $13\dfrac{4}{6} = \dfrac{82}{6}$

   The answer is WISDOM.

3. $\dfrac{22}{40} = \dfrac{11}{20}$; $\dfrac{35}{51}$; $\dfrac{62}{78} = \dfrac{31}{39}$

   $\dfrac{17}{22}$; $\dfrac{59}{114}$; $\dfrac{46}{84} = \dfrac{23}{42}$

   $\dfrac{11}{16}$; $\dfrac{23}{42}$

4. $\dfrac{27}{30}$ – B

$\dfrac{12}{30}$ – U

$\dfrac{6}{7}$ – C

$\dfrac{1}{4}$ – K

$\dfrac{1}{4}$ – T

$\dfrac{2}{3}$ – E

$\dfrac{12}{15}$ – E

$\dfrac{1}{11}$ – T

$\dfrac{3}{28}$ – H

The answer is BUCKTEETH.

5. 1. 1.0375
   2. 4.00006
   3. 25,000.5
   4. 6.099
   5. 87.09

Lesson 69

1. $13\dfrac{4}{3} = 14\dfrac{1}{3}$; $5\dfrac{12}{10} = 6\dfrac{2}{10} = 6\dfrac{1}{5}$

   $9\dfrac{13}{12} = 10\dfrac{1}{12}$; $27\dfrac{17}{12} = 28\dfrac{5}{12}$

2. $16\dfrac{19}{84}$ $77\dfrac{16}{39}$ $79\dfrac{19}{36}$

   $23\dfrac{7}{22}$ $8\dfrac{22}{45}$

3. $1\dfrac{1}{3}$ – E

   $5\dfrac{1}{12}$ – X

$7\dfrac{2}{3}$ – C

$11\dfrac{5}{6}$ – E

$6\dfrac{7}{9}$ – L

$2\dfrac{4}{7}$ – L

$3\dfrac{3}{4}$ – E

$6\dfrac{5}{8}$ – N

$9\dfrac{1}{6}$ – T

The answer is EXCELLENT.

4. 653   214   505
   116 R4   166 R2   199 R3

5.
2.	1	2	.	0	9	9	
3.	3	7	.	0	0	0	9
4.	2	6	.	3			
5.	1	6	.	0	7		
6.	9	2	.	0	2	6	
7.	8	1	.	0	0	4	6
8.		9	.	2	1	0	9

6. 1. $5\dfrac{13}{8} = 6\dfrac{5}{8}$ yards

   2. $\dfrac{5}{8}$ yard

Lesson 70

1. $5\dfrac{3}{6} = 5\dfrac{1}{2}$; $1\dfrac{7}{20}$; $4\dfrac{8}{18} = 4\dfrac{4}{9}$

   $5\dfrac{17}{30}$; $6\dfrac{10}{21}$; $5\dfrac{8}{10} = 5\dfrac{4}{5}$

   $2\dfrac{12}{35}$; $2\dfrac{9}{12} = 2\dfrac{3}{4}$

2. $79\dfrac{29}{21} = 80\dfrac{8}{21}$ $35\dfrac{118}{99} = 36\dfrac{19}{99}$ 2. $27\dfrac{13}{42};$ $18\dfrac{19}{30};$

$149\dfrac{24}{18} = 150\dfrac{6}{18} = 150\dfrac{1}{3}$ $24\dfrac{7}{12};$ $37\dfrac{7}{10}$

$177\dfrac{49}{30} = 178\dfrac{19}{30}$

3. $70\dfrac{17}{12} = 71\dfrac{5}{12}$

$118\dfrac{123}{84} = 119\dfrac{39}{84} = 119\dfrac{13}{28}$

$139\dfrac{21}{16} = 140\dfrac{5}{16}$

$87\dfrac{10}{9} = 88\dfrac{1}{9}$

3. $\dfrac{4}{3}$ – O $\dfrac{28}{5}$ – T

$\dfrac{14}{5}$ – D $\dfrac{84}{10}$ – O

$\dfrac{17}{4}$ – G $\dfrac{7}{2}$ – S

$\dfrac{28}{3}$ – P $\dfrac{19}{2}$ – O

$\dfrac{16}{5}$ – U $\dfrac{13}{2}$ – N

$\dfrac{29}{3}$ – D $\dfrac{18}{4}$ – C

$\dfrac{23}{7}$ – A $\dfrac{50}{7}$ – K

$\dfrac{67}{6}$ – E

The answer is HOTDOGS and
POUND CAKE.

4. 478,622 807,836
1,392,621 750,478

5. The answer is Counselor.

6. 1036.49 376.828

4. 159,002; 92,928; 168,393; 71,040

5.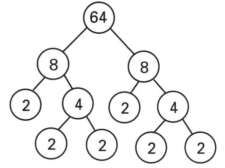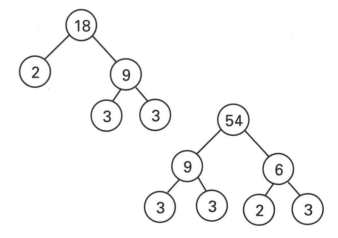

6. 1. $42.56
    2. 19 miles
    3. 122.8 meters
    4. $167.60

Lesson 71

1. <u>Across</u>   <u>Down</u>
    1. 529.2   1. 15.4
    2. 4.2   2. 39.2
    3. 3.78   3. 293.4
    4. 3.9   4. 32.85
    5. 5.49   5. 0.98

Lesson 72

1. Answers from least to greatest:

    0.3;   0.384;   0.52;   0.572

    3.48;   4.37;   5.44;   6.08

    6.49;   6.65;   7.497;   7.502

    16.64;   40.68

    The answer is: But, I say to you love your enemies and pray for those who persecute you.

2. $5\frac{31}{33}$ $55\frac{8}{12} = 55\frac{2}{3}$

    $31\frac{25}{36}$ $59\frac{7}{14} = 59\frac{1}{2}$

3. $40\frac{23}{20} = 41\frac{3}{20}$; $46\frac{11}{9} = 47\frac{2}{9}$

    $99\frac{15}{12} = 100\frac{3}{12} = 100\frac{1}{4}$

    $110\frac{13}{10} = 111\frac{3}{10}$

4. 777,898   19,888   63,889   28,580

5.

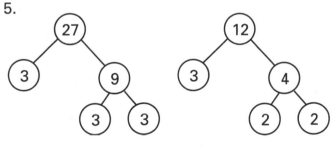

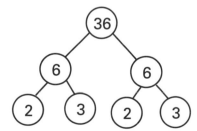

6. 1. $51.88

    2. 832.68 square meters

Lesson 73

1. 2.48   10.19   28.18   21.13

   67.18   88.12   98.53   71.57

2. 7.98;   7.03;   15.61;   0.365;   0.8844

   1.44;   2.295;   56.42   25.48;   0.833

   The answer is COMPLAIN.

3. 42.7   15.28   245.7   301.2

   28.5   24.04   341.5   1,718.2

4. $8\frac{7}{8}$; $21\frac{4}{12} = 21\frac{1}{3}$

   $44\frac{8}{18} = 44\frac{4}{9}$; $78\frac{11}{28}$

5. 160,861   87,089   57,284   6,432

6. Start

3	11	14	25	20	90
12	7	17	23	29	77
21	15	8	16	31	32
18	10	47	41	37	49
71	59	53	22	40	64

   Finish

7. right angle   acute angle

   straight angle   obtuse angle

Lesson 74

1. <u>tenths:</u>

   2.5   18.2   7.5   9.5

   <u>hundredths:</u>

   25.50   4.75   3.75   5.25

   <u>thousandths:</u>

   1.375   2.125   4.375   10.125

2. 7.88   18.49   45.68   91.73

3. 7.15   31.92   21.18   1.736

4. 15.92 B; 14.42 R; 161.28 O; 145.65 A

   29.68 D; 228.42 C; 145.65 A; 395.85 S

   235.8 T

   The answer is Broadcast.

5. 152 – 2
174 – 2, 3
310 – 2, 5, 10
993 – 3

6. rectangle; square; parallelogram
trapezoid; rhombus; pentagon

Lesson 75

1. 0.5   0.25   0.8
0.8   0.625   0.875

$0.8\overline{3}$ $0.8\overline{1}$ $0.\overline{1}$
$0.\overline{4}$ $0.1\overline{6}$ $0.\overline{3}$

2. 1.7   8.5   4.9   5.5

3. 2.18   78.59   7.01   91.61

4. 111.83   39.72   4.84   1.0075
0.2679

5. $\frac{1}{3}$ D $\frac{3}{6}$ A $\frac{1}{12}$ R

$\frac{1}{3}$ K $\frac{1}{4}$ N $\frac{7}{7}$ E

$\frac{2}{3}$ S $\frac{2}{9}$ S

The answer is Darkness.

6. 225.9   173.89
267.2   397.2

Lesson 76

1. 0.38   0.14   0.29   0.86
0.8   0.8   1.3   0.2

2. $\frac{1}{5}$ > .02 $\frac{1}{10}$ < 0.3 $\frac{3}{4}$ > 0.71

$\frac{2}{7}$ < 1.2 $\frac{1}{2}$ = 0.50 $\frac{1}{3}$ > 0.2

$\frac{4}{5}$ = 0.8 $\frac{3}{11}$ < 0.70 $\frac{1}{8}$ = 0.125

3. $0.\overline{54}$ $0.\overline{4}$ $1.\overline{3}$
$0.8\overline{3}$ $0.0\overline{5}$

4. 4.91   108.1   75.15   0.993
923.1   802.3   3.221   41.07   99.8

4	.	9	1	▨	9	▨	▨	▨	▨
1	▨	▨	0	.	9	9	3	▨	9
.	▨	8	▨	.	▨	.	▨	2	▨
0	▨	▨	.	8	0	2	.	3	▨
7	5	.	1	5	▨	▨	2	▨	.
▨	▨	▨	▨	▨	▨	▨	1	▨	1

5.

10^2	10 x 10	100	2	2
10^3	10 x 10 x 10	1,000	3	3
10^4	10 x 10 x 10 x 10	10,000	4	4
10^5	10 x 10 x 10 x 10 x 10	100,000	5	5
10^6	10 x 10 x 10 x 10 x 10 x 10	1,000,000	6	6

6. 4   15   6   16
85   21   58

Lesson 77

1.

	x 10
67.9	679
3.4	34.0
0.71	7.1
0.712	7.12

	÷10
13.92	1.392
3.09	0.309
0.254	0.0254
21.77	2.177

2. 0.1   0.2   0.9   0.8

3.
2.222   2.2 $2.\overline{2}$
0.055   0.1 $0.0\overline{5}$
0.277   0.3 $0.2\overline{7}$
0.333   0.3 $0.\overline{3}$
0.090   0.1 $0.0\overline{9}$

4. 3   2   9   12
8   10   6   7

5. 828;   1,391;   1,899
   1,409;   1,591

6. The answer is "your calves."

Lesson 78

1. 47)01.2‾

   521)910.‾

   422)038.‾

   29)19.‾

2. 1.99   13   32
   2.3   1.4   34

3.

	x 100
60.2	6,020
0.876	87.6
0.14	14
9.1	910

	÷ 100
33.72	0.3372
309	3.09
12	0.12
5.9	0.059

4. $\frac{1}{9} = .11\overline{1}$ $\frac{1}{4} < 0.3$ $\frac{2}{3} > 0.59$

   $\frac{4}{7} < .75$ $\frac{1}{3} = 0.33\overline{}$ $\frac{1}{11} < 0.9$

5. 5   11   9   1
   8   2   6   10

6. 222   180   99   284   291

7.

49.6	124
1,240	74.4

11,610	464.4
696.6	1,161

Lesson 79

1. 1. 5 groups

    2. 12.8 cm

    3. $3\frac{4}{5}$ cookie

    4. 4 people in 8 groups, 5 people in 1 group

2. 6.92   2.7   1.03
   6.81   89   12

3.

Division by 1,000	Division by 100	Division by 10	Given Number	Multiply x 10	Multiply x 100	Multiply x 1,000
0.1608	1.608	16.08	160.8	1,608	16,080	160,800
0.09312	0.9312	9.312	93.12	931.2	9,312	93,120
0.0088	0.088	0.88	8.8	88	880	8,800
0.71254	7.1254	71.254	712.54	7125.4	71,254	712,540
.0235	0.235	2.35	23.5	235	2,350	23,500

4. 0.63   0.47   0.86   0.71

5. 285 x 12 = 3,420
   405 x 13 = 5,265
   109 x 22 = 2,398
   411 x 17 = 6,987

Lesson 80

1.

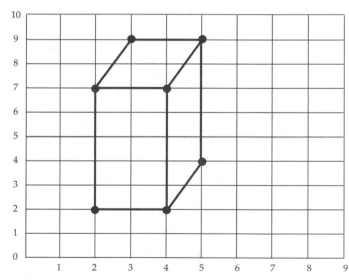

2. 1. 1.2 ounces

    2. 1 1/2 cupcakes

    3. 4 tins

    4. 5 people in 3 groups, and 4 people in the other group

3. $279\overline{)89.0}$

   $92\overline{)91.}$

   $175\overline{)8920}$

   $81\overline{)19.8}$

4.

	x 1,000
1.793	1793
345.4	345,400
0.0509	50.9
4.888	4,888

	÷ 1,000
17.984	0.017984
432	0.432
8,120	8.120
420	0.42

5.
$$\begin{array}{r} 737,050 \\ +\ 736,655 \\ \hline 1,473,706 \end{array}$$

$$\begin{array}{r} 582,755 \\ +\ 948,899 \\ \hline 1,531,604 \end{array}$$

   1,473,705   1,531,654

6. 7,241   4,082   10,416   7,695

Lesson 81

1. $\dfrac{7}{64}$; $\dfrac{2}{5}$; $\dfrac{2}{45}$; $\dfrac{3}{28}$

   $\dfrac{2}{9}$; $\dfrac{1}{9}$; $\dfrac{7}{30}$; $\dfrac{27}{80}$

2. 52 boxes
   16 packages
   6 boxes
   10 cabins total

3. 6.4;   3.6;   0.069;   .56

4. $16 + 8 + 0 + 2 + 1 = 27$
   $8 + 4 + 2 + 1 = 15$
   $8 + 0 + 0 + 1 = 9$
   $2 + 1 = 3$
   $16 + 4 + 2 = 22$
   $16 + 8 + 4 + 2 + 1 = 31$

5. 1 dollar, 3 quarters, 1 dime,
   1 penny = ($1.86)
   1 dollar, 2 quarters, 2 dimes,
   1 penny = ($1.71)
   2 dollars, 2 quarters, 2 dimes = ($2.70)
   1 dollar, 1 quarter = ($1.25)
   1 five, 2 ones, 3 quarters, 1 nickel,
   1 penny = ($7.81)

6. The answers will be as follows moving
   from the right to the left on the map.
   Eastern 9:00;   Central 8:00;
   Mountain 7:00;   Pacific 6:00;
   Alaska 5:00;   Hawaii 4:00

Lesson 82

1. 8;   3;   5
   6;   5;   16

2. $\dfrac{23}{125}$; $\dfrac{1}{4}$; $\dfrac{7}{32}$;

   $\dfrac{14}{25}$ $\dfrac{1}{2}$; $1\dfrac{1}{4}$

3. 83 people with 1 mini quiche left over
   11/2 lbs.
   3 boards with 24 inches left over
   8 times

4. 0.419;   3.13;   32.1;   5.67
   120;   0.0009; 0.094; 1.59

5. 111000_2; 111111_2; 1001_2; 10111_2

6. 10.24;   56.98;   0.37;
   0.09;   42.01;   19.73

7. $102.35 = 1 one hundred, 2 ones
            1 quarter, 1 dime
   $46.05   = 2 twenties, 1 five, 1 one
            1 nickel
   $89.75
   $118.10 = 1 one hundred dollar bill
            (unused from transaction)
            1 ten, 1 five, 3 ones

Lesson 83

1. $8\frac{1}{8}$; $22\frac{1}{10}$; $8\frac{11}{20}$

    22; $106\frac{15}{16}$; $19\frac{1}{32}$

2. $6\frac{2}{5}$;   5;   8;   50

    $30\frac{5}{8}$;   5;   40;   200

3. about 8 lines per second
    $10.00 left over
    4—5th grade classes
    No. There should be no remainders if the total is correct.

4. 65.3399;   15.502;   147.1372
    35.821;   4.8793

5. $2,797.30
    $9.00
    $79.90
    $149.53

6. DELIVERER

Lesson 84

1. $6\frac{2}{3}$; $27\frac{3}{4}$;   15

    $\frac{3}{10}$; $\frac{6}{7}$; $\frac{1}{6}$

2. $4\frac{4}{5}$; $26\frac{5}{14}$; $1\frac{7}{9}$; $3\frac{3}{5}$

    $3\frac{12}{35}$; $\frac{1}{12}$; $\frac{1}{10}$; $2\frac{1}{4}$

3. $569.73
    $37.90
    $47.63
    $309.17

4. < ;   > ;   >
    = ;   > ;   >

5. $78.75
    $4.06
    No
    Yes

6. All dresses $36.00
    All dress shorts $22.50
    All blouses $13.50
    All earrings $1.80 pr.
    All belts $4.50 ea.

7. 56.095   56.395   65.293   65.329
    100.010   101.010   101.011   101.110
    223.654   245.636   254.363   254.636

Lesson 85

1. $\frac{100}{12}$; $\frac{65}{45}$; $\frac{4}{2}$

    $\frac{19}{10}$; $\frac{8}{7}$; $\frac{5}{4}$

2. $\dfrac{5}{14}$; $\dfrac{2}{9}$; $\dfrac{1}{6}$; $\dfrac{1}{4}$

   $\dfrac{2}{5}$; $\dfrac{7}{19}$; $\dfrac{2}{3}$; $\dfrac{2}{3}$

3. $1\dfrac{2}{5} \times 2\dfrac{6}{7}$ – 4

   $4\dfrac{1}{3} \times 3\dfrac{6}{8}$ – $16\dfrac{1}{4}$

   $7\dfrac{2}{5} \times 2\dfrac{1}{7}$ – $15\dfrac{6}{7}$

   $3\dfrac{1}{4} \times 8\dfrac{1}{2}$ – $27\dfrac{5}{8}$

   $2\dfrac{3}{8} \times 2\dfrac{2}{3}$ – $6\dfrac{1}{3}$

   $4\dfrac{2}{3} \times 1\dfrac{4}{8}$ – 7

4. 24; 20; 9

   $\dfrac{1}{3}$; $\dfrac{1}{2}$; $\dfrac{3}{4}$

5. 0.257; 171.823; 31.55
   39.521; 2.415; 5.422

6. 4, 3, 7, 1, 2, 9, 6
   HOLINESS

7. 195; 504; 5,149
   663; 282; 9,168

Lesson 86

1. 8; 9; 48; 138
   192; 6; 10; 4

2. $\dfrac{98}{45}$; $\dfrac{78}{63}$; $\dfrac{45}{25}$; $\dfrac{72}{12}$; $\dfrac{255}{125}$; $\dfrac{33}{11}$

   $\dfrac{100}{65}$; $\dfrac{133}{98}$; $\dfrac{698}{245}$; $\dfrac{55}{14}$; $\dfrac{156}{143}$; $\dfrac{85}{74}$

Shading should show two crosses.

254

3. $6\dfrac{11}{32}$; $58\dfrac{1}{10}$; $9\dfrac{7}{9}$

   $32\dfrac{1}{7}$; $145\dfrac{3}{5}$; $4\dfrac{1}{5}$

4. The correct path is path 2 with answers totaling 485.261.

5. 9; 8; 5
   0; 7; 6

6. 134; 93; 1,018
   575; 963; 827

Lesson 87

1. 2; $2\dfrac{1}{2}$; 6; $1\dfrac{1}{3}$

   4; $1\dfrac{4}{5}$; 2; $2\dfrac{2}{3}$

2. 220; 2,817; 3,416
   6,832; 7,272; 2,025

3. $\dfrac{540}{91}$; $\dfrac{48}{343}$; $\dfrac{530}{88}$

   $\dfrac{26}{184}$; $\dfrac{31}{24}$; $\dfrac{56}{339}$

4. $\dfrac{10}{21}$; $\dfrac{13}{50}$; $\dfrac{13}{6} = 2\dfrac{1}{6}$ $\dfrac{1}{9}$

5. 6; 6; 8
   3; 6; 7

6.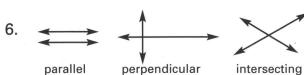
   parallel   perpendicular   intersecting

7. 63; 70; 3
   9; 18; 54

Lesson 88

1. $\dfrac{1}{100}$; $\dfrac{1}{20}$; $1\dfrac{4}{9}$

   $\dfrac{2}{3}$; $2\dfrac{1}{3}$; $\dfrac{7}{9}$

   $\dfrac{17}{48}$; $2\dfrac{2}{7}$

2. $\dfrac{5}{42}$; $\dfrac{9}{15} =$ $\dfrac{5}{24}$; $\dfrac{2}{35}$

3. 5;   4
   10;   18
   20;   24
   21;   3
   2;   6
   75;   7
   30;   14
   9;   40
   12;   8
   27;   50

4. $\dfrac{2}{1}$; $\dfrac{5}{4}$; $\dfrac{98}{45}$; $\dfrac{987}{101}$; $\dfrac{231}{760}$

   $\dfrac{70}{65}$; $\dfrac{56}{23}$; $\dfrac{334}{92}$; $\dfrac{510}{398}$; $\dfrac{1,010}{801}$

5. 0;   3;   3;   7
   3;   3;   7;   7

6.

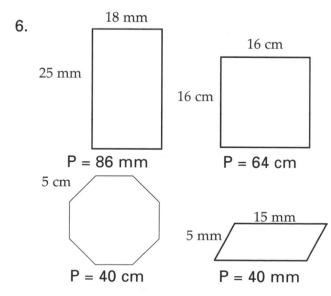

P = 86 mm   P = 64 cm

P = 40 cm   P = 40 mm

7. 189;   925;   1,068
   2;   4;   2

Lesson 89

1. $\dfrac{1}{2}$;   15; $1\dfrac{1}{2}$

   $4\dfrac{1}{2}$; $11\dfrac{1}{2}$;   6

   5; $43\dfrac{1}{2}$;   7

2. $\dfrac{1}{8}$; $\dfrac{3}{400}$; $\dfrac{1}{10}$

   $\dfrac{1}{80}$; $\dfrac{5}{48}$; $\dfrac{1}{8}$

3. $\dfrac{2}{3}$; $2\dfrac{5}{8}$; $\dfrac{8}{9}$; $9\dfrac{3}{5}$

   $3\dfrac{3}{4}$; $\dfrac{7}{88}$; $1\dfrac{1}{15}$; $3\dfrac{23}{25}$

4. $11.20
   $60.00
   $1,750.00
   $4,000.00
   $33.33

5. 9,150 sq. ft.
   2,025 sq. meters

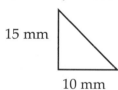

area = (15 x 10) ÷ 2 = 75 mm squared
Wall area = 375 ft squared
Window area = 18 ft squared
375 ft² − 18 ft² = 357 ft²

6. Corrected problems:

1,680	14,060	3,437
+ 2,960	+ 15,755	+ 4,550
4,640	29,815	7,987

2,986	1,215	4,514
+ 465	+ 689	+ 2.605
3,451	1,904	7,119

$$\begin{array}{r} 8,193 \\ +\ 1,390 \\ \hline 9,583 \end{array}$$

BE GODLY

Lesson 90

1. $3\dfrac{3}{4}$; $3\dfrac{1}{2}$; $\dfrac{3}{5}$

   $4\dfrac{2}{5}$;   37; $1\dfrac{3}{5}$

2. 1;   80;   7

   20; $1\dfrac{1}{2}$;   5

3. $\dfrac{2}{3}$; $\dfrac{2}{21}$; $\dfrac{1}{15}$

   $\dfrac{24}{35}$; $\dfrac{8}{63}$; $\dfrac{11}{15}$

   $\dfrac{26}{105}$; $\dfrac{2}{3}$; $\dfrac{3}{28}$

   GRACE

4. 160 cm³
   16 cm³
   27 cm³
   70 cm³
   4 layers
   168 cm³

5. 40,000;   582,030;   598,701
   66,214;   8,597;   24,865

6.
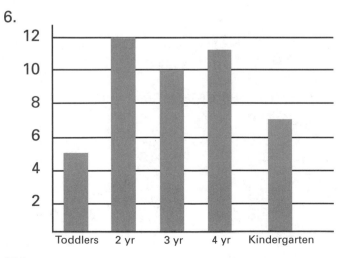

Lesson 91

1. $3\dfrac{2}{16}$

   $1\dfrac{15}{16}$

   $2\dfrac{4}{16}$

   $\dfrac{14}{16}$

2. $\dfrac{186}{20} = 9\dfrac{3}{10}$; $\dfrac{62}{9} = 6\dfrac{8}{9}$; $\dfrac{12}{20} = \dfrac{3}{5}$

   $\dfrac{22}{5} = 4\dfrac{2}{5}$; $\dfrac{222}{6} = 37$; $\dfrac{8}{5} = 1\dfrac{3}{5}$

3. $\dfrac{3}{4}$; $\dfrac{1}{4}$

   $\dfrac{1}{3}$; $\dfrac{1}{2}$

   $\dfrac{1}{4}$; $\dfrac{1}{2}$

4. $\dfrac{3}{24} = \dfrac{1}{8}$; $\dfrac{2}{9}$; $\dfrac{1}{4}$; $\dfrac{7}{16}$

   $\dfrac{9}{450} = \dfrac{1}{50}$; $\dfrac{3}{60} = \dfrac{1}{20}$

   $\dfrac{8}{64} = \dfrac{1}{8}$; $\dfrac{3}{15} = \dfrac{1}{5}$

5. 6 L;   7 O
   4 V;   2 E

   LOVE

6.
      Square

   Rhombus   Parallelogram   Square

   Rectangle   Trapezoid

7.
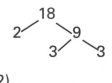

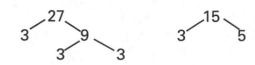

Lesson 92

1. Answers will vary.
   Sample answers are given.
   a baby;   a soda;   a car;   a table
   a washer;   a bag of potatoes

2. $3\dfrac{1}{16}$

   $1\dfrac{8}{16}$

   $5\dfrac{3}{16}$

   $2\dfrac{4}{16}$

3. $\dfrac{8}{7} = 1\dfrac{1}{7}$; $\dfrac{582}{198} = 2\dfrac{31}{33}$; $\dfrac{20}{7} = 2\dfrac{6}{7}$

   $\dfrac{100}{19} = 5\dfrac{5}{19}$; $\dfrac{1200}{131} = 9\dfrac{21}{131}$; $\dfrac{150}{19} = 7\dfrac{17}{19}$

4. Answers will vary. Possible answers follow:

   $\dfrac{9}{16}$; $\dfrac{1}{13}$; $\dfrac{11}{12}$

   $\dfrac{5}{12}$; 1; $\dfrac{1}{2}$

5. 1,004,561,332,879

   25,334,567

   350,008,495,229,314

   561,220,182,285,882

6. teacher check

7. 2, 13, 23, 19, 59, 3, 11, 31, 89, 17, 23, 73
   47, 5, 19, 7, 79, 67, 2, 7, 19, 97, 61, 19
   message: JOY

Lesson 93

1. 1;   1;   6
   1;   1; $\dfrac{1}{2}$
   4;   512;

2. 40 oz
   4 oz
   1lb for $1.05
   .899 = .90¢
   200 bags
   112 oz

3. teacher check

4. $5\dfrac{1}{3} \div 1\dfrac{1}{3}$ $=$ 4

   $3\dfrac{1}{12} \div 1\dfrac{1}{3}$ $=$ $2\dfrac{5}{16}$

   $4 \div 1\dfrac{1}{6}$ $=$ $3\dfrac{3}{7}$

   $9 \div 2\dfrac{1}{3}$ $=$ $3\dfrac{6}{7}$

   $12\dfrac{3}{6} \div 2\dfrac{1}{6}$ $=$ $5\dfrac{10}{13}$

5. 973,263;   1,278,668;   66,896;   5,023

6. 100°   45°
   60°   20°

7. 10^5
   10^3
   7^3
   4^2
   3^4
   5^5

Lesson 94

1. 1. C.
   2. A.
   3. D.
   4. B.

2. 16;   1

$\frac{1}{2}$;   2

$1\frac{1}{2}$;   16

3. (1 ton)   (10 oz)   (9 lb)   (1 lb)

4. 8;   8
   16;   3
   8;   1

5. 4,394;   10,053;   68,600
   55,369;   482,444

6. 90°;   30°
   7°;   94°

7. 36
   256
   78,125
   1,000,000
   27
   4,782,969

Lesson 95

1. 12.9 cm;   1,945 cm
   3.129 m;   60,900 dm
   1,970 mm;   253 mm

2. 87°;   54°;   -30°;   2°
   102°;   69°;   -15°;   17°

3. 1 cup;   1 gal
   1 quart;   1 pint

4. 48 oz;   80 oz;   32,000 oz
   160,000 oz;   35 oz;   224,000 oz

5.   **Across**   **Down**
   1. 107,092   1. 181,421
   2. 210,585   2. 267,605

6. 12;   25;   18;   20;   80;   33

7. $7\frac{7}{10}$; $22\frac{5}{6}$; $39\frac{19}{18} = 40\frac{1}{18}$; $11\frac{7}{12}$

Lesson 96

1. 0.009 Kg;   0.099 Kg;   0.820 Kg
   4,000 g;   35,000 g;   328,000 g

2. 100
   1
   1
   1000
   2.5
   900

3. thermometers must be colored to the
   indicated temperature
   (freezing point = 32° F)
   (boiling point = 212° F)

4. 24 pt, 3 gal; 2 gal, 8 qt; 36 pt, $4\frac{1}{2}$ gal

   12 qt, 3 gal; $17\frac{1}{2}$ qt, $4\frac{3}{8}$ gal

   40 qt, 80 pt

5. 50,000;   482,030;   498,007
   66,213;   7,597;   17,545

6. $7\frac{7}{10}$; $8\frac{3}{6} = 8\frac{1}{2}$; $19\frac{9}{20}$

   $15\frac{4}{9}$; $5\frac{5}{12}$

   SIGHT

7. 78;   19;   4;   11;   10;   32

Lesson 97

1. 5;   319;   0.015
   0.730;   2,000;   51,000

2. grams
   kilograms
   milligrams
   milligram
   kilogram
   gram

3. about 500 kilometers
   Note: All answers are approximations.

© MCMXCIX, Alpha Omega Publications, Inc.

Student answers may vary slightly due to measuring techniques
about 760 km
about 520 km
about 575 km
Boise to Col. Spr. = about 1,000 km
Salt Lake to Col. Spr. = about 600 km
Difference = 400

Casper to Col. Spr. = about 420 km
Col. Spr. to Provo = about 600 km
Total = 1,020 km

4. 3.16×10^6; 9.98×10^{-1}; 2.68×10^8
   9.55×10^1; 7.7×10^{-4}; 8.65×10^5

5. 4;   10;   5

   $\dfrac{10}{10}$; $\dfrac{4}{6}$;   1

6. $41.38 $13.45 $26.10
   $4.60 $1.50 $2.90

   $473.40 $269.77 $2,190.15
   $52.60 $29.98 $243.35

Lesson 98

1. 32° C   8° C   10° C   39° C

2.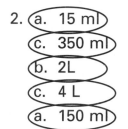
   a. 15 ml
   c. 350 ml
   b. 2L
   c. 4 L
   a. 150 ml

3. Answers will vary. Sample answers are given.
   a paper clip   a small kitten
   a bowling ball   a lemon

4. about $2\dfrac{1}{2}$ meters
   30 cm
   2 cm
   5 cm
   about 3 meters

5. 1,000,000
   5,870,000,000,000
   4.2×10^7
   0.0000073
   10,000
   2.36×10^{11}
   45,880,000,000,000,000,000
   9.8×10^{-5}

6. $33\dfrac{4}{7}$; $56\dfrac{1}{4}$; $28\dfrac{7}{12}$

   $21\dfrac{13}{15}$; $29\dfrac{7}{8}$; $29\dfrac{5}{6}$

7. book   – $23.40
   bracelet   – $53.98
   tent   – $112.95
   box of dishes   – $56.69
   ring   – $55.79
   pair of shorts – $22.95

Lesson 99

1. 560 x 5 = 2,800 ft
   (92 x 2) + (46 x 2) = 276 in
   350 ÷ 2 = 175;   175 + 15 = 190
   350 + 175 + 190 = 715 ft

2. 93° C;   36° C;   29° C;
   160° C;   7° C;   0° C

3. 0.345;   0.072
   34,000;   1.598
   175,000;   0.008

4. a feather   –   1 mg
   an egg   –   50 mg
   a TV set   –   50 Kg
   a baby kitten   –   1 Kg
   a hamster   –   4 g
   a hippopotamus   –   1,000 Kg
   MERCY

5.

		1	1	1	0	1	= 29
			1	0	1	0	= 10
	1	0	0	1	1	0	= 38
				1	1	1	= 7
1	1	1	1	0	1	0	= 122
	1	0	1	0	1	0	= 42

6. 5; 9; 4
   75; 3; 5

7. 304,192; 606,888; 172,491
   91,950; 19,440; 58,947

Lesson 100

1. $100.00

   $200.00

   Most: Food Concessions ($300.00)
   Least: Cotton candy ($100.00)

   $1,200.00 total sales combined

2. 100° C; 14° C; 28° C
   271° C; -4° C; 0° C

3. soda – 250 ml
   trash can – 700 L
   washing machine – 80 L
   carton of milk – 1 L

4. 1010_{two}; 10010_{two}; 1100_{two}; 1111_{two}
   10100_{two}; 11_{two}; 1001_{two}

5. 78; 15; 1,050
   71; 3; 443

6.
   4,739
   x   14
   66,346

   9,374
   x   33
   309,342

   9,786
   x   56
   548,016

7. 68 sit-ups
   19 were left

Lesson 101

1. 24 cm; 12 cm; 14 ft
   20 cm²; 18.2 cm²; 51.84 cm²

2. 26° F; 44° F; 10° F
   88° F; 92° F; 8° F

3. -14° C; -4° C; 72° C
   16° C; 36° C; 80° C

4. 17; 79; 70; 80
   88; 111; 325; 161

5.

1. 1		2. 3				4. 1	•	8
1. 9	•	2	9	3. 2		2		
•		•		9		•		5. 0
2. 2	•	8		3. 3	6	•	8	•
				•		8	9	
		5. 5	4	•	4	2		8

Down:
1. 19.2
2. 32.8
3. 293.4
4. 12.88
5. 0.98

Across:
1. 9.292
2. 2.8
3. 36.8
4. 1.8
5. 54.42

6. $\frac{1}{7}$; $\frac{1}{4}$; $\frac{2}{9}$; $\frac{1}{3}$
   $\frac{4}{9}$; 2; 1; $\frac{3}{16}$

Ananias

Lesson 102

1. 108 cm²; 19.8 cm²; 12 mm²
   846 cm²; 3,950 mm²; 1.449 m²

2. 13.4 cm; 23.56 cm; 18.6 cm
   46.6 mm; 63.2 cm; 18.8 m

3. teacher check

4. 251.37; 195.06
   40.57; 196.656

5. $\dfrac{1}{27}$; $\dfrac{40}{63}$; $\dfrac{3}{8}$; $\dfrac{4}{35}$; $\dfrac{8}{15}$; $\dfrac{3}{10}$; $\dfrac{3}{77}$

   $\dfrac{7}{10}$; $\dfrac{3}{8}$; $\dfrac{7}{12}$; $\dfrac{1}{54}$; $\dfrac{5}{9}$; $\dfrac{3}{28}$; $\dfrac{3}{25}$

   $\dfrac{3}{16}$; $\dfrac{24}{35}$; $\dfrac{25}{36}$; $\dfrac{1}{3}$; $\dfrac{1}{2}$; $\dfrac{3}{32}$; $\dfrac{3}{56}$

Faith, Hope, Love

6. 5;   8;   3

Lesson 103

1. 6 cm²;   35 mm²;   10 mm²
   360 cm²;   40 mm²;   31 cm²
   162 cm²;   270 mm²;   34 cm²

2. 182 cm²;   20.64 cm²;   19.2 mm²
   846 cm²;   395 mm²;   1.449 m²

3. 5 cm   20 cm
   5 cm

   4 cm   6 cm
   4 cm

4. 36 cm²;   25 cm²;   63 cm²

5. 280,423,224; 131,082,462; 17,227,764
   2,243,616,102;   151,871,976
   GRACE

6. $\dfrac{4}{5}$;   5; $\dfrac{1}{9}$; $\dfrac{3}{8}$

7. 1,089.78;   408.59;   11.172;   32.85

Lesson 104

1. 153.9 cm²;   10.2 m²

2. 78.5 cm²;   28.3 m²;   2.5 cm²

3. 128 cm²;   40 m²;   4.5 cm²
   154 m²;   39.4 m²;   7.8 cm²

4. 340 m²;   7.6 m²

5. $\dfrac{6}{11}$; $\dfrac{1}{12}$; $\dfrac{4}{9}$

   $\dfrac{1}{11}$;   1; $\dfrac{4}{21}$

6. 9.4 × 2.2 = 20.68
   3.1 × 5.2 = 16.12
   2.6 × 0.5 = 1.3

Lesson 105

1. 12 cm³;   24 cm³;   36 cm³

2. 28.3 cm²;   12.6 cm²;   50.2 cm²
   113.0 cm²;   63.6 cm²;   78.5 cm²

3. 24 cm²;   48 cm²
   12 cm²;   24 cm²

4. 97;   66;   43
   58;   552;   73

5. 15.4
   6.8
   3.7
   13

6. Shaded boxes from start to end:
   $\dfrac{1}{2}$; $\dfrac{1}{2}$; $\dfrac{1}{5}$; $\dfrac{1}{3}$

   $\dfrac{2}{9}$; $\dfrac{1}{4}$; $\dfrac{1}{5}$; $\dfrac{1}{4}$

Lesson 106

1. 301.4 m³;   100.5 m³
   508.7 m³;   192.3 m³
   2009.6 m³;   172.3 m³

2. 8 cm³;   36 cm³

3. 22.9 cm²;   45.3 cm²;   75.4 cm²
   4.9 m²;   314 cm²

4. 87 cm²;   60.4 cm²

5. 714

6. 0.17;   0.09;   2.16;   7.2;   0.62
   ALYRE

7. 1. South Carolina
   2. Rhode Island and New Hampshire
   3. West Virginia, Rhode Island
   4. 5,000,000 – 1,700,000 = 3,300,000
   5. 1,000,000 – 500,000 = 500,000

Lesson 107

1. Front: 300 cm², 600 cm²
   Top: 50 cm², 100 cm²
   Side: 150 cm², 300 cm²
   Total: 1,000 cm²

   Front: 375 cm², 750 cm²
   Top: 225 cm², 450 cm²
   Side: 375 cm², 750 cm²
   Total: 1,950 cm²

2. 1.) 40 cm³   2.) 64 cm³
   3.) 36 cm³   4.) 90 cm³

3. teacher check

4. 1. (The drawing should have a
      diameter of 6 cm)
   Area: 28.3 cm²

   2. (The drawing should have a
      diameter of 4 cm)
   Area: 12.6 cm²

5. 60.2
   5.68
   2.87
   3.09
   51.8
   PERCH

6. $\frac{1}{2}$; $\frac{3}{10}$; $\frac{1}{3}$; $\frac{3}{7}$

   $\frac{7}{16}$; $\frac{3}{10}$; $\frac{9}{11}$; $\frac{7}{10}$

   $\frac{2}{7}$; $\frac{9}{11}$; $\frac{3}{4}$; $\frac{4}{5}$

Lesson 108

1. 1. 20,000 cm²
   2. 32 cm³
   3. 100.48 cm³
   4. 40 cm

2. 72 cm², 144cm²
   12 cm², 24 cm²
   24 cm², 48 cm²
   Total: 216 cm²

3. 37.7 cm³;   904.3 cm³

4. 54 cm²   108 cm³
   9 m   10 m
   2 mm   25 mm
   6 cm   408 cm³
   144 m²   864 m³

5.   197   508   362
     x 4   x 9   x 5

6. $\frac{3}{16}$; $1\frac{1}{15}$; $\frac{5}{6}$; $\frac{10}{11}$

   $2\frac{1}{7}$; $\frac{35}{54}$; $\frac{32}{65}$; $\frac{9}{10}$

Lesson 109

1. 12:00 P.M.   4:00 P.M.   9:00 P.M.   10:00 P.M.
   8:00 A.M.   7:00 A.M.   5:00 A.M.   6:00 A.M.
   3:00 A.M.   7:00 A.M.   4:00 A.M.   6:00 A.M.

2. Triangle A has an area of 171 cm².
   Triangle B has an area of 102 cm².
   Triangle A has the greater area.

Rectangle A has an area of 36 cm².
Rectangle B has an area of 35.88 cm².
Rectangle A has the greater area.

3. 35.55 cm², 71.1 cm²
    35.55 cm², 71.1 cm²
    20.25 cm², 40.5 cm²
    <u>Total: 182.7 cm²</u>

4. 1570 cm³
    2411.5 cm³
    2659.6 cm³

5. 11.8; 21.5; 92.9; 230.1; 1.056
    197.4; 421.8; 14.85; 825.25; 20.308

6. 0.5   0.25   0.8
    0.8   0.625   0.875
    0.1   0.75   0.625

Lesson 110

1. 1. Addition, Division
    2. Addition, Division
    3. Addition, Multiplication
    4. Multiplication, Subtraction

2. teacher check (answers will vary)

3. 79.56 cm², 159.12 cm²
    30.6 cm², 61.2 cm²
    10.4 cm², 20.8 cm²
    <u>Total: 241.12 cm²</u>

4.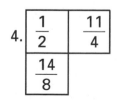

5. $19)\overline{1.52}$
    $53)\overline{106}$
    $123)\overline{86100}$
    $29)\overline{115.2}$

6. $1\frac{1}{2}$; $1\frac{3}{5}$
    $3\frac{1}{3}$; $\frac{18}{49}$

7. $\frac{5}{6}$; $\frac{9}{10}$; $\frac{4}{9}$; $\frac{1}{10}$; $\frac{2}{3}$; $\frac{2}{5}$
    $\frac{1}{8}$; $\frac{6}{89}$; $\frac{8}{9}$; $\frac{3}{13}$; $\frac{3}{4}$; $\frac{1}{4}$
    $\frac{3}{8}$; $\frac{1}{12}$; $\frac{19}{20}$; $\frac{1}{4}$; $\frac{3}{4}$; $\frac{7}{12}$

Lesson 111

1. 1. 15°
    2. 90°
    3. 120°

2. 6cm   7cm   12mm
    4.5cm   7cm   3.2mm
    13.5cm²   24.5cm²   19.2mm²

3. 1. $90.00
    2. $78.00 for 25 loaves. No.
    3. 10 hard cover books
        20 paperback books
        She can buy 10 more
        paperback books.
    4. 8 days

4. a. 7:00 A.M.   b. 6:00 A.M.
    c. 3:00 P.M.   d. 12:00 A.M.

5. 6   4   14
    40   12   9
    40   77   65

6. $0.\overline{45}$ $0.\overline{81}$ $0.\overline{1}$
    $1.2\overline{6}$ $0.\overline{6}$ $0.\overline{3}$
    $0.\overline{27}$ $0.\overline{53}$ $0.\overline{2}$

    0.2   0.5   0.875
    0.8   0.75   0.1
    0.625   0.8   0.9

7. 0.021; 0.1; 0.2; 0.22; 0.3; 0.41
    0.456; 0.544; 0.8; 0.801; 0.89; 0.9
    0.92; 0.99; 1.01; 1.075; 1.1; 1.125
    (picture should be of a hand)

Lesson 112

1. $\angle$LMN = 90°
    $\angle$NMP = 150°
    $\angle$PMO = 30°
    $\angle$OML = 90°

2. $\angle$AXB = 110°
    $\angle$DXC = 110°
    $\angle$AXD = 70°
    $\angle$CXB = 70°

    $\angle$EKF = 145°
    $\angle$GKH = 145°
    $\angle$EKG = 35°
    $\angle$FKH = 35°
    congruent

3. a. $75.00
    b. $100.00
    c. $145.00
    d. $190.00
    e. Yes

4. $0.\overline{4}$ $0.\overline{36}$ $0.\overline{76}$
    $0.\overline{5}$ $0.4\overline{6}$ $0.1\overline{6}$
    $0.\overline{27}$ $0.\overline{8}$ $0.\overline{18}$

5. a. 12:00 P.M.   b. 2:00 P.M.
    c. 2:00 P.M.   d. 11:00 A.M.

6. 5;   3;   11;   2;   67;   19;   53;   67
    31;   79;   89;   41;   29;   13

LESSON 113

1.
    (90°)   (120°)   (10°)

2. 120° + 105° + 135° = 360°

3. a. Total bill: $23.40
       Amount of change: $1.60

    b. Total bill: $21.28
       Amount of change: $3.72

    c. Total bill: $28.49
       Amount of change: $11.51

    d. Total bill: $39.23
       Amount of change: $0.77

4.

10^4	10 x 10 x 10 x 10	10,000	4	4
2^4	2 x 2 x 2 x 2	16	4	0
10^5	10 x 10 x 10 x 10 x 10	100,000	5	5
3^6	3 x 3 x 3 x 3 x 3 x 3	729	6	0

5. 9   4   3
    5   6   20

6. (1 ton)
    (4 oz.)
    (12 lbs.)
    (1 lb.)

Lesson 114

1. The lines given should be divided evenly by a straight line forming 4 right angles. These need to be graded by teacher observation.

2.

3. $\angle$EVF = 50°
    $\angle$EVH = 130°
    $\angle$GVH = 50°
    $\angle$GVF = 130°

    50° + 130° + 50° + 130° = 360°

4. 35°
    105°

5. What do you call a fish that plays poker? **A card shark!**

6. 8   5
    20   400

Lesson 115

1. Each angle should be bisected into two congruent angles. These need to be graded by teacher observation.

2. Each angle should be bisected into two congruent angles. These need to be graded by teacher observation.

3.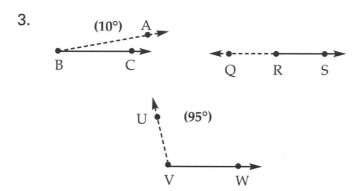

4. ∠CDE = 35°
    ∠EDF = 170°
    ∠CDF = 155°

    35° + 170° + 155° = 360°

5.
    121 – 11   361 – 19
    196 – 14   81 – 9
     64 – 8   225 – 15
    144 – 12   400 – 20
                   625 – 25

6.   90 mm
    4 cm   70 cm
    400 cm   800 cm
    4 km   2 km

Lesson 116

1. Hexagon should have sides measuring 3 centimeters. (Refer to example in explanation.)

2. Each angle should be bisected into two congruent angles. These need to be graded by teacher observation.

3. Line EF should be bisected forming 4 right angles. These need to be graded by teacher observation.

    EF = GH

4.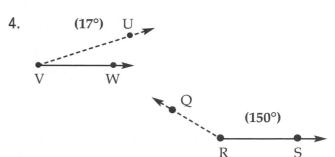

5. 11   2   4
     3   8   6
    13   9   5
    10   12   7

6.   80 mm
    450 cm   385 cm
    47.7 mm   1.18 cm
    7 km   0.23 km

Lesson 117

1. Triangle should be equilateral and should have line GH as one of its sides. It should be labeled △FGH. (Refer to example in Lesson 117 explanation.)

2. Hexagon should have sides measuring 4 centimeters. (Refer to example in explanation in Lesson 116.)

3. Each angle should be bisected into two congruent angles. These need to be graded by teacher observation.

4. Each angle should be bisected into two congruent angles. These need to be graded by teacher observation.

5. 10^{10} 10^2
    10^3 10^4
    300   5,000
    700,000   90,000

6.

ACROSS	**DOWN**
1. 3,408	2. 8,535
3. 756	3. 7,052
4. 5,790	5. 618
5. 603	6. 904
7. 2,460	
8. 585	

Lesson 118

1. Triangle should be a right triangle and should have line JK as one of its sides. It should be labeled △IJK. (Refer to example in Lesson 118 explanation.)

2. Triangle should be equilateral and should have line QR as one of its sides. It should be labeled △PQR. (Refer to example in Lesson 118 explanation.)

3. This section will be graded by teacher observation.

4. Each angle should be bisected into two congruent angles. These need to be graded by teacher observation.

5.

10,600	990,000
610	5,100
111,000	4,230,000
96,120	830

6.

2. 2,068;	3. 1,701;	4. 1,095
5. 4,564;	6. 1,936;	7. 4,035
8. 1,936;	9. 1,936;	10. 4,740

SQUARE FEET

Lesson 119

1. Square should have line XY as one of its sides and should be labeled VWXY. (Refer to example in explanation.)

2. Triangle should be a right triangle and should have line MN as one of its sides. It should be labeled △MNO. (Refer to example in Lesson 118 explanation.)

3. Triangle should be equilateral and should have line JK as one of its sides. It should be labeled △JKH. (Refer to example in Lesson 117 explanation.)

4.

55	15
841	76
733	4,040

5.

27,060;	11,368;	26,158;	33,934
20,502;	10,836;	22,163;	13,072
7,539;	16,484;	44,915;	25,542

6.

28 qt	896 oz
1 gal	24 c
8 qt	72 oz
14 c	20 c

Lesson 120

1. Parallelogram should have one side 5 cm in length and the other side 3 cm in length and should be labeled EFGH. The measure of the angle should be 60° (Refer to example in explanation.)

2. Square should have line OP as one of its sides and should be labeled OPQR. (Refer to example in Lesson 119 explanation.)

3. Triangle should be a right triangle and should have line ST as one of its sides. It should be labeled △STU. (Refer to example in Lesson 118 explanation.)

4. Triangle should be equilateral and should have line HI as one of its sides. It should be labeled △HIJ. (Refer to example in Lesson 117 explanation.)

5. 36,220;   57,744;   314,041;   85,680
   109,780;   256,920;   236,348;   153,630
   A REPTILE

6. 7 ft
   126 ft
   26,400 ft
   21,120 yd
   5 yd 2 ft
   29 yd 1 ft
   6 ft 7 in
   18 ft 3 in

Lesson 121

1. 25/$1.25
   15/$1.69
   5/$2.35
   15/27;   10/27;   3/27;   5/27

2. 733.33;   478.507
   311.303;   35.325
   102.19;   145.82

3. $\frac{32}{44}$
   $\frac{50}{98}$
   $\frac{51}{47}$
   $\frac{36}{98}$
   $\frac{33}{44}$
   $\frac{5}{47}$

4. 216 m²   810 cm²
   345 ft²   117.50 in²

5. 5 - $50.00 bills
   $250.00 – $225.98 = $24.02 in change
   $3.92
   $11.80
   $126.00

6. $7.00 $28.00
   $19.65 $78.60
   $39.80 $159.19
   $9.00 $36.00
   $5.00 $20.00
   $47.00 $188.00
   $15.10 $60.40

7. 113,141;   88,833;   91,377;   61,479
   LOST

Lesson 122

1.

12	15	18	21	24
4	5	6	7	8

6	8	10	12	14	16
3	4	5	6	7	8

3	4	5	6	7	8
6	8	10	12	14	16

2. 25/5
   5/25
   12/5
   15/32
   15/12
   20/12

3. 54.6   54.6   9.15   0.007
   45.9   61.71   12.86   665.3
   45.9   54.6   50.47   61.71
   60.28   6.19   26.46   9.15
   206.68   1.56   9.15   2.08
             178.66   108.09   738.247

4. $\frac{5}{8}$ $\frac{1}{2}$ $\frac{10}{12} = \frac{5}{6}$; $\frac{7}{20}$

5. 97.5 cm²;   92 ft²;   150 m²

6. $40.00
   $60.00
   10 weeks
   $225.00
   $643.50

7. $15.00 $60.00
   $639.65 $2558.60
   $19.80 $79.19
   $7.00 $28.00
   $11.00 $44.00
   $447.00 $1788.00
   $35.10 $140.40

Lesson 123

1. Answers will vary.

   $\dfrac{10}{15}, \dfrac{2}{3};$ $\dfrac{4}{30}, \dfrac{2}{15};$ $\dfrac{32}{16}, \dfrac{8}{4};$ $\dfrac{6}{21}, \dfrac{4}{14}$

   $\dfrac{9}{15}, \dfrac{3}{5};$ $\dfrac{40}{5}, \dfrac{8}{1};$ $\dfrac{110}{30}, \dfrac{22}{6};$ $\dfrac{494}{214}, \dfrac{247}{107}$

2.

4	6	8	10	12
48	72	96	120	144

6	9	12	15	18
2	3	4	5	6

60	72	84	96	108
5	6	7	8	9

3. 6/6; 6/12; 6/12; 2/6; 3/6; 1/3

4. 5.04;   3.01;   50.61
   29.00; 4.33;   17.12

5. $\dfrac{2}{9};$ $\dfrac{1}{29};$ $\dfrac{1}{2}$

   $\dfrac{3}{4};$ $\dfrac{1}{12};$ $\dfrac{7}{10}$

   $\dfrac{5}{6};$ $\dfrac{1}{8};$ 1

   $\dfrac{4}{5};$ $\dfrac{1}{4}$

   Praise the Lord

6. 37.5 m²;   157.5 in²;   405 mm²

Lesson 124

1.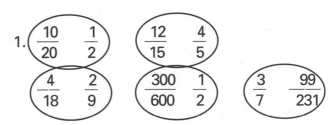

2. Answers will vary.

   $\dfrac{90}{70}, \dfrac{9}{7}.$ $\dfrac{65}{85}, \dfrac{13}{17}.$ $\dfrac{555}{575}, \dfrac{111}{115}.$ $\dfrac{50}{35}, \dfrac{10}{7}$

3. yes   no
   yes   no
   yes   yes
   yes   no

4. 1/3
   4/2
   2/1
   3/0

   5/3
   5/7
   4/5
   3/5

5. 2   20   40
   33   15   18
   4   8   48

6. Note: Some student books only list 12 possible triangles.

   Any order:
   1. 625 m²   9. 1250 m²
   2. 625 m²   10. 1250 m²
   3. 625 m²   11. 1250 m²
   4. 625 m²   12. 1250 m²
   5. 625 m²   13. 2500 m²
   6. 625 m²   14. 2500 m²
   7. 625 m²   15. 2500 m²
   8. 625 m²   16. 2500 m²

Lesson 125

1. 27; 18; 10; 15
   30; 6; 2; 60

2. | 81 | 72 | 63 | 54 |
   |----|----|----|----|
   | 18 | 16 | 14 | 12 |

4	6	8	10
10	15	20	25

2	4	6	8	10	12	14
3	6	9	12	15	18	21

6	5	4	3	2	1
18	15	12	9	6	3

3. REPENT

4. 254.4 in²   314 m²
   113 mm²   452.2 cm²

5. teacher check
   (freezing point = 0° C)
   (boiling point = 100° C)

6. 10 different rides will be taken

Lesson 126

1. 54   84   80   15
   20   25   10   50
   50   90   75   25

2. 5   9   40   32
   125 105 35   392

3. Answers will vary.

   $\dfrac{48}{40}$; $\dfrac{19}{43}$; $\dfrac{20}{40}$; $\dfrac{5}{8}$

   $\dfrac{20}{6}$; $\dfrac{4}{9}$; $\dfrac{12}{8}$; $\dfrac{11}{10}$

4. <;   <;   >
   =;   >;   <
   <;   =;   <

5. 78.5 in²;   706.5 ft²
   379.9 in²;   1256 ft²

6. B
   C
   E
   D
   A

Lesson 127

1. 1/8

   2/8 = 1/4

   Green = 1/8 + red = 2/8 = 3/8

   1/8

   Blue = 2/8 + red = 2/8 + green = 1/8 = 5/8

2. | $\dfrac{46}{100}$ | $\dfrac{26}{100}$ | $\dfrac{5}{50}$ | $\dfrac{3}{75}$ | $\dfrac{4}{5}$ |
   |------|------|------|------|------|
   | .46 | .26 | .10 | .04 | .80 |
   | 46% | 26% | 10% | 4% | 80% |
   | 70% | 96% | 5% | 25% | 136% |

3. 33   5   15
   25   14   20

4. $\dfrac{7}{10} = \dfrac{7}{10}$ $\dfrac{1}{6} = \dfrac{1}{6}$
   $-\dfrac{1}{5} = \dfrac{2}{10}$ $+\dfrac{2}{3} = \dfrac{4}{6}$
   $\dfrac{5}{10}$ $\dfrac{5}{6}$

   $\dfrac{1}{4} = \dfrac{2}{8}$
   $-\dfrac{2}{8} = \dfrac{2}{8}$
   $\dfrac{0}{8}$

5. 706.5 cm³   3,014.4 in³

6. teacher check
Example:

**1998 Bright Beginnings
Preschool Enrollment**

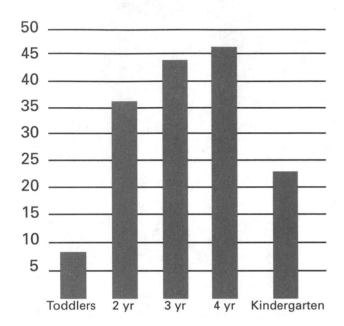

Lesson 128

1. 4/9

   5/9

   0/9

   1/9

   3/6 = 1/2

   one: 1/6;   four: 1/6;   three: 1/6

   All of the outcomes are 1/6 because they are all equally as likely.

2. 2. **brown dogs to all dogs**

   ratio: 4:25

   fraction: 4/25

   ratio/fraction per 100:
   $\dfrac{4}{25} = \dfrac{16}{100}$ = 16:100

   decimal: 16/100 = .16

   percent: 16%

3. **gray dogs to all dogs**

   ratio: 1:25

   fraction: 1/25

   ratio/fraction per 100:
   $\dfrac{1}{25} = \dfrac{4}{100}$ = 4:100

   decimal: 4/100 = .04

   percent: .4 = 4%

4. **tan/white dogs to spotted dogs**

   ratio: 4:10

   fraction: 4/10

   ratio/fraction per 100:
   $\dfrac{4}{10} = \dfrac{40}{100}$ = 40:100

   decimal: 40/100 = .4

   percent: .4 = 40%

5. **black dogs to brown dogs**

   ratio: 6:4

   fraction: 6/4

   ratio/fraction per 100:
   $\dfrac{6}{4} = \dfrac{150}{100}$ = 150:100

   decimal: 150/100 = 1.50

   percent: 1.50 = 150%

3. 5;   20;   5;   27
   4;   20;   21;   6

4. $5\dfrac{7}{12}$; $18\dfrac{29}{35}$; $1\dfrac{2}{6} = 1\dfrac{1}{3}$

   $67\dfrac{1}{5}$; $47\dfrac{4}{10} = 47\dfrac{2}{5}$; $5\dfrac{13}{24}$

5. 1,695.6 ft³   1,538.6 mm³

6.

Number of Rooms Rented at Round Ridge Mountain Inn During Summer Months

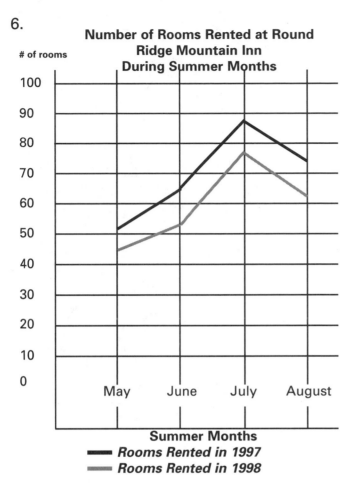

Summer Months
— **Rooms Rented in 1997**
— **Rooms Rented in 1998**

3.

Chet	23/26	.88 = 88%
Brian	19/26	.73 = 73%
Russell	21/25	.84 = 84%
John	17/20	.85 = 85%
Jeffrey	15/23	.652 = 65%
Alan	18/22	.818 = 82%
Mark	23/30	.766 = 77%
Lynn	10/21	.476 = 48%
Greg	9/15	.60 = 60%
Jim	16/26	.615 = 62%
Doug	8/17	.470 = 47%

4. 1; 1; 1; 2

$126\frac{1}{2}$; $10\frac{3}{11}$; $9\frac{2}{3}$; $321\frac{1}{6}$

5. 535   619   925

   448   649

6. Figure 1: $\angle B = 38°$

   Figure 2: e = 12
             d = 6

   Figure 3: x = 7
             y = 10

   Figure 4: $\angle M = 45°$
             $\angle N = 90°$
             $\angle O = 45°$

Lesson 129

1. $\dfrac{256}{1} = \dfrac{1{,}792}{7}$

   $\dfrac{27}{\$850} = \dfrac{54}{\$1700}$

   $\dfrac{3}{6} = \dfrac{27}{54}$

   $\dfrac{3{,}300}{2} = \dfrac{26{,}400}{16}$

   $\dfrac{4}{112} = \dfrac{1}{28}$

2. A 1   A 2   A 3   A 4
   B 1   B 2   B 3   B 4
   C 1   C 2   C 3   C 4
   D 1   D 2   D 3   D 4

Lesson 130

1. | | | | |
   |---|---|---|---|
   | 0.1 | 0.01 | 0.001 | 0.0001 |
   | 0.2 | 0.02 | 0.002 | 0.0002 |
   | 0.3 | 0.03 | 0.003 | 0.0003 |
   | 0.4 | 0.04 | 0.004 | 0.0004 |

2. 9
   .5 or $\frac{1}{2}$
   12
   67%
   63%

3. blue, 1   blue, 3   blue, 5   blue, 7
    red, 1   red, 3   red, 5   red, 7
    green, 1   green, 3   green, 5   green, 7
    yellow, 1   yellow, 3   yellow, 5   yellow, 7

4. $11\frac{1}{3}$; $257\frac{2}{9}$; $46\frac{4}{5}$;   35

   $3\frac{2}{8} = 3\frac{1}{4}$; $898\frac{1}{3}$; $10\frac{1}{7}$; $4\frac{5}{6}$

5. 53,923;   9,517;   67,214
   196;   22.09;   139,060

6. 75° each
   60°;   all sides are equal

Lesson 131

1. $\frac{1}{4} = \frac{25}{100} = 0.25 = 25\%$
   $\frac{1}{2} = \frac{50}{100} = 0.50 = 50\%$
   $\frac{3}{4} = \frac{75}{100} = 0.75 = 75\%$

2.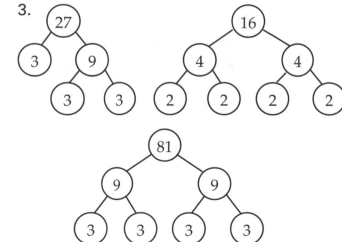
trapezoid   rectangle   rhombus
parallelogram   square

3.

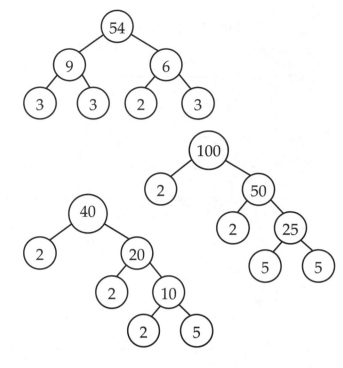

4. 14.8;   38.4;   444.8;   1,563
   33.25;   168.24;   6.35;   77.82
   6.02;   0.81

5. $\frac{1}{16}$; $\frac{6}{24} = \frac{1}{4}$; $\frac{12}{45} = \frac{4}{15}$; $\frac{1}{21}$
   $\frac{8}{3} = 2\frac{2}{3}$; $\frac{21}{72} = \frac{7}{24}$; $\frac{3}{8}$; $\frac{6}{7}$

6. Students should draw circles with appropriate measurement requirements.

7. 90°;   40°;   170°
   180°;   20°;   45°

Lesson 132

1. 20;   18.75;   5.76;   5.94
   6;   125;   7;   108

2.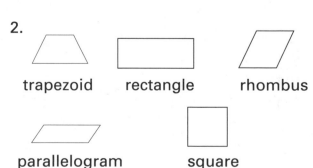
trapezoid   rectangle   rhombus
parallelogram   square

© MCMXCIX, Alpha Omega Publications, Inc.

3. 11;   13;   31;   7;   19
17;   23
WORSHIP

4. 2;   1;   4;   3

5. $\dfrac{160}{7} = 22\dfrac{6}{7}$; $\dfrac{1863}{32} = 58\dfrac{7}{32}$; $\dfrac{455}{12} = 37\dfrac{11}{12}$

$\dfrac{39}{16} = 2\dfrac{7}{16}$; $\dfrac{176}{20} = 8\dfrac{4}{5}$; $\dfrac{748}{55} = 13\dfrac{3}{5}$

6. 80°;   10°;   95°
30°;   130°;   160

Lesson 133

1.

Fraction	Decimal	Percent
-------	0.75	75%
$\dfrac{21}{100}$	-------	21%
$\dfrac{2}{100}$	0.02	-------
-------	0.99	99%
-------	-------	9%
-------	0.29	29%
$\dfrac{54}{100}$	0.54	-------
$\dfrac{100}{100}$	-------	100%

2. D
F
H
G
B
C
E
A

3. B = 60°;   I = 133°;   O = 70°

4. 32
19,683
64
64
2,401
27

5. 35.334;   1.274;   253.617;   318.25

6. $\dfrac{1}{5}$ $\dfrac{5}{12}$; $\dfrac{5}{8}$; $\dfrac{1}{2}$; $\dfrac{3}{10}$; $\dfrac{3}{7}$

Lesson 134

1. $\dfrac{1}{5}$; $\dfrac{7}{10}$; $\dfrac{5}{100} = \dfrac{1}{20}$
$\dfrac{3}{5}$; $\dfrac{33}{100}$; $\dfrac{19}{20}$
$\dfrac{27}{100}$; $\dfrac{9}{20}$; $\dfrac{13}{100}$

2. 70%; 38%; 27%; 100%; 19%; 29%
30%; 89%; 7%; 1%; 64%; 88%

3. $4.00
$6.00
$10.00
$8.00

4. 30°, 90°;   45°, 135°
125°;   90°, 90°, 90°

5. 10^6
7^2
9^4
5^5
12^2

6. $\dfrac{6}{1} = 6$; $\dfrac{28}{1} = 28$; $\dfrac{38}{1} = 38$; $\dfrac{72}{1} = 72$

8;   24;   4;   36

Lesson 135

1.

Fraction	Decimal	Percent
$\dfrac{21}{50}$	0.42	-------
-------	0.07	7%
$\dfrac{1}{50}$	-------	2%
-------	0.59	59%
$\dfrac{31}{50}$	0.62	-------
$\dfrac{39}{50}$	0.78	-------

Horizons Math 6 Answer Key

1. (cont.)

Fraction	Decimal	Percent
$\frac{9}{10}$	-------	90%
-------	0.05	5%
$\frac{1}{25}$	0.04	-------

2. 51%,   53%
   add 2 %

   0.31,   0.35
   add 0.04

   0.44,   44%
   add 0.11 then change to percent

   $\frac{5}{10}$,   40%

   subtract 10% alternating as % and

   fraction

   $\frac{3}{4}$,   125%

   add 50 % then subtract 25% alternating

   between fractions and percents

3. Church = $240
   Auto Expense = $500
   Food = $200
   Miscellaneous = $300
   Housing = $760

4. 25;   90;   11;   12;   15;   10
   WISDOM

5. 90.44;   11.305
   80.983;   40.4915

6. 2;   4;   2;   9
   8;   2;   8;   3

Lesson 136

1. $56.87; $67.79; $3.42; $109.26
   78.21;   456.65;   1,324.50;   0.34

2.

Fraction	Decimal	Percent
$\frac{11}{50}$	0.22	-------
-------	0.70	70%
$\frac{1}{5}$	-------	20%
-------	0.68	68%
-------	$0.3\overline{3}$	33%
-------	0.51	51%

3. 0.22, $\frac{27}{100}$

   Pattern: Add $\frac{5}{100}$ and write in

   repeating order as a percent, decimal,

   and fraction.

   $\frac{4}{15}$, $\frac{2}{15}$

   Pattern: Subtract $\frac{2}{15}$ and write in

   lowest terms.

   0%,   5%

   Pattern: Subtract 15% then add 5%.

   0.80,   92%

   Pattern: Add 0.12, subtract .03, then
   add .02 alternating between decimals
   and percents.

4. $(6 \times 10^3) + (8 \times 10^2) + (7 \times 10^1) + 5$

   $(7 \times 10^6) + (2 \times 10^5) + (1 \times 10^4) +$
   $(8 \times 10^3) + (4 \times 10^2) + (4 \times 10^1) + 3$

   $(5 \times 10^{12}) + (2 \times 10^{11}) + (3 \times 10^9) +$
   $(4 \times 10^8) + (5 \times 10^7) + (6 \times 10^6) +$
   $(7 \times 10^5) + (9 \times 10^4) + (8 \times 10^3) + 2$

   $(1 \times 10^6) + (9 \times 10^3) + (2 \times 10^2) +$
   $(4 \times 10^1) + 7$

5.

	2^2	3^2
3,000	4^2	6^2
40,000	6^2	9^2
500,000	8^2	12^2

6. 20;   1.50;   21.165;   0.9

Lesson 137

1. 10;   12;   7.5;   16;   40;   129.8
   8,725;   61.3;   8.7
   25.6;   897.2;   1,520.7

2.   0.03973   – 3.973×10^{-2}
    3,973,000,000   – 3.973×10^{9}
  3,973,000,000,000   – 3.973×10^{12}
       0.003973   – 3.973×10^{-3}
         39,730   – 3.973×10^{4}
     397,300,000   – 3.973×10^{8}

3. Percents shaded from left to right and top to bottom:
70, 38, 64, 99, 25, 6, 5, 3, 19,
40, 20, 10, 70, 10, 40, 29,
1, 89, 5, 17, 25, 40, 38, 10, 25, 89,
29, 3, 6, 1, 20, 29, 3
10, 41, 50, 17, 64, 1, 5
FAITH

4.

Fraction	Decimal	Percent
-------	0.60	60%
$\frac{3}{4}$	0.75	-------
$\frac{19}{100}$	0.19	-------
-------	0.40	40%
-------	0.12	12%

5. 458.93;   9,871,234.5;   149.78;   237.8
371;   4.57;   8.91;   742.06

6. 26;   8;   555;   1,946;   31

Lesson 138

1.

$120.00	$415.00
7.20	49.80
4.95	6.95
$132.15	$471.75
$102.00	$60.00
11.22	3.00
4.95	3.95
$118.17	$66.95

2. 68.57
548.30
369.40
5.89
67.3
26.38
254.64
736.20
Fountain

3. 50% $\frac{1}{2}$
75% $\frac{3}{4}$
99% $\frac{99}{100}$
70% $\frac{7}{10}$
63% $\frac{63}{100}$
34% $\frac{17}{50}$
1% $\frac{1}{100}$
4% $\frac{1}{25}$
60% $\frac{3}{5}$
12% $\frac{3}{25}$
85% $\frac{17}{20}$

4.

Across	Down
1. 5.001	2. 2.03
3. .004	4. 25.4
5. 5.922	6. 721.8

5. 100,000
6,880,000,000,000
           3.3×10^{7}
0.00000071
10,000
           2.36×10^{8}
6,521,000,000,000
           9.3×10^{-5}

6. 0.64; 0.4375; 0.20; 0.31; 0.625; 0.45
   0.6; 0.4; 0.2; 0.3; 0.6; 0.5

Lesson 139

1. $5,197.20 $20,788.80
   $70.49 $399.46
   $61.98 $1,177.52
   $10.00 $10.00
   $59.50 $535.50
   $59.21 $138.14

2. $39.76; $0.88; $2.89
   $7.13; $5.37; $1.61

3. 740   74
   193   19.3
   85   8.5
   1,451   145.1
   1,260   126
   12.1   1.21
   35.2   3.52

4.
```
                          24
        1   0   1   1
                          39
            1   1   1
                          127
    1   0   1   1   1   1
```

5. $\frac{3}{21} = \frac{1}{7}$; $\frac{1}{20}$; $\frac{2}{35}$; $\frac{1}{48}$

   $\frac{4}{12} = \frac{1}{3}$; $\frac{9}{15} = \frac{3}{5}$

   $\frac{10}{20} = \frac{1}{2}$; $\frac{5}{4} = 1\frac{1}{4}$

6. 76,465   76,564   76,654
   78,465   78,564   79,456
   79,546
   WORSHIP

Lesson 140

1. Brick   Brick   Brick   Brick
   Siding   Siding   Siding   Siding
   Cedar   Cedar   Cedar   Cedar
   Stucco   Stucco   Stucco   Stucco
   16 combinations

   Yellow shirt   Yellow shirt
   White shirt   White shirt
   Blue shirt   Blue shirt
   6 combinations

2. 1010_2 10010_2 1100_2
   1111_2 10111_2

3. 23,451   2,110   25,561
   5,803   34,512   40,315
   29,254   36,622   65,876

4. $\frac{48}{35} = 1\frac{13}{35}$; $\frac{22}{36} = \frac{11}{18}$

   $\frac{84}{63} = 1\frac{1}{3}$; $\frac{105}{120} = \frac{7}{8}$

   $\frac{72}{6} = 12$; $\frac{105}{4} = 26\frac{1}{4}$

   $\frac{69}{48} = 1\frac{7}{16}$; $\frac{88}{50} = 1\frac{19}{25}$

5. 42.25 sub-total   9.66 sub-total
   6.34 15% off   2.42 20% off
   35.91 total   7.24 total
   2.15 sales tax   0.72 sales tax
   38.06 grand total   7.96 grand total

   sub-total $2,248.00
   10% discount $224.80
   total $2,023.20
   8% sales tax $161.86
   Grand Total $2,185.06

6. 32,790.2;   649.3;   437.2
   1910.1;   679.1;   222.2

Lesson 141

1. +9
   -30
   +25
   +4
   -6
   +15
   -8

2.

Fraction	Decimal	Percent
$\frac{75}{100}$	0.75	75%
$\frac{99}{100}$	0.99	99%
$\frac{5}{100}$	0.05	5%
$\frac{30}{100}$	0.30	30%
$\frac{50}{100}$	0.50	50%
$\frac{16}{100}$	0.16	16%
$\frac{88}{100}$	0.88	88%
$\frac{25}{100}$	0.25	25%

3. (2 x 2.39) + 9.09 − 1.88 = 11.99
   14.9 + 2.7 + (3.1 x 8.2) = 43.02
   (56.2 ÷ 2) + 9 = 37.1
   3 x (8 + 13) − 33 = 30

4. Answers will vary.

5. 30 + 90 + 90 + 30 + 120 = 360

6. 42   20   48   21
   8   21   36   35

7.
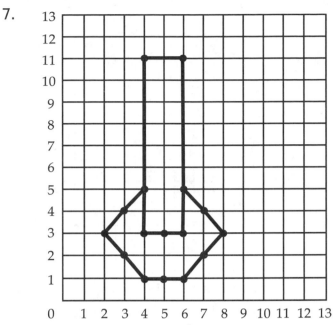

Lesson 142

1. 1.   +7
   2.   -19
   3.   +8
   4.   -25
   5. +346
   6.   0
   7.   +17
   8.   -99

2. A = +4
   B = +1
   C = -1
   D = -5

3. Area = 108 cm²
   Perimeter = 42 cm

4. 153   342   105   133
   44   138   212   360

5. $\frac{1}{4}$; $\frac{1}{25}$; $\frac{1}{20}$

   $\frac{7}{20}$; $\frac{1}{5}$; $\frac{1}{10}$

   $\frac{7}{10}$; $\frac{2}{25}$; $\frac{19}{20}$

5. (cont.)

50%	10%	40%
30%	60%	75%
20%	4%	40%

6.

A shooting star.

Lesson 143

1.

-6 < +2	-8 > -12	+2 < +7
-1 > -2	-4 < 0	+1 < +10
-9 < -4	-2 > -12	+8 < +14
+22 < +24	-10 > -18	+56 > +50

2. 1.   +1
    2.   -32
    3.   0
    4.   +12
    5.   +346
    6.   +14
    7.   +32
    8.   -41

3. Answers will vary.

4. 261,790,685   118,283,660
    147,501,047   480,094,032

5. Area = 100 cm²
        Area = 532 cm²

6.

7. 166.8   574.6
    456.35   210.32

Lesson 144

1.

-4	+2	-3
-7	+7	-6
-1	+4	+6

2. true;   true
    false;   true
    true;   true
    false;   false

3. 1. +37
    2. -42
    3. -24
    4. -83
    Answers will vary.

4. | Positive Integers | Negative Integers |
    |---|---|
    | 1. +56 <u>Y</u> | -5 <u>S</u> |
    | 2. +49 <u>O</u> | -29 <u>H</u> |
    | 3. +20 <u>U</u> | -44 <u>O</u> |
    | 4. +16 <u>R</u> | -45 <u>E</u> |

5. P = 14 cm   P = 21.2 cm
    A = 8.33 cm²   A = 25.35 cm²

6. teacher check

Lesson 145

1. +1;   -1
   -8;   -7
   +6;   -7
   -9;   +3
   +18;   +11

2. -28;   +24;   -35
   -13;   +18;   -53
   -19;   +31;   +57

3. -21 < -20   -8 > -9   -10 < +1
   -19 > -25   -1 < 0   +25 < +40
      -5 < -2   +3 > -3   +12 < +13

4. 1. $\dfrac{25}{27}$ A;   2. $\dfrac{3}{4}$ P;   3. $\dfrac{13}{20}$ O

   4. $\dfrac{4}{9}$ L;   5. $\dfrac{7}{18}$ I;   6. $\dfrac{11}{12}$ C

   7. $\dfrac{13}{15}$ E;   8. $\dfrac{7}{10}$ M;   9. $\dfrac{11}{18}$ A

   10. $\dfrac{9}{10}$ N

   A policeman

5. 3;   19 R2;   15 R1;   26

6. 2.7 cm²   32.55 mm²   9.25 mm²
   90 cm²;   32.49 mm²   40.95 cm²

7.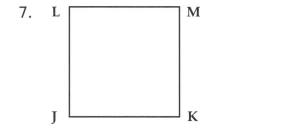

Lesson 146

1. -4;   8
   -2;   9
   -3;   3
   9;   -5

2. 10 degrees Celsius
   62 degrees Celsius

3.   -3 S
     -10 W
     +13 O
      -9 R
     +47 D
      +7 F
      -10 I
     +19 S
     -42 H
   Answer: Swordfish

4. true;   false
   false;   true
   true;   false
   true;   true

5. 231.1 cm²;   77.2 m²;   17.6 cm²

6.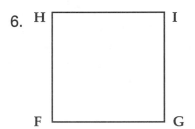

Lesson 147

1. -6;   12;   -7;   -25;   34;   1
    3;   3
   10;   10
   -5;   -5
   -2;   -2

2. 4;   -18;   0
   -6;   5;   12
   20;   -23;   16

3. +10;   -11
   -58;   -38
   +43;   -17
   -13;   +18
   +38;   +44

4. 1. -61 T   6.   0 I
   2. -55 R   7.   +1 N
   3. -41 U   8. +12 G
   4. -11 S   9. +32 O
   5. -1 T   10. +41 D
   Message: Trust In God

5. 8.1 x 8.1   4.6 x 4.6
   65.61   21.16
   206.0 cm²   66.4 cm²

6. 10.674;   83.351;   658.65
   320.417;   28.084;   35.09
   18.47;   319.35

Lesson 148

1.

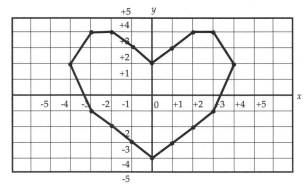

2. 20;   -23;   0
   -5;   +1;   +13
   100;   -1;   +45

3. +11;   -1
   -34;   -35
   +4;   +26
   -21;   +28
   +71;   0

4. A = 1670.5 cm²

5. $0.06 - 1 nickel, 1 penny
   $1.71 - 1 dollar, 2 quarters, 2 dimes,
   1 penny
   $8.50 - 1 five, 3 ones, 2 quarters
   $1.85 - 1 ones, 3 quarters, 1 dime
   $17.81 - 1 ten, 1 five, 2 ones,
   3 quarters, 1 nickel, 1 penny

Lesson 149

1. -18;   -20
   +49;   -36
   45;   +15
   -24;   6
   -72;   -54
   -77;   40

2. 6;   18
   0;   -12
   0;   -18
   -6;   12

3. 706.5   254.3
   362.1   254.1

4. A. (-2, 2);   B. (-1, 3);   C. (3, 3);
   D. (2, 2);   E. (-2, -2);   F. (2, -2);
   G. (3, -1)

5. Answers: Each angle should be bisected into two congruent angles. These need to be graded by teacher observation.

6. This needs to be graded by teacher observation.

Lesson 150

1. +3;   -9
   -1;   -4
   3;   +5
   -6;   6
   -2;   +9
   -3;   4

2. Answers will vary.

3. $\frac{4}{11}$; $\frac{1}{27}$; $\frac{7}{8}$; $\frac{4}{21}$; $\frac{2}{15}$

4.

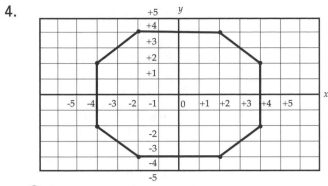

Octagon

5. V = 664.7m³;   V = 268.6m³

6. 2; $\dfrac{7}{10}$; $\dfrac{7}{24}$; $1\dfrac{7}{9}$; $\dfrac{5}{27}$

$2\dfrac{11}{12}$; $1\dfrac{9}{26}$; $2\dfrac{19}{22}$; 1; $\dfrac{1}{9}$

Lesson 151

1.

Salary	3,825.00
Extra Income	1,075.00
Total Monthly Income	$4,900.00
Tithe	490.00
Taxes	1,225.00
Housing	
Rent/Mortgage	950.00
Electricity	150.00
Gas	0.00
Water	27.00
Telephone	45.00
Total Housing	$1,172.00
Food	$250.00
Automobile	
Payments	1,025.00
Gas & Oil	350.00
Insurance	0.00
Taxes	0.00
Maint/Repair	0.00
Total Automobile	$1,375.00
Insurance	
Life	110.00
Medical	0.00
Other	
Total Insurance	$110.00

Debts	
Credit Cards	300.00
Loans	75.00
Other	
Total Debts	$375.00
Entertainment $ Recreation	
Eating Out	100.00
Trips	
Other	
Total Entertain/Recreation	$100.00
Clothing	$40.00
Medical Expenses	
Doctor	50.00
Total Medical	$50.00
Miscellaneous	
Lunches	225.00
Laundry	30.00
Spending Money	200.00
Cell Phone	75.00
Tuition	435.00
Allowance	25.00
Total Miscellaneous	$990.00
TOTAL MONTHLY EXPENSE	**$6,177.00**

INCOME VS. EXPENSE

Spendable Income	**$4,900.00**
Less Expense	**$6,177.00**
SURPLUS	**–1,277.00**

*Tom needs to cut down on his expenses. He is spending $1,277.00 per month more than he is making.

2. 6,678;   239,191;   89,026
880,164;   10,769;   9,655

3.

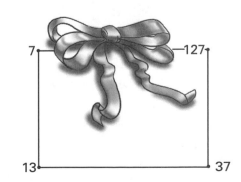

7   127

13   37

4. 3.45;   0.1794;   233.29;   552.123
    0.00012;   3.63;   6901.422;   144.287

5. $\frac{7}{64}$; $\frac{3}{35}$; $\frac{4}{40} = \frac{1}{10}$; $\frac{8}{45}$

    $\frac{16}{63}$; $\frac{8}{27}$; $\frac{35}{132}$; $\frac{5}{84}$

6. 45 cm × 12 cm = 540 cm²

    12 yd × 10 yd = 120 yd² ÷ 2 = 60 yd²

    21 m × 21 m = 441 m²

    (7 ft × 7 ft = 49 ft²) +

    [(1/2 ft × 3 ft = 10.5 ft²) × 2] = 70 ft²

7. Some answers may vary. Examples are given.

    $\frac{1}{3}$; $\frac{6}{7}$; $\frac{3}{4}$; $\frac{1}{2}$; $\frac{1}{4}$; $\frac{1}{3}$

Lesson 152

1. Answer: made to Dr. Mann for $52.00
    Answer: made to ABC Electric Co. for $154.25
    Answer: made to Walker Mortgage Co. for $897.38
    Answer: made to Walton Water Co. for $25.50

2. Yearly income: $36,000.00

$3,600	--------
--------	$325
$28,500	$2,375
$7,500	--------
$2,100	--------
--------	$240
--------	$100
--------	$125
$1,380	--------
$600	--------
--------	$85
$1,320	--------

Totals
(items 3-12) $20,400 $1,700

Yes, because he/she is spending less than he/she makes

Excess money should be placed in savings

3. 83,762;   212,985;   63,786
    26,789;   21,294;   419,859

4. 45.96 ÷ 1.3   = 35.35
    4.596 ÷ .013   = 353.54
    459.6 ÷ 130.0   = 3.54
    45.96 ÷ 10.13   = 4.54

5. $2\frac{1}{10}$; $26\frac{5}{8}$; $38\frac{1}{2}$

    $20\frac{1}{4}$; $2\frac{11}{12}$; $4\frac{1}{4}$

CHARACTER

6. total surface area = 1,600 cm²
    total surface area = 702 cm²
    total surface area = 73.5 in²

7. $40.00 $4.00
    $60.00 $5.25
    $63.00 $3.27
    $30.00 $31.36

Lesson 153

1. Investment Services
    a savings account
    a checking account
    IRAs

2.

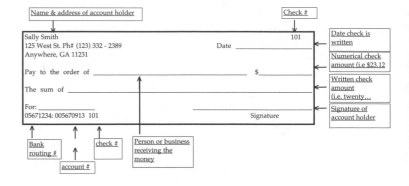

© MCMXCIX, Alpha Omega Publications, Inc.

3. I. Tithe – 10% of our gross earnings needs to be given to God.

   II. Government – taxes must be paid on the money we earn.

   III. Family – needs family necessities must come next. This would include food, shelter, clothing.

   IV. Debts – money that has been borrowed such as school loans, credit cards, car notes, etc.

   V. Surplus – there should always be a surplus of money that needs to go into savings or used to respond to the needy.

4. 1,024

   729

   64

   25

   10^7

   10^2

   12^2

   15^2

5. $\frac{43}{100}$; $\frac{25}{1,001}$; $\frac{123}{100} = 1\frac{23}{100}$

   $\frac{670}{988} = \frac{335}{494}$ $\frac{366}{467}$; $\frac{183}{100} = 1\frac{83}{100}$

   Shape should be cross and crown.

6. 0.09

   0.3

   0.62

   0.4

   0.75

   0.073

   0.60

   0.427

   0.089

   CHARACTER

7. 450;   125;   2,000;   21,100

   161;   2,967;   5,000;   32

Lesson 154

1. $60 $154.20

   $660 $1,439.20

   $105 $1,177

   $1,605 $11,877

   $988.13 $1,584

   $8,738.13 $10,384

   $93.75 $42.25

   $1,343.75 $367.25

2. Answers will vary according to name, date, and account number. Total should be $47.23.

3. teacher check

4. teacher check
   total = $2,558.09

5. 1. $3,068

   2. $30,680

   3. $147.50

   4. $32,214

6. $\frac{8}{9}$; $\frac{2}{12} = \frac{1}{6}$; $\frac{9}{9} = 1$

   $\frac{11}{20}$; $\frac{21}{27} = \frac{7}{9}$; $\frac{5}{15} = \frac{1}{3}$

7. 0.5;   0.625;   0.9

   $0.\overline{6}$; $0.\overline{81}$; $0.\overline{7}$

8.
City One	City Two	Diff.
$30.00	$40.00	$10.00
$150.00	$200.00	$50.00
$1,527.90	$2,037.20	$509.30
$11,340.00	$15,120.00	$3,780.00

Lesson 155

1. $9.50; $13.75
   $18.67; $162.50
   $337.50; $2.63

2. $1,260 $3,000
   $13,260   23,000

   $688.75 $3,355
   $10,188.75 $33,855

3. teacher check

4. Balance:
   $2,492.21
   $2,462.71
   $3,674.71
   $3,658.72
   $3,500.82
   $4,712.82

5.
7	0	8	1
7	8	7	3
2	3	7	8

   197,033;   901,404;   7,004;   68,580

6. =;   >;   >;   <
   >;   >;   >;   <

7. $325.00
   $325.00
   $487.50
   $325.00
   $422.50
   $390.00

Lesson 156

1. January $715.00
   February $715.00 $10.73 $425.73
   March $6.39 $132.12
   April $132.12 $1.98 $134.10

2. $1,800
   $27.50
   $280.00
   $600
   $308.75

3. $1,500
   $1,350
   $1,200
   $1,050
   $900

   1. 6%
   2. 10%
   3. $600.00
   4. $150.00

4. $129.90 $6,754.80
   $56.50 $2,938
   $290.00 $15,080
   $301.20 $15,662.40

5.
1	0	0	1	0	0	0	=	72
	1	1	1	1			=	15
	1	0	0	0	1	0	=	34
	1	0	1	1	1		=	23
1	1	0	1	0	0	1	=	105
1	0	1	0	1	1		=	43

6. $\frac{8}{12} = \frac{2}{3}$; $\frac{38}{70} = \frac{19}{35}$; $\frac{54}{60} = \frac{9}{10}$; $\frac{51}{105} = \frac{17}{35}$

   $\frac{13}{56}$; $\frac{21}{60} = \frac{7}{20}$; $\frac{11}{18}$; $\frac{11}{26}$

7. $\frac{75}{20} = 3\frac{3}{4}$; $\frac{42}{12} = 3\frac{1}{2}$; $\frac{12}{20} = \frac{3}{5}$

   $\frac{22}{5} = 4\frac{2}{5}$; $\frac{222}{6} = 37$; $\frac{8}{5} = 1\frac{3}{5}$

© MCMXCIX, Alpha Omega Publications, Inc.

Lesson 157

1. 1. (140.00 at 15% off)
   2. (5 for 1)
   3. (3 for $1.20)
   4. (2 for $2.50)

2.
2nd mo.	+$1.27	-$25.00	$102.77
3rd mo. $102.77	+$1.03	-$25.00	$78.80
4th mo. $78.80	+$0.79	-$25.00	$54.59
5th mo. $54.59	+$0.55	-$25.00	$30.14
6th mo. $30.14	+$0.30	-$25.00	$5.44
7th mo. $5.44	+$0.05	$5.49	--------

3. $120.00
   $62.50
   $60.00
   $18.00

4. $n = 40$; $n = 24$; $n = 180$
   $n = 175$; $n = 60$; $n = 4,500$

5. square;   pentagon;   hexagon
   decagon;   trapezoid;   parallelogram

6.
100;	32;	59,049
15,625;	10,000;	2,197
343;	121;	531,441
81;	144;	7,776
512;	4,096;	243
100,000;	16,384;	279,936
256;	27;	81
1,024;	9;	729

   Shape should be a HEART.

7.
	Across		Down
	1. 16.436		1. 19.459
	3. 48.22		2. 4.62
	4. 9.951		5. 518.24
	6. 6.8		

Lesson 158

1. $307 $51.17
   $510 $85

2. 1. (Pay 50 cents for two and get one free.)
   2. ($10 with 40% off)
   3. (2 for $40)
   4. ($7 with 15% off)

3.
2nd mo.	$177.50	$1.78	$75.00	$104.28
3rd mo.	$104.28	$1.04	$75.00	$30.32
4th mo.	$30.32	$0.30	$30.62	--------

4. $5.00; $60.00
   $9.19; $112.50

5. 999
   11

6. 256 cm^2

7. Answers may vary. Some possible answers are given.

   $\frac{4}{6}, \frac{2}{3}$; $\frac{9}{36}, \frac{1}{4}$; $\frac{70}{490}, \frac{7}{49}$; $\frac{6}{21}, \frac{4}{14}$

   $\frac{10}{30}, \frac{1}{3}$; $\frac{8}{10}, \frac{4}{5}$; $\frac{36}{18}, \frac{2}{1}$; $\frac{77}{44}, \frac{7}{4}$

Lesson 159

1. 1. <u>How many more</u>   6
   2. <u>how many</u>   28
   3. <u>How many more</u>   4
   4. <u>total number</u>   22

2. $19.47

3.
$0.15	$0.10	($0.09)
$0.17	$0.22	($0.16)

4. Clockwise from top right:
   12, 6, 16, 4, 3, 8

5. 722,152;   193,978;   4,853;   21,872
   54,244;   163,678;   3,678;   13,678

6. $\frac{71}{72}$; $\frac{5}{18}$; $\frac{9}{9} = 1$

   $\frac{15}{20} = \frac{3}{4}$; $\frac{14}{21} = \frac{2}{3}$; $\frac{19}{55}$

7. 0.5;   0.625;   0.9
   $0.\overline{6}$; $0.\overline{81}$; $0.\overline{7}$

6. 24, 3;   4, 16;
   $6\frac{1}{4}$, 50   3, 12;
   8, 32;   80, 160

7. 53;   154;   63
   91;   19;   109

Lesson 160

1. 1. 2-$20's
   2. 1-$10
   3. $48.49
   4. $456.75

2. 1. Division
   2. Multiplication
   3. Subtraction
   4. Addition

3. January $19.99
   February $16.78
   March   0
   April   0
   May $25.01
   June   0
   July $23.04
   August $12.90
   September   0
   October $32.44
   November $58.24
   December $100.12

   Avg. monthly expenditure: $24.04

4. Prime numbers:
   2, 19, 3, 23, 5, 41, 73, 7, 89, 11, 97, 13
   The letter is X.

5. 5.2;   2.37;   1.19
   4.89;   8.92;   1.26

Horizons Mathematics 6

Test

Answer
Key

Test 1

1. 348,128,000,007,321
   717,322,701,000,000
   8,112,651,000,000
   8,000,062,000,000

2. 16,745,099,000,126
   1,003,000,000,047
   945,000,819,000,302
   81,000,000,000,005

3. <
   >
   <
   <

4. ten thousandths
   tenths
   thousandths
   hundredths
   hundred thousandths
   hundredths
   tenths
   thousandths

5. 79,000,000,000   800,000,000   5,000
   50,000,000,000   863,000,000   810,000
   34,803,000   711,905,300   800,000,000

6. <;   <
   <;   >
   <;   >
   >;   <

7. 234;   212;   133;   316
   99;   508;   410;   135

Test 2

1. 15;   32;   12
   68;   18;   15

2. 0, Zero Property of Addition
    0, Zero Property of Subtraction
    12, Addition is Commutative
    9, Addition is Associative

3. 86,826;   44,938;   66,331;   108,540
   1,011,256;   723,448

4. 61,702;   30,342;   41,899;   122,339
   220,693;   437,466

5. 92,000;   14,000;   75,000;   11,000

6. t = 9;   m = 7;   z = 4;   b = 9

7. 57;   667;   72
   134;   32;   368

8. Commutative Property – 2 x 4 = 8,
                           so 4 x 2 = 8

   Associate Property   – (3 x 9) x 2 = 3 x (9 x 2)

   One Property   – 9 x 1 = 9
   of Multiplication

   Distributive Property – 4 x (7 + 2) =
   of Multiplication   (4 x 7) + (4 x 2)

   Division by One   – 8 ÷ 1 = 8

9. 4131;   4015;   3896;   1752
   1785;   1488;   2244;   2805

10. 18073;   27, 993;   19, 162;   3,232
    34143;   249823;   109344;   159,213

Test 3

1. 3,200;   4,500;   1,800;   2,100

2. 376;   198;   719;   296

3. 58;   87;   41;   62

4. 88;   33;   81;   58

5. 18;   79
   358;   87

6. 1,831,720;   4,149,751
   6,457,314;   9,974,799
   GOOD

7. 400,711,500;   221,915,036
   827,046,360;   880,683,092

8. 320,000;   180,000;   280,000
   120,000;   2,000,000;   24,000,000

9. 13;   37;   28;   41

10. 19;   12;   23

Test 4

1. too high   too high
   too low   too high

2. 120;   90;   80;   126

3. $12.18
   89 cm

4. 1 penny, 2 quarters, 2 ones
   3 pennies, 1 nickel, 3 quarters, 2 ones
   1 penny, 1 dime
   1 penny, 2 dimes, 1 dollar
   1 nickel, 1 quarter, 3 ones

5. 1. $11.99
   2. 4 pizzas
   3. 6 pizzas
   4. Yes. $0.24

6.
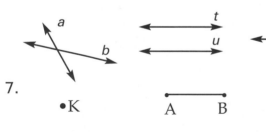

7.
   •K   A   B

   C   D   L   M

8. 1. acute;   5. right
   2. right;   6. right
   3. acute;   7. obtuse
   4. obtuse;   8. acute

9. 5;   5;   5
   6;   6;   9
   8;   8;   20
   10;   10;   35

10.

Square   Rhombus   Rectangle

Parallelogram   Trapezoid

11.

Test 5

1. scalene
    equilateral
    isosceles
    equilateral
    scalene

2. 60°;   40°;   33°

3. 1. AB and CD
    2. XY
    3. CZ, DZ, AZ, BZ, VZ
    4. 1.4 cm

4. Triangular –   This figure has one polygon
   Pyramid   base. All faces are triangles and
                  meet at a point.

   Cylinder –   This figure has curved sides with
                  2 parallel bases that are not
                  polygons.

   Sphere –   All points are the same distance
                  from the center.

   Rectangular – This figure has 2 parallel
   Prism   polygon bases and all other
                  faces are rectangles.

   Cone   This figure has curved sides and
                  the base is not a polygon.

5.

6. 3 6 9 12 15 18 21 24 27 30 33 36
   5 10 15 20 25 30 35 40 45 50 55 60
   7 14 21 28 35 42 49 56 63 70 77 84
   9 18 27 36 45 54 63 72 81 90 99 108

7. Prime numbers:
   3, 19, 29, 73, 13, 41, 43, 5, 7, 37, 2, 23
   11, 53, 17, 47

8.

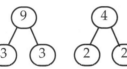

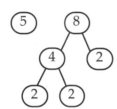

9. 1,000;   16;   125;   64
   144;   100,000;   243;   10,000

10. 11;   7;   4
    3;   8;   12
    13;   9;   5

Test 6

1. 12;   2;   12;   6

2. 20;   8;   30;   12

3. 10,800;   992,000
   950;   5,500
   731,000;   7,040,000

4. 1111two;   10011two;   100010two
   10101two;   10001two;   10100two

5. 1. 76
   2. white, gray
   3. 8
   4. white
   5. 32

6. **Read:**
   88 and 39034 hundred thousandths
   Written:
   Eighty-eight and thirty-nine thousand
   thirty-four hundred thousandths
   Expanded Form:
   80 + 8 + 0.3 + 0.09 + 0.000 + 0.0003
   + 0.00004

   Read:
   42 and 89 hundredths
   Written:
   Forty-two and eighty-nine hundredths
   Expanded Form:
   40 + 2 + 0.8 + 0.09

7. 0.4996 | 10.187 | 9.087 | 34.019
   0.5012 | 11.150 | 9.807 | 34.091
   0.5090 | 11.151 | 9.870 | 34.199
   0.5091 | 12.152 | 10.087 | 35.109

8. 14.527 G;   105.10 B;   32.15 I
   100.931 B;   1,132.932 W
   21.321 N;   970 E
   WEBBING

9. 9.999;   79.503;   770.56;
   391.414;   3.573   14.792
   269.852

10. 91;   298;   1;   45
    9.7;   35.0;   110.0;   8.0

Test 7

1. 5,887.4;   405.03;   194.11
   1,087.01;   18,449.02;   2,390

2. LXXXIV;   XVIII or XIIX ;   CMXC
   XLVII;   CLII;   XVI
   XC;   MIX;   MMCM

3. Range: 36   Range: 102
   Mean: 82   Mean: 186

   Range: 8   Range: 83
   Mean: 16   Mean: 172

4. Mode: 6   Mode: 18
   Median: 9   Median: 18

   Mode: 24   Mode: none
   Median: 26   Median: 111

5. 1. <u>They earned $1,400 doing car washes in 1998.</u> $1,934

   2. Not enough information

6. $\frac{3}{4}$; $\frac{1}{4}$; $\frac{5}{9}$; $\frac{1}{5}$; $\frac{9}{13}$; $\frac{9}{20}$

   $\frac{1}{2}$; $\frac{1}{6}$; $\frac{8}{9}$; $\frac{14}{39}$; $\frac{7}{15}$; $\frac{1}{4}$

7. $\frac{7}{8}$; $\frac{1}{2}$; $\frac{7}{12}$

   $\frac{8}{15}$; $\frac{3}{5}$; $\frac{3}{5}$

8.   21;   12;   40
   10;   8;   18;   40

9. <;   >;   <;   >
   =;   <   >   <

10. $\frac{14}{15}$; $\frac{5}{14}$; $\frac{7}{9}$; $\frac{1}{8}$; $\frac{1}{4}$

Test 8

1. $\frac{30}{4}$; $\frac{25}{8}$; $\frac{58}{7}$; $\frac{22}{5}$

   $\frac{20}{9}$; $\frac{29}{3}$; $\frac{71}{8}$; $\frac{58}{11}$

2. $4\frac{1}{5}$;   7; $11\frac{1}{3}$; $2\frac{1}{4}$

   $6\frac{2}{3}$; $4\frac{1}{3}$;   1; $7\frac{3}{7}$

3. $12\frac{7}{9}$; $54\frac{2}{3}$; $59\frac{25}{56}$; $\frac{7}{8}$; $23\frac{7}{10}$

4. $15\frac{1}{4}$; $18\frac{9}{20}$; $17\frac{1}{4}$; $75\frac{5}{14}$

5. $3\frac{2}{9}$; $5\frac{4}{5}$; $2\frac{1}{2}$; $17\frac{9}{14}$

6. 30.1; 17.7;   338; 64.56; 5.94

   67.16; 8.82;   15.57; 6.96;   5.8117

7. 1.18;   45.79;   44.19;   64.12

8. 1.5;   7.5;   17.5;   7.2
   4.75;   3.80;   62.50;   6.25
   4.375;   3.125;   5.625;   10.125

9. 0.4;   0.875;   0.625
   $0.\overline{2}$; $0.\overline{6}$; $0.\overline{3}$

Test 9

1. 0.5;   1.17;   1.57;   0.4

2.   459   1.89
            88   0.389
            31.7   0.0110
   0.902   902.71

3. $0.47\overline{)0.094}$

   $31.1\overline{)279.9}$

4. 1. 19 bags of candy

   2. 11.74 cm

   3. 1 1/4 candy bar

5.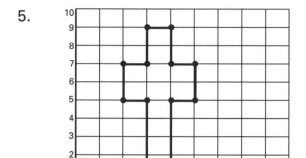

6. $\frac{7}{27}$; $\frac{2}{35}$; $\frac{7}{72}$; $\frac{21}{63} = \frac{1}{3}$

   $\frac{4}{77}$; $\frac{3}{35}$; $\frac{35}{108}$; $\frac{1}{8}$

7. 8; 4; 6; 5

8. $14\frac{7}{14} = 14\frac{1}{2}$; $32\frac{4}{10} = 32\frac{2}{5}$; $9\frac{2}{6} = 9\frac{1}{3}$

   $8\frac{4}{9}$; $38\frac{2}{6} = 38\frac{1}{3}$; $7\frac{1}{32}$

9. $\frac{1}{5}$; 3; $9\frac{1}{4}$; $23\frac{1}{3}$

10. $\frac{12}{2}$; $\frac{99}{47}$; $\frac{47}{35}$; $\frac{105}{11}$; $\frac{22}{17}$; $\frac{58}{49}$

Test 10

1. 24; 48; 180; 150
   153; 22; 76; 108

2. 6; $1\frac{19}{21}$; $1\frac{9}{15} = 1\frac{3}{5}$; $1\frac{1}{15}$

   $1\frac{1}{4}$; $3\frac{4}{12} = 3\frac{1}{3}$; $\frac{12}{18} = \frac{2}{3}$; $3\frac{5}{9}$

3. $\frac{7}{36}$; $\frac{3}{32}$; $1\frac{1}{8}$; $1\frac{1}{28}$

4. $5\frac{1}{2}$; $14\frac{1}{2}$; $11\frac{1}{2}$

5. $2\frac{14}{63} = 2\frac{2}{9}$; $1\frac{63}{91} = 1\frac{9}{13}$; $2\frac{4}{20} = 2$; $2\frac{4}{27}$

6. $\frac{9}{16}$

   $1\frac{5}{16}$

7. Small can of corn – 11 oz
   Van – 2 T
   Hamburger – 4 oz
   Weight of a cat – 14 lb
   Golf Ball – 1.5 oz

8. 1; 2; $\frac{1}{2}$
   18; 10; $2\frac{1}{2}$

9. 30° F; 212° F
   38° F; -12° F

10. 8
    4,000
    700
    5
    90
    2,000
    4

Test 11

1. Fly - 1 gram
   Rabbit - 1 kilogram
   Turtle - 1 kilogram
   Paper Clip - 1 gram

2. 1,000
   5,900
   330
   0.001
   4.7
   0.109

3. 703
   3
   9,800
   15,000
   0.6

4. 110° C; 85° C
   35° C; 37° C

5. 46 feet

6. 1. $50.00
   2. $150.00
   3. April
   4. 12 cars
   5. January

7. 36 cm;   18.2 cm;   44 cm
   32 cm²   20.4 cm²;   121 cm²

8. 80 cm²;   54 cm²

9. 16 cm²;   18 cm²

10. 78.5 cm²   452.16 cm² = 452.2 cm²

11 12 cm³;   48 cm³

Test 12

1. 785 m³;   197.82 m³ = 197.8 m³

2. 262 cm²

3. 96 cm³;   401.92 cm³

4. earlier
   Later
   Ahead
   International Date Line or Prime Median

5. 1. Multiplication, division
      There are 60 pieces of candy in all.
      Each player gets two pieces.

   2. Subtraction, subtraction
      Katrina will have $70.13 left in
      savings.

6. 1. 35°
   2. 110°

7. ∠ABC = 40°
   ∠CBE = 140°
   ∠EBD = 40°
   ∠DBA = 140°
   40° + 140° + 40° + 140° = 360°

8.

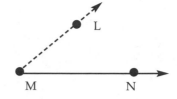

9.

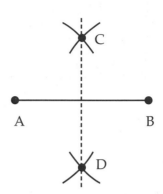

10.

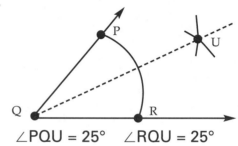

∠PQU = 25°   ∠RQU = 25°

Test 13

1.

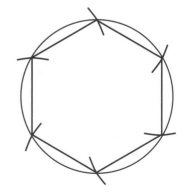

2.

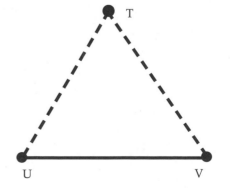

3.

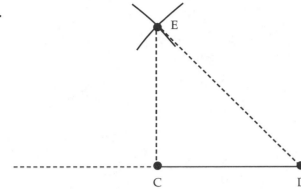

4.

5.

6. 1. $\frac{2}{8}$

2. $\frac{2}{8}$

3. $\frac{2}{2}$

4. $\frac{2}{2}$

5. $\frac{2}{8}$

7. 6; 9; 12; 15; 18; 21
   2; 3; 4; 5; 6; 7

8. Answers will vary. Several possible
   answers are given.

   $\frac{80}{100}$, $\frac{4}{5}$; $\frac{9}{45}$, $\frac{1}{5}$; $\frac{24}{21}$, $\frac{8}{7}$; $\frac{30}{90}$, $\frac{3}{9}$

9. 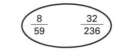 $\frac{7}{15}$ $\frac{28}{60}$ $\frac{8}{59}$ $\frac{32}{236}$

10. N = 2;   N = 16;   N = 18;   N = 50

Test 14

1. 60;   95;   16;   80

2. 1. $\frac{3}{10}$;   2. $\frac{5}{10}$;   3. $\frac{5}{10}$

   4. $\frac{1}{10}$;   5. $\frac{1}{10}$;   6. $\frac{3}{10}$

3. 85 boxes
   146 bags

4. $\frac{1}{10}$ 0.1 1×10^{-1}

   $\frac{1}{100}$ 0.01 1×10^{-2}

   $\frac{1}{1,000}$ 0.001 1×10^{-3}

   $\frac{1}{10,000}$ 0.0001 1×10^{-4}

   $\frac{1}{100,000}$ 0.00001 1×10^{-5}

   $\frac{1}{1,000,000}$ 0.000001 1×10^{-6}

5. 10%
   20%
   33%
   25%
   8%
   40%

6. 80;   50;   7;   25

7.
$\frac{88}{100}$	0.88	88%
$\frac{55}{100}$	0.55	55%
$\frac{7}{100}$	0.07	7%
$\frac{29}{100}$	0.29	29%
$\frac{89}{100}$	0.89	89%
$\frac{33}{100}$	0.33	33%
$\frac{79}{100}$	0.79	79%

8. $\frac{1}{2}$; $\frac{9}{10}$; $\frac{1}{25}$

$\frac{1}{5}$; $\frac{4}{25}$; $\frac{49}{50}$

9.
$\frac{3}{25}$	0.12	12%
$\frac{2}{25}$	0.08	8%
$\frac{3}{50}$	0.06	6%
$\frac{89}{100}$	0.89	89%
$\frac{1}{20}$	0.05	5%
$\frac{22}{25}$	0.88	88%
$\frac{1}{5}$	0.2	20%
$\frac{8}{10}$	0.8	80%
$\frac{6}{25}$	0.24	24%

Test 15

1. $2.07; $30.81; $903.01; $0.07
93.31; 6.65; 0.09 0.15

2. 2.5; 59.0; 91.7; 900.8; 1,120.80

3.
Bible Covers	–	$111.93
Read and Sing Bible Stories	–	$119.80
Memory Verse Pkg.	–	$52.50

Total	$284.23
6% sales tax	$17.05
Shipping	$10.00
Grand Total	$311.28

4.
$6.40	$25.60
$2.00	$17.95
$0.75	$14.20
$5.99	$33.96
$2.50	$22.50

5. 27 different combinations:

ham, rye, provolone	ham, white, provolone	ham, whole wheat, provolone
ham, rye, swiss	ham, white, swiss	ham, whole wheat, swiss
ham, rye, american	ham, white, american	ham, whole wheat, american

turkey, rye, provolone	turkey, white, provolone	turkey, whole wheat, provolone
turkey, rye, swiss	turkey, white, swiss	turkey, whole wheat, swiss
turkey, rye, american	turkey, white, american	turkey, whole wheat, american

salami, rye, provolone	salami, white, provolone	salami, whole wheat, provolone
salami, rye, swiss	salami, white, swiss	salami, whole wheat, swiss
salami, rye, american	salami, white, american	salami, whole wheat, american

6. 1. (-10)
2. (+9)
3. (-10)
4. (+6)
5. (+10)
6. (-10)

7. (+15)
(-11)
(-10)
0
(+39)
(-10)

8. <; <; <; >
>; <; >; >

9. (-8);   (+8);   (-29)
    (-22);   (-24);   (-69)
    (-48);   (+90);   (+76)

10. (+1);   (-11);   (+32)
    (-17);   (-9);   (-3)
    (+65);   (-3)

Test 16

1. 6;   6
   15;   15
   -15;   -15
   -7;   -7

2.

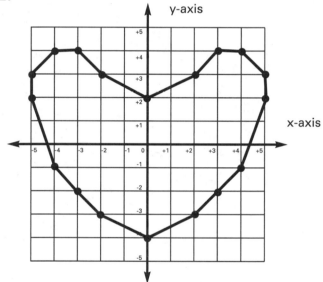

3. (-72)
   (+28)
    27
   (-48)
   (+49)

   (-9)
   (-8)
   (-4)
   (+9)
    6

4. $164.63
  $302.90
  $17.90
  $1,872.00

5. $40.00
  $21.00
  $23.40
  $500.00
  $120.00

6.

1st month	$100.00	+$1.00	-$20.00	$81.00
2nd month	$81.00	+$0.81	-$20.00	$61.81
3rd month	$61.81	+$0.62	-$20.00	$42.43
4th month	$42.43	+$0.42	-$20.00	$22.85
5th month	$22.85	+$0.23	-$20.00	$3.08
6th month	$3.08	+$0.03	-$3.11	00

7. CD World $17.99

   Discounts Galore $16.14

   Gallow's Music $15.19

8.

Item	Quantity	Price/item	Total Cost
Tennis Racquet	10	$13.99 ea	139.90
Tennis Balls (case)	10	$15.99 ea	159.90
Racquetball Racquet	15	$15.50 ea	232.50
Total			$532.30
6% sales tax			31.94
Shipping			10.00
Grand Total			574.24

Worksheets

Reproducible Worksheets
for use with Horizons
Mathematics 6

DEFINITION

Expanded form is writing a number to illustrate each place value.

Model: In expanded form, 527 is written: 500 + 20 + 7

Check the following chart.

TRILLIONS			BILLIONS			MILLIONS			THOUSANDS			UNITS		
hundreds	tens	ones	hundreds	tens	ones	hundreds	tens	ones	hundreds	tens	ones	hundreds	tens	one
0	0	0 ,	0	0	0 ,	0	0	0 ,	0	0	0 ,	0	0	0

(1) Write 726 in expanded form. _____

(2) Write the number equal to 20,000 + 7,000 + 500 + 20 + 9. _____

LARGE NUMBERS

A digit followed by six zeros is a multiple of a million. What about a number with nine zeros or twelve zeros? The numbers are multiples of a *billion* or *trillion* respectively.

Model: Write the number that begins with the digit 6 followed by eight zeros, and write its name.

600,000,000 is six hundred million.

(3) Write the number that starts with the digit 8 followed by eight zeros, and write its name.

a. _____   b. _____

(4) Write the number that starts with the digit 5 followed by nine zeros, and write its name.

a. _____   b. _____

(5) Write six billion in numerals. _____

(6) Write four trillion in numerals. _____

PLACE VALUE

The location of the decimal point is very important. This place value chart will help you choose the correct placement of the decimal point.

MILLIONS	HUNDRED THOUSAND	TEN THOUSAND	THOUSANDS	HUNDREDS	TENS	ONES (UNITS)		TENTHS	HUNDREDTHS	THOUSANDTHS	TEN THOUSANDTHS	HUNDRED THOUSANDTHS	MILLIONTHS
◯	◯	◯	◯	◯	◯	◯	●	◯	◯	◯	◯	◯	◯

Model: Show the location of the decimal point in the fraction $\frac{213}{1,000}$.

On the chart, $\frac{1}{1,000}$ is the third place to the right of

the decimal point, so $\frac{213}{1,000} = 0.213$.

(1) Show the location of the decimal point in the fraction $\frac{145}{1,000}$. _____

(2) Show the location of the decimal point in the fraction $\frac{456}{10,000}$. _____

(3) Show the location of the decimal point in the fraction $5\frac{45}{100}$. _____

(4) Show the location of the decimal point in the fraction $127\frac{9}{1,000}$. _____

(5) State fifty-six and fourteen hundredths in numerals. _____

(6) Show the location of the decimal point in the fraction $\frac{35}{1,000}$. _____

(7) The decimal sixty-three and twenty-nine hundredths in numerals is _____.
   a. 63.029   b. 63.29   c. 6.329   d. 630.29

(8) The correct location of the decimal point in the fraction $\frac{327}{1,000}$ is _____.

   a. 0.327   b. 3.27   c. 0.0327   d. 32.7

(9) On the number line the starting point is _____.
   a. zero   b. one   c. any place   d. one hundred

(10) The correct location of the decimal point in the fraction $\frac{3}{10,000}$ is _____.

   a. 0.3   b. 0.03   c. 0.003   d. 0.0003

Numbers of any value can be rounded to a given place.

Round 27 to tens' place.

Find the digit in tens' place. (2) 27 rounds to 30
Look at the digit to the right of 2. (7)
If the digit is 5 or more, round to the next higher tens' number. (30)
If the digit is less than 5, round to the lower tens' number. (20)

(1) **Round to the nearest tens' place.**

37 _____   45 _____   63 _____   98 _____   51 _____   12 _____

Round 395,467 to one thousands' place.

Find the digit in one thousands' place. (5) 395,467 rounds to 395,000
Look at the digit to the right of the 5. (4)
If the digit is 5 or more, round to the next higher thousands' number. (6,000)
If the digit is less than 5, round to the lower thousands' number. (5,000)

(2) **Round to the nearest ...**

a. hundreds' place.   1,574 _____   778,386 _____   16,360 _____

b. thousands' place.   6,127 _____   48,963 _____   312,615 _____

c. ten thousands' place. 104,262 _____   4,851,243 _____   56,921 _____

We can round a number when 9 is the digit to be rounded.

Round 24,976 to hundreds' place. 24,976 rounds to 25,000
9 is in hundreds' place. The digit to the right is 7.
Round 900 to the next higher hundreds. (1,000)
Write a zero in hundreds' place. Change 4,000 to 5,000.

(3) **Round to the nearest ...**

a. one thousands' place.

549,848 _____   19,672 _____   1,329,032 _____

b. one millions' place.

29,730,114 _____   9,320,647 _____   549,842,149 _____

c. ten millions' place.

49,267,849 _____   989,360,543 _____   29,367,851 _____

d. one billions' place

569,876,054,293 _____   29,587,313,263 _____

To compare numbers, begin with the digits
  with the largest place value (4 and 4).
  If the numbers are the same, continue comparing
  until the numbers are different (5 and 6).
  Because we know that 5 is less than 6,
    we know that …

436,259,630 (>?<) 436,261,817

436,25……   436,26……
    5   <   6
436,259,630   <   436,261,817

(1) Circle the correct symbol.

a. 3,864,291 (>, <) 3,568,691   5,840,376 (>, <) 5,843,076   9,818,369 (>, <) 9,881,369

b.   630,208 (>, <) 603,208   72,369,945 (>, <) 72,396,954   13,254 (>, <) 13,542

c.   84,592 (>, <) 85,594   295,486,310 (>, <) 295,486,031   549,281 (>, <) 548,291

(2) Write the numbers in number order from smallest to largest.

a. 3,865,924   6,685,942   3,685,942   6,835,492   3,856,924

_____ _____ _____ _____ _____

b. 2,397,102   1,397,102   1,973,102   2,973,102   2,379,103

_____ _____ _____ _____ _____

The symbols greater than (>) and less than (<) can be written with the equal sign (=).

(3) Write number sentences in digits and operation symbols.

a. Four is less than five. _____   Ten is greater than nine.   _____

b. Six is greater than two. _____   Seven is less than eleven.   _____

c. Thirty-five divided by seven is equal to fifteen divided by three.   _____

d. Fourteen minus two is not equal to eight plus five.   _____

Numbers can be arranged in order using the symbols greater than (>) and less than (<).

2,341 < 2,568 < 3,554   or   3,554 > 2,568 > 2,341

(4) Arrange numbers using the greater than (>) and less than (<) symbol . or , , …

a. from small to large.   4,558   3,957   6,492   _____   _____   _____

b. from large to small.   4,558   3,957   6,492   _____   _____   _____

1 **Add or subtract.**

102,637	117,685	255,718
+ 100,941	+ 106,320	+ 127,489

155,734	290,232	225,430
+ 125,466	+ 110,200	+ 207,561

263,111	312,954	325,441
+ 250,047	+ 284,000	+ 315,078

101,115	199,999	207,123
− 100,009	− 150,444	− 158,627

233,816	251,042	292,724
− 222,556	− 193,008	− 263,114

346,636	333,498	395,283
− 201,751	− 300,001	− 350,586

Equations are special number sentences.
The values on both sides of the equal sign are equal to each other.

(1) **Circle the correct symbol (5, ≠), (Y, N) if the expression is an equation or not.**

a. $92 + 87$ (=, ≠) 189 (Y, N) $63 - 49$ (=, ≠) 14 (Y, N) 3×8 (=, ≠) 4×6 (Y, N)

b. 10×32 (=, ≠) 320 (Y, N) $76 \div 4$ (=, ≠) 18 (Y, N) $25 \div 5$ (=, ≠) 2×3 (Y, N)

c. $8 + 6$ (=, ≠) 2×7 (Y, N) 9×0 (=, ≠) $13 - 3$ (Y, N) $36 - 4$ (=, ≠) 5×6 (Y, N)

d. $53 + 29$ (=, ≠) 83 (Y, N) $81 - 45$ (=, ≠) 46 (Y, N) $48 \div 6$ (=, ≠) $72 \div 9$ (Y, N)

Equations may be written with a missing number (N).

(2) **Use fact families to find the missing numbers.**

a. $8 + N = 17$ N = _____ $9 + N = 13$ N = _____ $N + 4 = 12$ N = _____

b. $15 - N = 9$ N = _____ $N - 7 = 7$ N = _____ $N - 3 = 8$ N = _____

Equations may have numbers larger than the fact families.
Follow the steps to find the missing number (N).

$187 + N = 341$ N must be the only number on one side of the equation.
$187 (- 187) + N = 341 (- 187)$ Addition and subtraction are opposite operations.
$N = 154$ Subtract 187 from the left side of the equation.
To keep the equation equal, 187 must also be subtracted
from the right side of the equation.

$187 + 154 = 341$ $N = 154$ Substitute and prove.

(3) **Follow the steps to solve for the missing number (N). Prove.**

a. $236 + N = 529$ $N + 417 = 631$ $518 + N = 874$ $N + 316 = 522$

Prove.

(4) **Solve for the missing number (N). Prove.**

a. $N - 439 = 518$ $N - 347 = 625$ $N - 238 = 671$ $N - 312 = 526$

Prove.

6   *Horizons Math 6 Worksheet*

(1) **Solve. (Write c. as a multi-operation problem and solve.)**

a. $(3 + 4) \times (15 \div 3) = N$ $8 + (2 \times 3) + 9 = N$ $(9 - 2) \times (5 + 5) = N$

_____ = N   _____ = N   _____ = N

b. $14 + 16 + (4 \times 2) = N$ $(37 - 9) \div (2 \times 2) = N$ $(52 + 8) + (46 - 6) = N$

_____ = N   _____ = N   _____ = N

c. David was keeping a record of the number of hits he had during the ball games. He had 7 hits the first week, 6 hits each the second and third weeks, and 8 hits each the fourth and the fifth weeks. How many hits did he have altogether?

_____ = N

_____ = N

In multi-operation problems, the operations in the parentheses are always completed first.

(2) **Complete the problems.**

a. $8 + (27 \div 3) - (5 \times 3) =$ _____ $(6 \times 7) - (4 \times 5) + 9 =$ _____

b. $14 + (3 \times 2) - 10 =$ _____ $17 - (5 \times 3) + (4 \times 4) =$ _____

c. $(7 \times 6) + (32 \div 4) - 16 =$ _____ $(2 \times 0) \times (5 \times 7) =$ _____

Some multi-operation problems require operations within operations.

Operations in parentheses ( ) are written within operations in **brackets [ ]**. The innermost operation is always completed first. Parentheses are then used for the remaining operations	$5 \times [(30 - 25) + 3]$ $5 \times (5 + 3)$ 5×8 40	$[4 + (6 \times 3)] \div 2$ $(4 + 18) \div 2$ $22 \div 2$ 11

(3) **Complete the multi-operation problems. Follow the examples.**

a. $3 \times [(2 \times 6) - 5] =$ _____ $[7 + (3 \times 6)] \div 5 =$ _____ $8 + [5 \times (4 + 3)] =$ _____

b. $[2 \times (9 - 5)] - 6 =$ _____ $36 \div [13 - (2 \times 2)] =$ _____ $[3 + (4 \times 6)] \div 9 =$ _____

c. $[(54 - 12) \div 6] \times 3 =$ _____ $4 \times [9 + (3 \times 4)] =$ _____ $64 \div [4 + (28 \div 7)] =$ _____

① Multiply.

322 x 200	304 x 165	247 x 151
568 x 302	871 x 498	644 x 437
532 x 469	602 x 385	813 x 296
371 x 364	672 x 430	736 x 149

1 **Divide.**

a.
$$24\overline{)7,560} \qquad 56\overline{)1,967} \qquad 43\overline{)2,623} \qquad 28\overline{)880} \qquad 72\overline{)2,592}$$

b.
$$31\overline{)6,328} \qquad 62\overline{)9,672} \qquad 18\overline{)7,391} \qquad 55\overline{)9,297} \qquad 84\overline{)4,284}$$

c.
$$61\overline{)26,352} \qquad 28\overline{)22,540} \qquad 47\overline{)18,941} \qquad 56\overline{)39,312} \qquad 35\overline{)16,100}$$

d.
$$13\overline{)11,700} \qquad 26\overline{)19,422} \qquad 81\overline{)55,728} \qquad 65\overline{)48,165} \qquad 48\overline{)25,536}$$

e.
$$16\overline{)12,224} \qquad 82\overline{)42,066} \qquad 74\overline{)31,894} \qquad 25\overline{)21,000} \qquad 53\overline{)17,649}$$

f.
$$27\overline{)16,821} \qquad 90\overline{)26,010} \qquad 36\overline{)29,556} \qquad 21\overline{)19,257} \qquad 44\overline{)31,944}$$

Find the average of the following numbers: 42, 25 and 39.
To find the average, add the numbers and divide by the number of addends. If you have a remainder, round to the nearest whole number.

$$42 + 25 + 39 = 106 \qquad 106 \div 3 = 35\tfrac{1}{3}$$

If the fraction is $\tfrac{1}{2}$ or greater, round the fraction to the next higher whole number. If the fraction is less that $\tfrac{1}{2}$, the whole number remains the same.

In $35\tfrac{1}{3}$ the fraction is less that $\tfrac{1}{2}$ so $35\tfrac{1}{3}$ becomes 35.

The average of the three numbers is 35.

(1) **Find the average of these numbers. If there is a remainder, round it to the nearest whole number.**

a.   16, 23, 18, 14   30, 32, 53, 75   26, 27, 32, 39

b.   9, 16, 23, 45, 16   19, 46, 57, 82, 37   48, 21, 35, 18, 15

c.   546, 384, 467   376, 160, 249   290, 320, 652

d.   9, 12, 26, 32, 8, 18   11, 20, 35, 12, 43, 18, 26

e.   4, 3, 7   6, 11, 12, 14   3, 8, 10, 11, 22

f.   13, 16, 21   18, 17, 24, 35   16, 23, 24, 32, 44

g.   87, 99, 24, 95   84, 77, 56, 98   261, 991, 441, 851

h.   53, 993, 614, 354   356, 127, 443, 52, 8

i.   5,611; 5,651; 292; 7,921; 2,776

① **Multiply.**

1,206	1,500	1,914
x 1,003	x 1,465	x 1,010

1,875	1,325	1,661
x 1,146	x 1,215	x 1,400

2,999	2,233	2,604
x 1,808	x 2,150	x 2,000

3,333	3,550	3,855
x 2,222	x 3,421	x 1,447

(1)   **Multiply.**

12,200	15,575	20,656
x 10,005	x 13,874	x 17,931

25,116	28,888	30,000
x 21,457	x 27,664	x 25,100

32,487	38,159	40,750
x 31,251	x 35,527	x 36,193

1 Divide. Show any remainder as a fraction of the divisor and simplify.

a. $7,252\overline{)37,849}$ $1,405\overline{)157,500}$ $2,604\overline{)329,664}$

b. $4,813\overline{)284,557}$ $3,578\overline{)156,870}$ $8,973\overline{)791,811}$

c. $7,182\overline{)681,122}$ $5,368\overline{)179,488}$ $4,521\overline{)1,123,672}$

d. $2,738\overline{)989,128}$ $4,792\overline{)3,603,517}$ $7,522\overline{)1,688,992}$

Geometry begins with lines and how lines relate to each other.

1 **Match the name of the line to the definition and to the drawing.**

a. _____ _____ vertical

b. _____ _____ parallel

c. _____ _____ horizontal

d. _____ _____ intersecting

e. _____ _____ perpendicular

1. lines that cross each other

2. lines straight up and down

3. lines the same distance apart along their entire length

4. lines that form 90° angles where they meet

5. lines parallel to the horizon

6.

7.

8.

9.

10.

2 **Match the name to the definition and to the drawing.**

a. _____ _____ line

b. _____ _____ line segment

c. _____ _____ end point

d. _____ _____ ray

e. _____ _____ angle

1. has one end point

2. marks the beginning and ending

3. distance between two rays with a common end point

4. has no beginning and no end

5. has a beginning and end

6.

7.

8.

9.

10.

3 **Match the name of the angle to the definition and to the drawing.**

a. _____ _____ right

b. _____ _____ acute

c. _____ _____ obtuse

d. _____ _____ straight

1. equal to 180°

2. greater than 90°, but less than 180°

3. less than 90°

4. equal to 90°

5.

6.

7.

8.

4 **Identify each measurement on the protractor. Describe as right, acute, obtuse, or straight.**

A _____ _____

B _____ _____

C _____ _____

D _____ _____

E _____ _____

F _____ _____

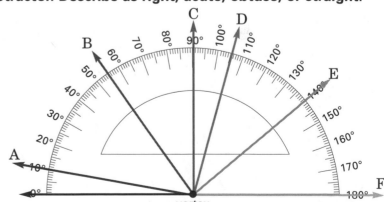

Polygons are closed, plane shapes with three or more sides.

(1) **Name two of the plane shapes that are not polygons.** _____ _____

A **regular polygon** has sides of equal length and angles of equal measure. Other polygons are **irregular polygons**.

(2) **Match irregular polygons to their names.**

1. triangle
2. pentagon
3. hexagon
4. octagon

a. _____   b. _____   c. _____   d. _____

Vertex is the point where the rays of an angle meet.
Vertices is the plural of vertex.

vertex →

(3) **How many vertices in …**

 ____ ____  ____ 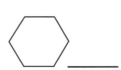 ____ 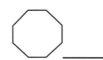 ____

Diagonals are lines that join vertices.

(4) The diagonals have been drawn between all of the vertices of the pentagon. Look carefully on the inside. Can you find a shape similar to the large shape? **Outline it with your pencil.**   **Name the shape.** _____

(5) **Draw diagonals in each shape. Outline the small shape similar to the large shape. Name the shape.**

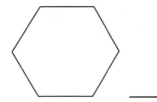 _____   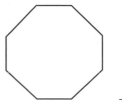 _____

A **quadrilateral** is a 4-sided polygon.
A **parallelogram** is a quadrilateral with opposite sides parallel and equal.
  Rectangles and squares are parallelograms with four right angles.
  A **rhombus** is a parallelogram with 4 sides of equal length.
    Its diagonals are perpendicular to each other
      and divide each other into equal lengths.
    There are usually 2 obtuse angles and 2 acute angles.

(1) Draw $\overline{RS}$ $1\frac{1}{2}$ in. long. Mark point O on $\overline{RS}$ at $\frac{3}{4}$ in.
Draw $\overline{MN}$ 2 in. long *perpendicular* to $\overline{RS}$ at point O.
$\overline{RS}$ should divide $\overline{MN}$ into 2 equal parts (1 in.).
$\overline{MN}$ should divide $\overline{RS}$ into 2 equal parts ($\frac{3}{4}$ in.).
Draw lines connecting the end points.
Measure the lines. $\overline{RM}$ _____ $\overline{MS}$ _____ $\overline{SN}$ _____ $\overline{NR}$ _____

(2) **Match the name of the quadrilateral to the definition and to the drawing.**

a. _____ _____ parallelogram

b. _____ _____ rhombus

c. _____ _____ rectangle

d. _____ _____ square

1. opposite sides parallel and equal usually two acute, two obtuse angles

2. opposite sides parallel and equal with four right angles

3. opposite sides parallel, four sides equal, with four right angles

4. opposite sides parallel

5.

6.

7.

8.

(3) **Select numbers from the second and third column. Match to the first column.**
Each number may be used only once. Look for the best match.

_____ _____ a. polygon

_____ _____ b. quadrilateral

_____ _____ c. parallelogram

_____ _____ d. rhombus

_____ _____ e. rectangle

_____ _____ f. square

1.

2.

3.

4.

5.

6.

7. 4-sided polygon, opposite sides parallel and equal

8. polygon with 4 equal sides, opposite sides parallel, having 4 right angles

9. closed plane shape with 3 or more sides and angles

10. polygon with 4 equal sides, opposite sides parallel, usually having 2 acute and 2 right angles

11. 4-sided polygon

12. 4-sided polygon, opposite sides parallel and equal, having 4 right angles

Congruent lines and shapes are exactly the same in size and shape as their congruent figures.

We use the word incongruent to describe two figures that are not congruent.

Similar shapes have the same shape but are different sizes.

1 **Describe these figures as similar, congruent, or not congruent.**

Triangles may be identified by their angles.

A triangle containing ...
   one angle equal to 90° is a **right** triangle.
   all angles less than 90° is an **acute** triangle.
   an angle more than 90° is an **obtuse** triangle.

right   acute   obtuse

Triangles may be identified by their sides.

A triangle containing ...
   3 equal sides is an **equilateral** triangle.
   2 equal sides is an **isosceles** triangle.
   no equal sides is a **scalene** triangle.

equilateral   isosceles   scalene

(1) **Identify the first row of triangles as (R) right, (A) acute, or (O) obtuse, and the second row of triangles as (E) equilateral, (I) isosceles, or (S) scalene.**

a. ____ ____ ____ ____ ____ ____

b. ____ ____ ____ ____ ____ ____

(2) How many angles are there in a triangle? _____

The angles of triangle ABC measure _____°, _____°, and _____°

The sum of the angles of triangle ABC is equal to _____°

C 60°
A 80°   40° B

Using a protractor, we can measure the angles of any given triangle.
No matter what triangle is drawn, the sum of the angles will always be 180°.

(3) Can a triangle have two right angles? _____ two obtuse angles? _____

Why not? _____

(4) **Answer the questions.**

a. What is the measure of *each* angle of an equilateral triangle?   _____

b. An isosceles triangle has one angle that measures 30°.
   What is the measure of the other two angles that are equal?   _____

c. A scalene triangle has angles of 53° and 69°
   What is the measure of its third angle?   _____

18   *Horizons Math 6 Worksheet*

© MCMXCIX, Alpha Omega Publications, Inc.

A **circle** is a continuous closed line always
   the same distance from a center point.
An **arc** is any part of the curve of a circle.
A **chord** is a line drawn between two
   points on the curve of a circle.
The **diameter** is a chord drawn through
   the center point of a circle.
The **radius** is that part of the diameter
   from the center point to the curve.
The radius is equal to one-half the diameter.
The **circumference** is the perimeter of the circle.
The **area** is the surface of the circle.

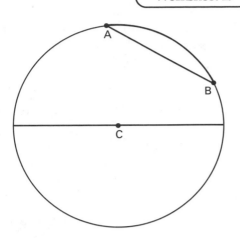

A circle is a plane shape. It can be measured for its circumference and its area.
The special ratio between the diameter of a circle and its circumference is 3.14:1.
The mathematics symbol pi(π) represents the value 3.14.
The formula for the circumference of a circle is 3.14 *times* the diameter or $C = \pi d$.
Because the diameter is twice the size of the radius,
   the formula is sometimes shown as 2 *times* 3.14 *times* the radius or $C = 2\pi r$.

(1) **Match the letter to the name.**

center _____   diameter   _____

radius _____   circumference   _____

arc _____   chord   _____

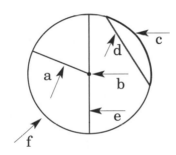

(2) **Match.**

_____ a. circle   1. the perimeter of the circle

_____ b. arc   2. a line drawn through the center point of the circle

_____ c. chord   3. ratio of the diameter to the circumference

_____ d. diameter   4. part of the diameter from the center point to curve

_____ e. radius   5. measure of the surface of a circle

_____ f. circumference   6. a line drawn between two points on the curve of a circle

_____ g. area   7. any part of the curve of a circle

_____ h. pi (3.14)   8. a continuous closed line always the same distance from a center point

Two kinds of solid shapes are prisms and pyramids.
   Prisms have bases that are parallel congruent faces. **Pyramids** have one base.
Prisms and pyramids are named by the shape of their bases.

1   **Name the plane shape that describes the base of the prism or pyramid.**

a. _____   b. _____   c. _____   d. _____

2   **Match the name with the shape. Then shade the base(s) of each shape.**

_____ a. rectangular prism

_____ b. square prism

_____ c. triangular prism

_____ d. rectangular pyramid

_____ e. square pyramid

_____ f. triangular pyramid

1.

2.

3.

4.

5.

6.

3   **Match the name to the illustration.**

1.

2.

3.

4.

_____ a. triangular prism

_____ b. rectangular prism

_____ c. square prism

_____ d. hexagonal prism

_____ e. triangular pyramid

_____ f. rectangular pyramid

_____ g. square pyramid

_____ h. hexagonal pyramid

5.

6.

7.

8.

4   **Match the name with the shape. Then shade the base(s) of each shape.**

_____ a. rectangular prism

_____ b. square prism

_____ c. triangular prism

_____ d. rectangular pyramid

_____ e. square pyramid

_____ f. triangular pyramid

1.

2.

3.

4.

5.

6.

1 **Use a factor tree to find the prime factors.**

a.   20   42   15   27

20 = ____ × ____ × ____   42 = ____ × ____ × ____   15 = ____ × ____   27 = ____ × ____ × ____

b.   25   36   56   40

25 = ____ × ____

36 = ____ × ____
× ____ × ____

56 = ____ × ____
× ____ × ____

40 = ____ × ____
× ____ × ____

2 **Use a factor tree to find the prime factors.**

a.   84   225   156

Prime factors
of 84 are …

____ × ____
× ____ × ____

Prime factors
of 225 are …

____ × ____
× ____ × ____

Prime factors
of 156 are …

____ × ____
× ____ × ____

b.   126   72   420

Prime factors
of 126 are …

____ × ____
× ____ × ____

Prime factors
of 72 are …

____ × ____
× ____ × ____
× ____

Prime factors
of 420 are …

____ × ____
× ____ × ____
× ____

Factors are all of the numbers that can be multiplied together for a certain product.
Factors are always written in number order.
Prime numbers are numbers that have only two factors, one and themselves.
Composite numbers are numbers with three or more factors.

(1) Write the factors for each number in number order. Circle (P) for prime or (C) for composite.

a.   3 _____ (P, C)   4 _____ (P, C)   15 _____ (P, C)

b.   18 _____ (P, C)   23 _____ (P, C)   27 _____ (P, C)

c.   7 _____ (P, C)   24 _____ (P, C)   16 _____ (P, C)

d.   9 _____ (P, C)   5 _____ (P, C)   32 _____ (P, C)

Multiples are the answers to multiplication facts.   The multiples of 6 are
Multiples are written in patterns. Multiply by 1, 2, 3, ...   6, 12, 18, 24, 36, ...
Multiples can be written to any size.   54, 60, 66, 72, 78, ...

Multiples can be written for any number (17).   17, 34, 51, 68, 85, ...

(2) Write multiples of ...

a.   4 beginning with 20.   _____ _____ _____ _____ _____ _____ _____ _____

b.   9 beginning with 45.   _____ _____ _____ _____ _____ _____ _____ _____

c.   15 beginning with 15.   _____ _____ _____ _____ _____ _____ _____ _____

(3) Write all of the multiplication facts with the product of 18.

$\times$ _____ $\times$ _____ $\times$ _____ $\times$ _____ $\times$ _____ $\times$ _____
    18   18   18   18   18   18

Factors are all of the numbers than can be multiplied together for a certain product.
Factors are always written in number order.

(4) Write the factors of 18.   _____ _____ _____ _____ _____ _____

Prime numbers are numbers that have only two factors, one and themselves.
Composite numbers are numbers with three or more factors.

(5) Write the factors for each number. Circle (P) for prime or (C) for composite.

a.   5 _____ (P, C)   20 _____ (P, C)

b.   14 _____ (P, C)   23 _____ (P, C)

c.   30 _____ (P, C)   15 _____ (P, C)

d.   27 _____ (P, C)   29 _____ (P, C)

© MCMXCIX, Alpha Omega Publications, Inc.

There is another operation symbol for multiplication.
A small number (2) is written above 3^2
and to the right of a number (3).
The symbol tells us to use 3 as a factor 2 times.
We can write the prime factors of 18 as ... $2 \times 3^2 = 18$

The name of this type of operation symbol is **exponential notation**.
The number (3) is the **base factor**. The small number (2) is the **exponent**.

3^2	is read "three to the second power or three squared."	$3 \times 3 = 9$
3^3	is read "three to the third power or three cubed."	$3 \times 3 \times 3 = 27$
3^4	is read "three to the fourth power."	$3 \times 3 \times 3 \times 3 = 81$
3^5	is read "three to the fifth power."	$3 \times 3 \times 3 \times 3 \times 3 = 243$

The pattern may continue to any power.
We say the number (3) is increasing exponentially.

The *base factor* is 7. The *exponent* is 2. 7×7
Write the number in *exponential notation*. 7^2
The *product* of 7 squared is 49. 49

(1) Fill in the blanks for each set of prime factors.

	Base Factor	Exponent	Exponential Notation	Product
a. $2 \times 2 \times 2 \times 2$	_____	_____	_____	_____
b. $5 \times 5 \times 5$	_____	_____	_____	_____
c. $3 \times 3 \times 3 \times 3$	_____	_____	_____	_____
d. $7 \times 7 \times 7$	_____	_____	_____	_____
e. $2 \times 2 \times 2 \times 2 \times 2$	_____	_____	_____	_____

Exponential notation is a way of expressing multiplication.
6 is the base number. 3 is the exponent. The operation is multiplication.
6 is multiplied by itself 3 times. 6 is called the repeated factor. $6^3 = 6 \times 6 \times 6 = 216$

(2) Write the value of the number.

4^3 _____ 9^2 _____ 2^6 _____ 5^4 _____ 3^5 _____

Numbers can be expressed in exponential notation.

4 is the base number (factor). 5 is the exponent. The operation is multiplication.
4 is multiplied by itself 5 times.
4 is called a repeated factor. $4^5 = 4 \times 4 \times 4 \times 4 \times 4 = 1,024$

(3) Write the value of the number.

3^4 _____ 7^2 _____ 5^3 _____ 2^5 _____ 0^5 _____

The expression 2^2 means two squared or 2×2.
 Whenever a number is multiplied by itself,
 the product is the *square* of the number.
 The number being multiplied is the **square root**.

$$2^2 = 2 \times 2 = 4$$

4 is the square of 2.
2 is the square root of 4.

(1) **Write the square of each number.**

3 ____   4 ____   5 ____   6 ____   7 ____   8 ____   9 ____   10 ____   11 ____   12 ____

(2) **Write the square root of each number.**

144 ____   121 ____   100 ____   81 ____   64 ____   49 ____   36 ____   25 ____   16 ____   9 ____

(3) **Write the ...**

a.   square of each number.

2 ____   3 ____   5 ____   6 ____   7 ____   8 ____   9 ____   10 ____   11 ____   12 ____

b.   square root of each number.

144 ____   121 ____   100 ____   81 ____   64 ____   49 ____   36 ____   25 ____   9 ____   4 ____

A **perfect square** is a number with a square root that is a whole number.
Each of the numbers in ex. 3b is a *perfect square*.
The **radical sign** $\sqrt{}$ expresses square root.

$\sqrt{121}$ =   11

(4) **Circle the perfect squares.**

$\sqrt{49}$ $\sqrt{72}$ $\sqrt{81}$ $\sqrt{25}$ $\sqrt{48}$ $\sqrt{21}$ $\sqrt{36}$ $\sqrt{121}$

Numbers can be written in scientific notation using powers of 10.
The formula is easy to remember. Move the decimal point until there is just one number in front of the decimal. Use the number of spaces moved as the exponent.

For 573,654,000,000   We write 5.73654×10^{11}, *the decimal was moved 11 spaces*

For 259,862   We write 2.59862×10^5, *the decimal was moved 5 spaces*

(1) Write the following numbers in scientific notation using powers of 10.

a.   437,295,086,191   _____

b.   276,049,568   _____

c.   7,239,567,446   _____

d.   51,468,332   _____

e.   9,367   _____

f.   273,854   _____

g.   Pluto is 3,600,000,000 miles from the sun.   Pluto is _____ miles from the sun.

h.   Jupiter is 480,000,000 miles from the sun.   Jupiter is _____ miles from the sun.

i.   Venus is   67,000,000 miles from the sun.   Venus is _____ miles from the sun.

By writing numbers in powers of ten, it is easier to compare the numbers.

j.   Arrange the planets by their distance from the sun.   _____ _____ _____

(2) Expand these numbers written in scientific notation.

a. 7×10^{12} _____

b. 4.2×10^8 _____

c. 3.5×10^2 _____

(3) Write these numbers in scientific notation.

a.   486,237,154,008 _____   32,158,994 _____

b.   9,116,482,305 _____   854,231,647 _____

c.   367,254,938,152 _____   28,946,157 _____

d.   93,857,116,038 _____   5,382,194 _____

Model 1: Change 156 to base 2. Begin with the largest possible power of 2.

$156 =$ 128 + 0 + 0 + 16 + 8 + 4 + 0 + 0

2^8	2^7	2^6	2^5	2^4	2^3	2^2	2^1	2^0
256	128	64	32	16	8	4	2	1

$156 =$ 1   0   0   1   1   1   0   0 $= 10011100_2$

(1) **Change the following base ten numerals to base two.**

a. 6 _____   f. 31 _____

b. 12 _____   g. 45 _____

c. 15 _____   h. 50 _____

d. 17 _____   i. 100 _____

e. 24 _____   j. 128 _____

Model 2: Change 10110_2 to base 10. Beginning with the units place, put the numbers under the chart and add the values.

Sixteens	Eights	Fours	Twos	Units
2^4	2^3	2^2	2^1	2^0
16	8	4	2	1

1   0   1   1   0

16 + 0 + 4 + 2 + 0 = 22

$10110_2 = 22$

(2) **Change the following base two numerals to base ten.**

a. 11_2 _____   f. 100110_2 _____

b. 1000_2 _____   g. 1000000_2 _____

c. 11100_2 _____   h. 111_2 _____

d. 111111_2 _____ i. 1010101_2 _____

e. 10011_2 _____   j. 11001100_2 _____

(1) **Rewrite the problems and solve.** (You will need scratch paper.)

a.   3.68 + 24.0 + .578 = _____   .004 + 62.5 + 4.3 = _____   .25 + 1.4 + 67 = _____

b.   27.6 + 59 + .031 = _____   .56 + .07 + .039 = _____   3.54 + 12 + 8.9 = _____

c.   36.4 + .07 + .25 = _____   53.09 + .36 + .18 = _____   .31 + .03 + .406 = _____

d.   9.05 − 3.2 = _____   8.3 − .78 = _____   7 − .56 = _____   6.41 − 3.9 = _____

e.   4.8 − 1.76 = _____   7.041 − .357 = _____   9 − 5.04 = _____   15.4 − 12.03 = _____

f.   13 − 5.6 = _____   29.3 − 15.2 = _____   .834 − .295 = _____   6.1 − 4.35 = _____

(2) **Rewrite and add.** (You will need scratch paper.)

a.   21.3 + 7.5 + .054 = _____   6.3 + 5.042 + .49 = _____   .56 + .423 + 7.002 = _____

b.   36.1 + .008 + 8.7 = _____   .78 + .0624 + .5439 = _____   .467 + .095 + 51.42 = _____

c.   .678 + 3.04 + .1352 = _____   5 + 2.3 + 8.006 = _____   9.05 + 3.18 + 4 = _____

d.   12.6 + 8.12 + .317 = _____   6.1 + 3.45 + 8.2 = _____   15 + 7.002 + 19 = _____

Decimal numbers are subtracted by lining
  numbers in place value column.
9.37 does not have a number in thousandths' place.
We must add a zero to complete the subtraction.

$$9.37 - 4.826 = \quad \begin{array}{r} 9.370 \\ 2.836 \\ \hline 6.343 \end{array}$$

(3) **Rewrite and subtract.** (You will need scratch paper.)

a.   63.081 − 42.376 = _____   42.38 − 7.845 = _____   92.04 − 26.931 = _____

b.   .085 − .07 = _____   9.85 − 6.371 = _____   38.64 − 4.762 = _____

c.   9.41 − 6.317 = _____   18 − .541 = _____   .0367 − .0054 = _____

d.   5.08 − 3.6 = _____   .0483 − .0312 = _____   4.81 − .0009 = _____

The **mean** is the same as the average. $(90 + 84 + 65 + 71 + 90 + 74) \div 6 = 79$

The **median** is located exactly in the middle.   65   71   74   84   90   90
The numbers are written in number order. $(74 + 84) \div 2 = 79$
(If two numbers are in the middle, find their average.)

The **mode** appears most of the time.   90 appears two times.

(1) Find the average number.

a.   16, 23, 18, 7 _____   28, 32, 53, 75 _____   25, 27, 31, 37 _____

b.   9, 15, 23, 47, 16 _____   19, 46, 57, 82, 36 _____   48, 21, 35, 17, 14 _____

c.   546, 382, 467 _____   376, 159, 248 _____   290, 321, 655 _____

d.   9, 12, 26, 32, 8, 15 _____   11, 20, 35, 8, 43, 18, 26 _____

(2) List the mean, median, and mode for each set of numbers.

		mean	median	mode
a.	18 9 15 14 14	____	____	____
b.	70 77 81 70 86 92 70	____	____	____
c.	25 42 30 33 37 45 33	____	____	____
d.	2 9 7 6 8 4 10 2	____	____	____
e.	22 13 25 19 17 22 22	____	____	____

(3) Answer the questions. Select mean, median, or mode.

a. The youth group was planning a bake sale. They wanted to know the most popular item from last year's sale. What statistic did they need to know? _____

b. Linda was deciding on clothes to take for her vacation. Which temperature statistic would be most helpful? _____

c. The leaders planned to divide the campers into two groups based on age. What statistic did they need to know? _____

d. Joseph managed to do 23 sit-ups on Monday, 23 on Tuesday, 18 on Wednesday, 23 on Thursday, and 21 on Friday. Which statistic was probably most important to Joseph? _____

Why? _____

(4) Find the mean, median, and mode of each set of numbers.

		mean	median	mode
a.	3, 15, 9, 8, 15, 6, 7	____	____	____
b.	11, 14, 21, 16, 15, 3, 11	____	____	____
c.	13, 29, 11, 13, 5, 17, 10	____	____	____
d.	43, 68, 59, 28, 34, 68	____	____	____

1 **Add or subtract fractions. Simplify answers.**

a.
$\frac{7}{8}$ $+\frac{3}{8}$

$\frac{2}{5}$ $+\frac{3}{5}$

$\frac{5}{12}$ $+\frac{1}{12}$

$\frac{13}{20}$ $+\frac{5}{20}$

$\frac{15}{16}$ $+\frac{4}{16}$

$\frac{9}{24}$ $+\frac{7}{24}$

b.
$\frac{5}{9}$ $-\frac{2}{9}$

$\frac{15}{16}$ $-\frac{5}{16}$

$\frac{17}{20}$ $-\frac{3}{20}$

$\frac{13}{18}$ $-\frac{5}{18}$

$\frac{11}{12}$ $-\frac{3}{12}$

$\frac{19}{21}$ $-\frac{12}{21}$

2 **Add or subtract. Simplify answers.**

a.
$\frac{1}{8}$ $+\frac{7}{8}$

$\frac{11}{15}$ $+\frac{12}{15}$

$\frac{9}{10}$ $+\frac{7}{10}$

$\frac{4}{9}$ $+\frac{3}{9}$

$\frac{5}{24}$ $+\frac{11}{24}$

b.
$\frac{11}{12}$ $-\frac{5}{12}$

$\frac{9}{14}$ $-\frac{1}{14}$

$\frac{5}{8}$ $-\frac{3}{8}$

$\frac{13}{16}$ $-\frac{9}{16}$

$\frac{5}{6}$ $-\frac{1}{6}$

3 **Add or subtract. Simplify answers.**

a.
$\frac{3}{10}$ $+\frac{5}{10}$

$\frac{7}{15}$ $+\frac{8}{15}$

$\frac{5}{12}$ $+\frac{4}{12}$

$\frac{9}{16}$ $+\frac{11}{16}$

$\frac{1}{9}$ $+\frac{5}{9}$

b.
$\frac{17}{20}$ $-\frac{13}{20}$

$\frac{2}{3}$ $-\frac{2}{3}$

$\frac{7}{8}$ $-\frac{1}{8}$

$\frac{13}{15}$ $-\frac{4}{15}$

$\frac{9}{10}$ $-\frac{4}{10}$

We can write equivalent fractions.
   Divide denominator by denominator.
   Multiply the numerator.
   Write the missing numerator.

$$\frac{3}{5} = \frac{?}{20} \qquad \frac{3}{5} = \frac{12}{20}$$

$$20 \div 5 = 4 \qquad 4 \times 3 = 12$$

(1) Write equivalent fractions.

a. $\frac{3}{5} = \frac{}{20}$ $\frac{1}{2} = \frac{}{12}$ $\frac{4}{9} = \frac{}{36}$ $\frac{3}{7} = \frac{}{21}$ $\frac{7}{8} = \frac{}{24}$ $\frac{5}{6} = \frac{}{30}$

b. $\frac{5}{11} = \frac{}{22}$ $\frac{3}{8} = \frac{}{24}$ $\frac{4}{15} = \frac{}{30}$ $\frac{3}{4} = \frac{}{28}$ $\frac{2}{9} = \frac{}{18}$ $\frac{2}{3} = \frac{}{12}$

c. $\frac{1}{4} = \frac{}{16}$ $\frac{3}{7} = \frac{}{21}$ $\frac{7}{10} = \frac{}{20}$ $\frac{2}{5} = \frac{}{10}$ $\frac{1}{2} = \frac{}{14}$ $\frac{5}{12} = \frac{}{24}$

A set of fractions can be compared for number order using equivalent fractions. Decide on a common denominator (24). Write equivalent fractions. Compare. Write the original set of fractions in number order.

$$\frac{5}{6} \quad \frac{2}{3} \quad \frac{1}{4} \quad \frac{7}{8}$$

$$\frac{5}{6} = \frac{20}{24} \quad \frac{2}{3} = \frac{16}{24} \quad \frac{1}{4} = \frac{6}{24} \quad \frac{7}{8} = \frac{21}{24}$$

$$\frac{1}{4} \quad \frac{2}{3} \quad \frac{5}{6} \quad \frac{7}{8}$$

(2) Write equivalent fractions with a common denominator for each row. Write the original set in number order.

a. $\frac{7}{16}$ ___ $\frac{5}{8}$ ___ $\frac{1}{2}$ ___ $\frac{3}{4}$ ___   ___ ___ ___ ___

b. $\frac{7}{8}$ ___ $\frac{3}{4}$ ___ $\frac{5}{6}$ ___ $\frac{2}{3}$ ___ $\frac{19}{24}$ ___   ___ ___ ___ ___ ___

c. $\frac{13}{18}$ ___ $\frac{1}{2}$ ___ $\frac{7}{9}$ ___ $\frac{2}{3}$ ___ $\frac{5}{6}$ ___   ___ ___ ___ ___ ___

d. $\frac{4}{9}$ ___ $\frac{2}{3}$ ___ $\frac{7}{12}$ ___ $\frac{5}{6}$ ___ $\frac{25}{36}$ ___   ___ ___ ___ ___ ___

e. Jess had read $\frac{2}{3}$ of the book, James had read $\frac{3}{4}$, Karen had read $\frac{5}{6}$, and Mark had read $\frac{7}{12}$. Write the names of the students in order from the one who read the least amount of the book to the one who read the most. ___ ___ ___ ___

1 Find a denominator common to the six fractions. Change to equivalent fractions. Compare. Write the original six fractions in number order.

a. $\dfrac{5}{18} =$ $\dfrac{1}{3} =$ $\dfrac{5}{9} =$ $\dfrac{1}{2} =$ $\dfrac{5}{6} =$ $\dfrac{7}{9} =$

_____   _____   _____   _____   _____   _____

b. $\dfrac{3}{4} =$ $\dfrac{1}{6} =$ $\dfrac{2}{3} =$ $\dfrac{7}{12} =$ $\dfrac{11}{24} =$ $\dfrac{5}{8} =$

_____   _____   _____   _____   _____   _____

To prove two fractions are equivalent, multiply the numerator of each fraction times the opposite denominator. If the products are equal the fractions are equal.

$\dfrac{5}{8}$ (=, $\neq$) $\dfrac{2}{3}$

$5 \times 3 = 15 \qquad 2 \times 8 = 16$

$\dfrac{3}{5}$ (=, $\neq$) $\dfrac{6}{10}$

$3 \times 10 = 30 \qquad 6 \times 5 = 30$

2 Cross multiply. Circle the correct symbol.

a. $\dfrac{6}{8}$ (=, $\neq$) $\dfrac{2}{3}$ _____ $\dfrac{7}{8}$ (=, $\neq$) $\dfrac{4}{5}$ _____

b. $\dfrac{2}{7}$ (=, $\neq$) $\dfrac{6}{21}$ _____ $\dfrac{3}{9}$ (=, $\neq$) $\dfrac{4}{12}$ _____

c. $\dfrac{4}{9}$ (=, $\neq$) $\dfrac{8}{15}$ _____ $\dfrac{2}{8}$ (=, $\neq$) $\dfrac{5}{16}$ _____

d. $\dfrac{5}{15}$ (=, $\neq$) $\dfrac{10}{30}$ _____ $\dfrac{4}{10}$ (=, $\neq$) $\dfrac{6}{15}$ _____

Two fractions can be compared using cross multiplication. Multiply numerators by opposite denominators. The numerator that produces the larger product is the numerator of the larger fraction. If the products are the same, the fractions are equal.

$\dfrac{5}{9}$ (>, =, <) $\dfrac{2}{3}$

$5 \times 3 = 15 \qquad 2 \times 9 = 18$

$\dfrac{3}{4}$ (>, =, <) $\dfrac{6}{8}$

$3 \times 8 = 24 \qquad 6 \times 4 = 24$

3 Compare two fractions. Use cross multiplication. Circle the correct symbol.

a. $\dfrac{3}{5}$ (>, =, <) $\dfrac{4}{7}$ $\dfrac{6}{9}$ (>, =, <) $\dfrac{2}{3}$ $\dfrac{3}{8}$ (>, =, <) $\dfrac{5}{12}$ $\dfrac{7}{10}$ (>, =, <) $\dfrac{5}{9}$

b. $\dfrac{3}{12}$ (>, =, <) $\dfrac{2}{8}$ $\dfrac{4}{6}$ (>, =, <) $\dfrac{8}{10}$ $\dfrac{12}{15}$ (>, =, <) $\dfrac{5}{7}$ $\dfrac{6}{18}$ (>, =, <) $\dfrac{7}{21}$

c. $\dfrac{1}{2}$ (>, =, <) $\dfrac{7}{12}$ $\dfrac{10}{15}$ (>, =, <) $\dfrac{8}{12}$ $\dfrac{2}{4}$ (>, =, <) $\dfrac{8}{16}$ $\dfrac{6}{10}$ (>, =, <) $\dfrac{4}{5}$

d. $\dfrac{2}{9}$ (>, =, <) $\dfrac{1}{3}$ $\dfrac{7}{8}$ (>, =, <) $\dfrac{21}{24}$ $\dfrac{9}{10}$ (>, =, <) $\dfrac{4}{5}$ $\dfrac{7}{12}$ (>, =, <) $\dfrac{3}{8}$

Fractions with unlike denominators cannot be added.
The denominators in this problem are 5 and 4.
The fractions must be changed to
equivalent fractions with a common denominator.

$$\begin{array}{r} \frac{3}{5} \\ + \frac{1}{4} \\ \hline \frac{?}{?} \end{array}$$

① **To find a common denominator, find the smallest (least) common multiple of the two numbers.**

a. Write five multiples of 5. _____ _____ _____ _____ _____

Write five multiples of 4. _____ _____ _____ _____ _____

Write the smallest multiple that they have in common. _____

Write the common denominator for the fractions $\frac{3}{5}$ and $\frac{1}{4}$. _____

b. Write the new denominator after each fraction.

Write the equivalent fractions.

$$\frac{3}{5} = \underline{\quad}$$
$$+ \frac{1}{4} = \underline{\quad}$$

Add the numerators and
write the difference over the common denominator.

② **Find the least common multiple (LCM) of 6 and 8.**
Write the new denominator after each fraction.
Write the equivalent fractions.
Subtract the numerators and write
the difference over the common denominator. Simplify.

$$\frac{3}{6} = \underline{\quad}$$
$$- \frac{3}{8} = \underline{\quad}$$

③ **Find the common denominator (LCM). Write equivalent fractions.**
Add or subtract. Simplify.

a.
$$\begin{array}{r} \frac{4}{9} \\ + \frac{2}{3} \\ \hline \end{array} \qquad \begin{array}{r} \frac{5}{16} \\ + \frac{3}{4} \\ \hline \end{array} \qquad \begin{array}{r} \frac{3}{8} \\ + \frac{5}{12} \\ \hline \end{array} \qquad \begin{array}{r} \frac{2}{5} \\ + \frac{7}{15} \\ \hline \end{array} \qquad \begin{array}{r} \frac{3}{8} \\ + \frac{5}{6} \\ \hline \end{array} \qquad \begin{array}{r} \frac{1}{2} \\ + \frac{1}{3} \\ \hline \end{array}$$

b.
$$\begin{array}{r} \frac{7}{12} \\ - \frac{1}{4} \\ \hline \end{array} \qquad \begin{array}{r} \frac{2}{3} \\ - \frac{1}{5} \\ \hline \end{array} \qquad \begin{array}{r} \frac{15}{16} \\ - \frac{1}{2} \\ \hline \end{array} \qquad \begin{array}{r} \frac{5}{6} \\ - \frac{3}{4} \\ \hline \end{array} \qquad \begin{array}{r} \frac{9}{10} \\ - \frac{3}{5} \\ \hline \end{array} \qquad \begin{array}{r} \frac{4}{5} \\ - \frac{1}{2} \\ \hline \end{array}$$

c.
$$\begin{array}{r} \frac{5}{12} \\ + \frac{4}{9} \\ \hline \end{array} \qquad \begin{array}{r} \frac{5}{8} \\ + \frac{1}{3} \\ \hline \end{array} \qquad \begin{array}{r} \frac{4}{7} \\ + \frac{5}{14} \\ \hline \end{array} \qquad \begin{array}{r} \frac{2}{3} \\ - \frac{5}{12} \\ \hline \end{array} \qquad \begin{array}{r} \frac{7}{10} \\ - \frac{4}{15} \\ \hline \end{array} \qquad \begin{array}{r} \frac{8}{9} \\ - \frac{1}{6} \\ \hline \end{array}$$

A **proper** fraction represents an amount
　less than one whole.
The numerator is *less* than the denominator.

$\frac{1}{3}$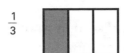

An **improper** fraction represents an amount
　equal to or *more* than one whole.
The numerator is *equal* to or
　more than the denominator.

$\frac{7}{3}$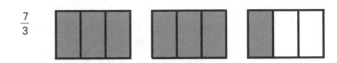

A **mixed number** represents an amount
　more than one whole.
A mixed number contains a whole number
　and a proper fraction.

$2\frac{1}{3}$

---

(1) **Describe each number as ...**   a. proper   b. improper   c. mixed number

a. $\frac{3}{4}$ _____ $5\frac{1}{2}$ _____ $\frac{4}{7}$ _____ $\frac{18}{3}$ _____ $\frac{49}{5}$ _____ $7\frac{3}{16}$ _____ $2\frac{1}{2}$ _____ $\frac{15}{16}$ _____

b. $\frac{7}{10}$ _____ $4\frac{2}{3}$ _____ $\frac{13}{10}$ _____ $9\frac{4}{5}$ _____ $\frac{7}{5}$ _____ $\frac{6}{8}$ _____ $\frac{3}{2}$ _____ $8\frac{1}{4}$ _____

---

(2) **Change improper fractions to mixed numbers or whole numbers.**

a. $\frac{14}{7} =$ $\frac{24}{6} =$ $\frac{21}{5} =$

b. $\frac{17}{9} =$ $\frac{20}{4} =$ $\frac{17}{2} =$

c. $\frac{9}{3} =$ $\frac{11}{4} =$ $\frac{8}{7} =$

---

(3) **Simplify the improper fractions.**

a. $\frac{6}{3} =$ $\frac{9}{5} =$ $\frac{8}{4} =$ $\frac{12}{5} =$

b. $\frac{7}{2} =$ $\frac{6}{4} =$ $\frac{10}{3} =$ $\frac{8}{8} =$

If the fractions have unlike denominators, find a common denominator, write equivalent fractions, and complete the problem.

$$8\frac{5}{6} = \frac{5}{6}$$
$$+\ 3\frac{1}{3} = \frac{2}{6}$$
$$\overline{11\ \ = \frac{7}{6} = \boxed{1\frac{1}{6}}}$$

$$11$$
$$+\ \boxed{1\frac{1}{6}}$$
$$\overline{12\frac{1}{6}}$$

(1) Add or subtract. Simplify.

a.
$$5\frac{4}{5}$$ $$6\frac{2}{3}$$ $$5\frac{1}{2}$$ $$11\frac{7}{12}$$ $$9\frac{7}{10}$$ $$21\frac{13}{15}$$
$$+\ 7\frac{3}{10}$$ $$+\ 8\frac{1}{4}$$ $$+\ 3\frac{5}{8}$$ $$+\ 6\frac{2}{3}$$ $$+\ 4\frac{3}{5}$$ $$+\ 8\frac{2}{9}$$

b.
$$15\frac{5}{8}$$ $$7\frac{8}{9}$$ $$8\frac{3}{4}$$ $$16\frac{13}{15}$$ $$18\frac{9}{14}$$ $$9\frac{7}{12}$$
$$-\ 10\frac{1}{4}$$ $$-\ 2\frac{2}{3}$$ $$-\ 5\frac{7}{16}$$ $$-\ 7\frac{2}{5}$$ $$-\ 11\frac{2}{7}$$ $$-\ 2\frac{5}{18}$$

c.
$$2\frac{5}{8}$$ $$7\frac{4}{5}$$ $$9\frac{2}{3}$$ $$8\frac{7}{20}$$ $$13\frac{1}{2}$$ $$24\frac{1}{6}$$
$$+\ 3\frac{3}{4}$$ $$+\ 6\frac{7}{15}$$ $$+\ 5\frac{5}{6}$$ $$+\ 3\frac{9}{10}$$ $$+\ 18\frac{1}{3}$$ $$+\ 15\frac{5}{8}$$

d.
$$14\frac{3}{5}$$ $$8\frac{5}{6}$$ $$11\frac{7}{8}$$ $$7\frac{2}{3}$$ $$19\frac{3}{4}$$ $$35\frac{8}{15}$$
$$-\ 10\frac{1}{3}$$ $$-\ 2\frac{4}{5}$$ $$-\ 3\frac{5}{6}$$ $$-\ 3\frac{1}{7}$$ $$-\ 12\frac{2}{5}$$ $$-\ 16\frac{4}{9}$$

e.
$$14\frac{1}{3}$$ $$10\frac{5}{8}$$ $$11\frac{1}{5}$$ $$9\frac{4}{5}$$ $$8\frac{5}{9}$$ $$15\frac{1}{2}$$
$$+\ 21\frac{2}{3}$$ $$+\ 13\frac{7}{8}$$ $$+\ 14\frac{2}{3}$$ $$-\ 6\frac{3}{5}$$ $$-\ 2\frac{2}{9}$$ $$-\ 4\frac{1}{4}$$

f.
$$7\frac{5}{8}$$ $$6\frac{4}{5}$$ $$12\frac{4}{9}$$ $$38\frac{5}{7}$$ $$18\frac{5}{6}$$ $$27\frac{11}{12}$$
$$+\ 4\frac{1}{3}$$ $$+\ 5\frac{7}{10}$$ $$+\ 18\frac{5}{6}$$ $$-\ 24\frac{5}{7}$$ $$-\ 11\frac{2}{3}$$ $$-\ 15\frac{3}{4}$$

When adding whole numbers and mixed numbers,
  bring down the fraction.
  Add the whole numbers.

$$4$$
$$+\ 7\frac{3}{8}$$
$$\overline{11\frac{3}{8}}$$

$$15\frac{7}{12}$$
$$+\ 22$$
$$\overline{37\frac{7}{12}}$$

When subtracting whole numbers and mixed numbers,
  if the fraction is in the minuend,
  bring down the fraction and subtract the whole numbers.

$$9\frac{3}{4}$$
$$-\ 6$$
$$\overline{3\frac{3}{4}}$$

(1) Add or subtract.

8	$7\frac{5}{6}$	$14\frac{1}{3}$	$6\frac{1}{2}$	$18\frac{3}{4}$	3	$21\frac{5}{6}$
$+\ 3\frac{1}{8}$	$+\ 2$	$-\ 7$	$+\ 3$	$-\ 15$	$+\ 2\frac{1}{9}$	$-\ 18$

When subtracting whole numbers and fractions,
or whole numbers and mixed numbers, if the
fraction is in the subtrahend, we need to borrow.
Borrow 1 whole from the whole number.
Change to a fraction with the same
        denominator as the problem.
Subtract fractions. Subtract whole numbers.

$$10$$
$$-\ \frac{5}{8}$$
$$\overline{?}$$

$$\overset{9}{\cancel{10}}\frac{8}{8}$$
$$-\ \frac{5}{8}$$
$$\overline{9\frac{3}{8}}$$

$$15$$
$$-\ 6\frac{3}{7}$$
$$\overline{?}$$

$$\overset{14}{\cancel{15}}\frac{7}{7}$$
$$-\ 6\frac{3}{7}$$
$$\overline{8\frac{4}{7}}$$

(2) Subtract. Remember to borrow.

7	16	14	17	22	9	15
$-\ \frac{2}{3}$	$-\ \frac{7}{12}$	$-\ \frac{4}{5}$	$-\ 12\frac{2}{9}$	$-\ 16\frac{3}{10}$	$-\ 7\frac{9}{15}$	$-\ 4\frac{5}{8}$

(3) Add or subtract. Borrow when necessary.

a.

$15\frac{7}{8}$	19	$23\frac{3}{4}$	$16\frac{1}{2}$	7	11
$-\ 12$	$-\ 5\frac{1}{3}$	$-\ 18$	$+\ 4$	$+\ 6\frac{3}{5}$	$+\ 8\frac{5}{7}$

b.

14	$7\frac{4}{11}$	$9\frac{5}{12}$	8	13	$14\frac{7}{12}$
$+\ \frac{5}{9}$	$+\ 2$	$+\ 8$	$-\ \frac{7}{10}$	$-\ 6\frac{3}{4}$	$-\ 11$

c.

21	$11\frac{1}{2}$	6	$9\frac{1}{3}$	3	7
$-\ 15\frac{3}{5}$	$-\ 7$	$-\ \frac{3}{4}$	$-\ 5$	$-\ 2\frac{1}{6}$	$-\ 4\frac{5}{8}$

Decimals do not need to be lined up by place value for multiplication.

Multiply as in whole numbers.	23.5	1 place
Count the decimal places in the multiplicand	× .075	3 places
and in the multiplier. Add.	1175	
Moving from right to left, count the same	16450	
number of decimal places in the product.	1.7625	4 places

(1) Multiply.

a.
$$\begin{array}{r} .37 \\ \times\ .56 \\ \hline \end{array}$$
$$\begin{array}{r} 9.2 \\ \times\ .64 \\ \hline \end{array}$$
$$\begin{array}{r} 5.06 \\ \times\ .42 \\ \hline \end{array}$$
$$\begin{array}{r} 38.4 \\ \times\ .027 \\ \hline \end{array}$$
$$\begin{array}{r} .486 \\ \times\ .079 \\ \hline \end{array}$$

b.
$$\begin{array}{r} 4.31 \\ \times\ .08 \\ \hline \end{array}$$
$$\begin{array}{r} 73.6 \\ \times\ .59 \\ \hline \end{array}$$
$$\begin{array}{r} 8.40 \\ \times\ 3.2 \\ \hline \end{array}$$
$$\begin{array}{r} .128 \\ \times\ 6.4 \\ \hline \end{array}$$
$$\begin{array}{r} 39 \\ \times\ .06 \\ \hline \end{array}$$

(2) Multiply. Remember to count decimal places.

a.
$$\begin{array}{r} 3.6 \\ \times.4 \\ \hline \end{array}$$
$$\begin{array}{r} 9.02 \\ \times\ 3 \\ \hline \end{array}$$
$$\begin{array}{r} 6.59 \\ \times\ .08 \\ \hline \end{array}$$
$$\begin{array}{r} 29.3 \\ \times\ .7 \\ \hline \end{array}$$
$$\begin{array}{r} .312 \\ \times\ .06 \\ \hline \end{array}$$
$$\begin{array}{r} 1.84 \\ \times\ .2 \\ \hline \end{array}$$

b.
$$\begin{array}{r} 23.4 \\ \times\ 4.9 \\ \hline \end{array}$$
$$\begin{array}{r} .083 \\ \times\ .56 \\ \hline \end{array}$$
$$\begin{array}{r} .490 \\ \times.38 \\ \hline \end{array}$$
$$\begin{array}{r} 7.57 \\ \times\ 6.1 \\ \hline \end{array}$$
$$\begin{array}{r} .437 \\ \times\ .86 \\ \hline \end{array}$$
$$\begin{array}{r} 95.2 \\ \times\ .73 \\ \hline \end{array}$$

(3) Multiply.

$$\begin{array}{r} 9.42 \\ \times\ .067 \\ \hline \end{array}$$
$$\begin{array}{r} 73.6 \\ \times\ .005 \\ \hline \end{array}$$
$$\begin{array}{r} .124 \\ \times\ .49 \\ \hline \end{array}$$
$$\begin{array}{r} 672 \\ \times\ 3.8 \\ \hline \end{array}$$
$$\begin{array}{r} 54.6 \\ \times\ 7.1 \\ \hline \end{array}$$

(4) Multiply.

$$\begin{array}{r} 3.07 \\ \times\ .8 \\ \hline \end{array}$$
$$\begin{array}{r} .093 \\ \times\ .24 \\ \hline \end{array}$$
$$\begin{array}{r} 5.62 \\ \times.041 \\ \hline \end{array}$$

Decimals can be divided by whole numbers.
Follow the steps to divide whole numbers.
Use long or short division.
Place the decimal point in the quotient
 directly above its place in the dividend.
Use zero (0) place holders, if necessary.

$$
\begin{array}{r}
1.54 \\
4\overline{)6\uparrow32} \\
4 \\
\hline
2\ 3 \\
2\ 0 \\
\hline
32 \\
32 \\
\hline
0
\end{array}
\qquad
\begin{array}{r}
.064 \\
4\overline{)\uparrow256} \\
24 \\
\hline
16 \\
16 \\
\hline
0
\end{array}
$$

(1) **Divide. Remember zero (0) place holders.**

a.

$8\overline{)2.72}$ $5\overline{).45}$ $3\overline{).006}$ $8\overline{)34.4}$ $4\overline{)16.08}$

b.

$9\overline{)196.2}$ $4\overline{).2752}$ $5\overline{)347.0}$ $6\overline{).318}$ $4\overline{)1.564}$

(2) **Divide. Remember zero (0) place holders. Round answers to the nearest decimal place.**

a.

$4\overline{)3.27}$ $8\overline{)63.7}$ $6\overline{).043}$ $9\overline{)6.32}$ $3\overline{).946}$

b.

$5\overline{).167}$ $7\overline{).493}$ $6\overline{).754}$ $4\overline{)28.3}$ $8\overline{)52.5}$

c.

$5\overline{)4.57}$ $3\overline{).248}$ $2\overline{).041}$ $3\overline{)3.07}$ $9\overline{)73.6}$

(3) **Divide to hundredths' place. Round to tenths' place.**

$6\overline{)7.00}$ $8\overline{)3.00}$ $7\overline{)9.00}$ $9\overline{)6.00}$ $6\overline{)5.00}$

Fractions can be converted to decimals.
  Write as a problem in division.
  Divide the denominator into the numerator.
  Add the understood decimal point to the dividend.
  Divide until the quotient is an even number, or
  divide to hundredths' place and round the answer.

$$\frac{7}{9} = \quad \begin{array}{r} .77 \\ 9\overline{)7.00} \\ \underline{6\ 3} \\ 70 \\ \underline{63} \\ 7 \end{array} \quad \frac{7}{9} = .78$$

(1) **Convert fractions to decimals.**

a. $\frac{3}{5} =$ _____ $\frac{5}{8} =$ _____ $\frac{3}{4} =$ _____ $\frac{1}{3} =$ _____ $\frac{5}{6} =$ _____

b. $\frac{1}{2} =$ _____ $\frac{2}{9} =$ _____ $\frac{1}{6} =$ _____ $\frac{7}{12} =$ _____ $\frac{3}{8} =$ _____

To find the decimal equivalent of a fraction
  divide the denominator into the numerator.
  To divide, add the understood decimal point and zeros.

(2)   **Find decimal equivalents. Divide until the quotient is an even number.**

$\frac{1}{5} =$ $\frac{1}{4} =$ $\frac{1}{2} =$ $\frac{3}{4} =$ $\frac{4}{5} =$

(3)   **Rewrite each number substituting a decimal number for the mixed number.**

$19\frac{1}{5}$ _____ $23\frac{1}{4}$ _____ $15\frac{1}{2}$ _____ $67\frac{3}{4}$ _____ $58\frac{4}{5}$ _____

Each of the fractions in ex. 2 & 3 converted evenly to a decimal.
There was no remainder. This type of decimal is a terminating
decimal. When the division is not even and the numbers in the
quotient begin to repeat, the decimal is a repeating decimal.
Repeating decimals are written with a bar over the numbers
that repeat.

$$\begin{array}{r} .16\overline{6} \\ 6\overline{)1.000} \\ \underline{6} \\ 40 \\ \underline{36} \\ 40 \\ \underline{36} \\ 4 \end{array} = .1\overline{6}$$

(4)   **Change fractions to decimals. Divide until the numbers terminate or repeat.**
   Write the repeating decimals with a bar over the numbers that repeat.

a. $\frac{5}{8} =$ $\frac{1}{3} =$ $\frac{1}{8} =$ $\frac{2}{5} =$ $\frac{5}{6} =$

b. $\frac{2}{9} =$ $\frac{3}{8} =$ $\frac{7}{9} =$ $\frac{3}{5} =$ $\frac{7}{8} =$

The rule for rounding decimals is the same as the rule for whole numbers.
   Decide on the place the number is to be rounded to (100th's).
   Look at the first digit to the right of that place.
   Follow the same rules as whole numbers.   .6352 rounds .6400
   Because of equivalent decimals, we may drop the zero(s).   .6400 = .64

(1) **Round decimal numbers to ...**

  a.   10ths' place.   2.74 _____   36.09 _____   .843 _____   7.546 _____   .2917 _____

  b.   100ths' place.   3.482 _____   .3169 _____   41.065 _____   .471 _____   6.038 _____

(2)   a. **Divide to the 100ths. Round to the nearest 10th.**

      $5 \overline{)47}$ $6 \overline{)215}$ $3 \overline{)572}$ $9 \overline{)95}$ $8 \overline{)379}$

  b. **Divide to the 1,000ths. Round to the nearest 100th.**

      $3 \overline{)8.6}$ $5 \overline{).37}$ $8 \overline{)9.4}$ $7 \overline{)36}$ $2 \overline{).39}$

(3)   a. **Round to the nearest whole number.**

      $29 \overline{)3,754}$ $63 \overline{)7,891}$ $48 \overline{)1,128}$ $19 \overline{)658}$

  b. **Round to the nearest decimal place.**

      $43 \overline{)69.3}$ $21 \overline{)79.3}$ $71 \overline{)32.67}$ $59 \overline{)36.41}$

(4) **Round decimal numbers to ...**

  a.   tenths' place.   3.48 _____   9.72 _____   .657 _____

  b.   hundredths' place.   7.068 _____   .4279 _____   58.213 _____

To divide decimals, the *divisor* must be a whole number.

We have learned to write equivalent fractions by multiplying the numerator and the denominator by the same number.

$$\frac{5 \times 10}{8 \times 10} = \frac{50}{80}$$

Suppose we want to show a ratio of two decimal numbers. We can write the ratio as a fraction. If we multiply the numerator and denominator by the same number, the ratio remains the same, but now the ratio shows two whole numbers.

3.25 : 4.25

$$\frac{3.25 \times 100}{4.25 \times 100} = \frac{325}{425}$$

In division of decimals, to make the divisor a whole number, multiply by 10, 100, or 1,000. Then multiply the dividend by the same number. The ratio between the two numbers remains the same.

Multiply .5 by 10. It is now a whole number.
Multiply .75 by 10. Divide 7.5 by 5.
Place the decimal point in the quotient directly above its new position in the dividend.

$$.5\overline{).7\,5} \quad \frac{1.5}{}$$

Multiply .06 by 100. It is now a whole number.
Multiply .372 by 100. Divide 37.2 by 6.
Place the decimal point in the quotient directly above its new position in the dividend.

$$.06\overline{).37\,2} \quad \frac{6.2}{}$$

(1) Follow the steps shown in the examples.
Make the divisor a whole number. Multiply by 10, 100, or 1,000. Multiply the dividend by the same number. Divide. Place the decimal point in the quotient directly above its new position in the dividend.

a.
$$.7\overline{).91} \qquad .8\overline{)12.8} \qquad .02\overline{)9.8} \qquad .007\overline{)5.74} \qquad .04\overline{).36}$$

b.
$$1.6\overline{)4.8} \qquad .15\overline{).75} \qquad 1.3\overline{).52} \qquad 2.4\overline{).144} \qquad .035\overline{).105}$$

c.
$$4.2\overline{).252} \qquad .53\overline{)4.24} \qquad .07\overline{)14} \qquad .6\overline{).84} \qquad .05\overline{).930}$$

There may be a remainder in the division problem.

Complete the division.
Write the decimal point in the quotient.
Write the remainder as a fraction.
Round.

$$8.4\tfrac{4}{7} = 8.5$$
$$.7\,)\overline{5.9.2}$$
$$\underline{5\ 6}$$
$$3\ 2$$
$$\underline{2\ 8}$$
$$4$$

(1) Complete the division. Round to the nearest decimal place or whole number.

a.

$.03\,)\overline{4.28}$ $.8\,)\overline{.253}$ $.2\,)\overline{4.73}$ $.09\,)\overline{.786}$

b.

$.5\,)\overline{45.6}$ $.14\,)\overline{7.57}$ $3.2\,)\overline{8.93}$ $.47\,)\overline{.563}$

c.

$2.3\,)\overline{41.6}$ $.84\,)\overline{.2189}$ $5.3\,)\overline{6.37}$ $6.2\,)\overline{23.58}$

(2) Complete the division. Round to the nearest decimal place.

a.

$.4\,)\overline{8.36}$ $.06\,)\overline{.72}$ $.003\,)\overline{9.72}$ $.09\,)\overline{.194}$

b.

$3.2\,)\overline{.64}$ $.29\,)\overline{.744}$ $7.3\,)\overline{.146}$ $.13\,)\overline{3.9}$

(3) Divide. Round answers to the nearest decimal place.

$6\,)\overline{36.8}$ $4\,)\overline{8.63}$ $.03\,)\overline{.943}$ $.2\,)\overline{.731}$

(4) Divide. Round answers to the nearest decimal place.

$8\,)\overline{4.39}$ $5\,)\overline{.451}$ $.06\,)\overline{.583}$ $.9\,)\overline{18.37}$

To graph an ordered-pair number, we find the first number on the horizontal scale, then move up the graph to find the second number on the vertical scale. Remember: First number, horizontal scale; second number, vertical scale.

Locate (1, 2), (2, 3), (4, 5) on a graph

To locate (1, 2), go to 1 on the horizontal scale, then go up 2 units on the vertical scale.
Place a dot where the two come together.

(2, 3) is over 2 and up 3.
(4, 5) is "east" 4, "north" 5.

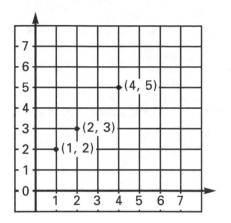

① **Graph the points.**
(1, 1) (2, 2) and (3, 3)

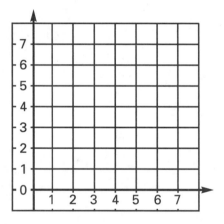

Graph the points (1, 4), (2, 3),
(3, 7), (4, 6), (5, 0) and (6, 1)

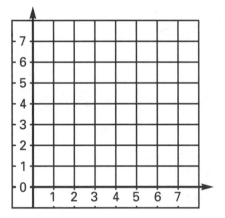

② **Determine the ordered-pair numbers for each letter.**

A _____

B _____

C _____

D _____

E _____

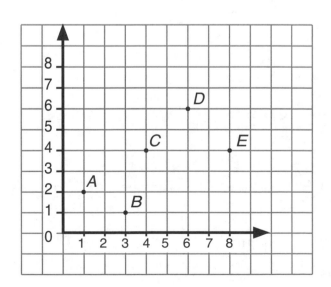

Suppose we have four cans of paint each $\frac{2}{3}$ full.
How many full cans is that?
Multiply $4 \times \frac{2}{3}$ of a can.
4 times $\frac{2}{3}$ cans of paint is
   $2\frac{2}{3}$ cans of paint.

$$\frac{4}{1} \times \frac{2}{3} = \frac{8}{3} = 2\frac{2}{3}$$

(1)   Solve the problem.

a.   10 cans each $\frac{3}{5}$ full   = _____ cans   12 boxes each $\frac{3}{4}$ full   = _____ boxes

b.   8 jars each $\frac{1}{2}$ full   = _____ jars   6 pails each $\frac{2}{3}$ full   = _____ pails

c.   There are 8 boxes of cards. $\frac{5}{8}$ of each box is birthday cards.
     If there are 18 cards in each box,
          how many birthday cards are there altogether in the 8 boxes?   _____

(2)   Write the fractions in simplest terms. Divide by the (GCF) greatest common factor.

a. $\frac{9}{27} =$ $\frac{16}{18} =$ $\frac{15}{20} =$ $\frac{6}{8} =$ $\frac{10}{16} =$ $\frac{21}{24} =$

b. $\frac{15}{30} =$ $\frac{24}{36} =$ $\frac{11}{22} =$ $\frac{12}{15} =$ $\frac{20}{25} =$ $\frac{9}{21} =$

Some problems can be simplified before multiplying.
     Find a common factor for one *numerator* and
     one *denominator*. Simplify in the problem.
     8 and 10 have a common factor of 2.
     9 and 15 have a common factor of 3.
     Complete the multiplication.

$$\frac{\overset{4}{\cancel{8}}}{\underset{5}{\cancel{15}}} \times \frac{\overset{3}{\cancel{9}}}{\underset{5}{\cancel{10}}} = \frac{12}{25}$$

(3)   Multiply. Simplify in the problem where possible. Write answers in simplest terms.

a. $\frac{3}{8} \times \frac{4}{9} =$ $\frac{5}{7} \times \frac{14}{15} =$ $\frac{8}{9} \times \frac{3}{4} =$ $\frac{7}{24} \times \frac{6}{7} =$ $\frac{11}{12} \times \frac{8}{9} =$

b. $\frac{7}{16} \times \frac{4}{5} =$ $\frac{9}{10} \times \frac{15}{16} =$ $\frac{4}{25} \times \frac{5}{8} =$ $\frac{16}{21} \times \frac{15}{24} =$ $\frac{14}{15} \times \frac{10}{13} =$

c. $\frac{3}{5} \times \frac{25}{27} =$ $\frac{4}{5} \times \frac{7}{8} =$ $\frac{1}{2} \times \frac{10}{21} =$ $\frac{11}{16} \times \frac{4}{11} =$ $\frac{9}{10} \times \frac{5}{18} =$

d. $\frac{2}{3} \times \frac{15}{16} =$ $\frac{5}{9} \times \frac{9}{20} =$ $\frac{16}{21} \times \frac{7}{8} =$ $\frac{24}{25} \times \frac{5}{8} =$ $\frac{30}{49} \times \frac{7}{10} =$

Mixed numbers can be changed to improper fractions.
  Multiply the denominator times the whole number.
  Add the numerator. Write the answer over the denominator.

$$2\frac{5}{7} = (7 \times 2) + 5 = \frac{19}{7}$$

(1) Change mixed numbers to improper fractions.

$3\frac{1}{2} =$ $5\frac{3}{4} =$ $9\frac{4}{5} =$ $6\frac{2}{3} =$ $12\frac{5}{6} =$ $8\frac{3}{7} =$ $4\frac{5}{8} =$

Mixed numbers can be multiplied.
Change the mixed number to an improper fraction.
Multiply as in other fraction problems.

$$5\frac{3}{5} \times \frac{5}{7} = \frac{\overset{4}{\cancel{28}}}{\cancel{5}} \times \frac{\overset{1}{\cancel{5}}}{\cancel{7}} = \frac{4}{1} = 4$$

(2) Change mixed numbers to improper fractions. Multiply.

a. $6\frac{2}{3} \times \frac{3}{5} =$ $\frac{2}{7} \times 10\frac{1}{2} =$ $4\frac{4}{5} \times 8\frac{1}{3} =$

b. $12\frac{1}{4} \times \frac{4}{7} =$ $\frac{9}{10} \times 5\frac{5}{6} =$ $8\frac{2}{5} \times 2\frac{1}{2} =$

c. $3\frac{3}{8} \times \frac{16}{21} =$ $\frac{1}{6} \times 7\frac{1}{5} =$ $8\frac{2}{3} \times 6\frac{3}{4} =$

d. $7\frac{1}{2} \times \frac{2}{5} =$ $\frac{5}{8} \times 5\frac{1}{5} =$ $6\frac{3}{4} \times 5\frac{1}{3} =$

e. $14\frac{2}{3} \times \frac{3}{11} =$ $\frac{15}{16} \times 9\frac{1}{3} =$ $12\frac{1}{2} \times 7\frac{1}{5} =$

f. $4\frac{1}{5} \times \frac{5}{7} =$ $\frac{5}{12} \times 3\frac{1}{5} =$ $2\frac{1}{2} \times 3\frac{1}{3} =$

(3) Multiply.

a. $\frac{2}{3} \times 4\frac{1}{8} =$ $6\frac{2}{3} \times \frac{2}{5} =$ $\frac{15}{16} \times \frac{8}{25} =$ $5\frac{1}{7} \times 3\frac{1}{2} =$

b. $\frac{7}{10} \times \frac{5}{9} =$ $\frac{3}{8} \times 10\frac{2}{3} =$ $3\frac{3}{7} \times \frac{5}{12} =$ $5\frac{4}{9} \times 2\frac{4}{7} =$

c. $\frac{8}{9} \times 4\frac{1}{2} =$ $\frac{11}{12} \times 6 =$ $\frac{8}{11} \times 16\frac{1}{2} =$ $\frac{14}{15} \times \frac{5}{7} =$

d. $10\frac{2}{3} \times 5\frac{1}{4} =$ $6\frac{7}{8} \times 3\frac{1}{5} =$ $\frac{4}{9} \times 15 =$ $11\frac{2}{3} \times \frac{3}{7} =$

Problems in multiplication of fractions can be understood by substituting the word 'of' for the multiplication sign.

$\frac{1}{2} \times \frac{1}{5} = \frac{1}{10}$

$\frac{1}{2}$ of $\frac{1}{5} = \frac{1}{10}$

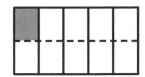

(1) **Solve the problems. Color the part that illustrates your answer.**

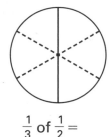

$\frac{1}{3}$ of $\frac{1}{2} =$

$\frac{1}{4}$ of $\frac{2}{3} =$

$\frac{1}{3}$ of $\frac{2}{5} =$

Multiplication of fractions is made easier by simplifying in the problem. Find the (GCF) greatest common factor (5) for a number in the numerator (5) and in the denominator (15). Simplify and multiply.

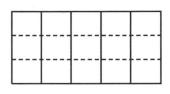

(2) **Solve problems by simplifying in the problem.**

$\frac{2}{3} \times \frac{1}{2} =$ $\frac{7}{8} \times \frac{4}{5} =$ $\frac{3}{10} \times \frac{5}{6} =$ $\frac{5}{9} \times \frac{3}{5} =$ $\frac{6}{7} \times \frac{7}{8} =$ $\frac{7}{8} \times \frac{16}{21} =$

Every whole number has an understood denominator of one (1). To multiply a fraction and a whole number, write the understood denominator beneath the whole number.

$\frac{5}{12} \times 6 = \frac{5}{\overset{12}{\underset{2}{}}} \times \frac{\overset{1}{6}}{1} = \frac{5}{2} = 2\frac{1}{2}$

(3) **Solve problems by adding the understood denominator. Simplify in the problem.**

$\frac{1}{4} \times 6 =$ $10 \times \frac{3}{8} =$ $14 \times \frac{3}{7} =$ $\frac{3}{4} \times 24 =$ $\frac{11}{12} \times 16 =$ $15 \times \frac{7}{9} =$

To multiply mixed numbers, change the mixed number to an improper fraction. (Multiply the whole number by the denominator, add the numerator.) Simplify and multiply.

$7\frac{1}{2} \times \frac{3}{5} = \frac{\overset{3}{15}}{2} \times \frac{3}{\underset{1}{5}} = \frac{9}{2} = 4\frac{1}{2}$

(4) **Solve problems by changing mixed numbers to improper fractions. Simplify.**

a. $2\frac{4}{5} \times \frac{5}{7} =$ $6 \times 9\frac{1}{3} =$ $\frac{3}{10} \times 8\frac{8}{9} =$ $5\frac{1}{3} \times 4\frac{1}{8} =$ $\frac{4}{9} \times 6\frac{3}{4} =$

b. $1\frac{2}{5} \times 3\frac{4}{7} =$ $3\frac{3}{4} \times \frac{4}{5} =$ $8\frac{3}{4} \times 2\frac{2}{7} =$ $3\frac{1}{3} \times 1\frac{1}{2} =$ $7\frac{1}{2} \times 3\frac{1}{5} =$

We can divide a fraction by a fraction.
  The illustration shows $\frac{3}{4}$ of a rectangle. We want to find
out how many half rectangles there are in $\frac{3}{4}$ of rectangle.
There are $1\frac{1}{2}$ half rectangles in $\frac{3}{4}$ of a rectangle.

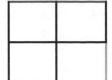

size
of a
half
rectangle

Write the problem.
Find the reciprocal of the divisor.
Change the division sign to a multiplication sign.
Complete as a multiplication problem.

$$\frac{3}{4} \div \frac{1}{2} = \frac{3}{\underset{2}{4}} \times \frac{\overset{1}{2}}{1} = \frac{3}{2} = 1\frac{1}{2}$$

---

(1) **Divide fractions by fractions. Simplify in problem.**

a. $\frac{4}{5} \div \frac{2}{3} =$ $\frac{3}{8} \div \frac{3}{4} =$ $\frac{5}{18} \div \frac{5}{9} =$ $\frac{7}{10} \div \frac{1}{5} =$ $\frac{4}{9} \div \frac{2}{6} =$

b. $\frac{3}{4} \div \frac{1}{3} =$ $\frac{1}{2} \div \frac{2}{5} =$ $\frac{7}{12} \div \frac{2}{3} =$ $\frac{1}{3} \div \frac{5}{6} =$ $\frac{3}{5} \div \frac{1}{2} =$

---

(2) **Divide.**

a. $4 \div \frac{1}{3} =$ $\frac{3}{5} \div 9 =$ $6 \div \frac{3}{8} =$ $\frac{1}{2} \div 7 =$

b. $\frac{1}{3} \div \frac{5}{6} =$ $\frac{4}{9} \div \frac{7}{12} =$ $\frac{7}{10} \div \frac{2}{5} =$ $\frac{3}{8} \div \frac{4}{9} =$

---

(3) **Divide. Simplify in the problem, if possible. Simplify answers.**

a. $\frac{5}{8} \div \frac{3}{4} =$ $\frac{2}{3} \div 14 =$ $18 \div \frac{3}{5} =$ $\frac{5}{6} \div \frac{5}{6} =$ $49 \div \frac{7}{9} =$ $\frac{1}{2} \div \frac{3}{4} =$

---

(4) **Divide.**

a. $\frac{3}{8} \div 6 =$ $14 \div \frac{1}{2} =$ $\frac{9}{10} \div \frac{3}{5} =$ $\frac{8}{15} \div \frac{2}{3} =$ $\frac{7}{10} \div \frac{2}{3} =$

To divide mixed numbers, change the mixed numbers to improper fractions. Find the reciprocal of the divisor. Change the division sign to a multiplication sign. Complete as a multiplication problem.

$$2\frac{1}{2} \div 3\frac{1}{4} =$$

$$\frac{5}{2} \div \frac{13}{4} = \frac{5}{\underset{1}{\cancel{2}}} \times \frac{\overset{2}{\cancel{4}}}{13} = \frac{10}{13}$$

(1) **Divide with mixed numbers in the problem.**

a. $7\frac{1}{3} \div 11 =$ $8 \div 6\frac{2}{5} =$ $2\frac{5}{8} \div 7 =$ $9 \div 6\frac{3}{4} =$

b. $3\frac{1}{8} \div \frac{5}{12} =$ $\frac{9}{10} \div 3\frac{3}{4} =$ $5\frac{3}{5} \div \frac{7}{15} =$ $\frac{5}{8} \div 2\frac{6}{7} =$

c. $4\frac{1}{2} \div 5\frac{1}{4} =$ $6\frac{2}{3} \div 4\frac{1}{6} =$ $9\frac{3}{4} \div 8\frac{1}{4} =$ $3\frac{1}{3} \div 1\frac{5}{6} =$

d. $8 \div 3\frac{1}{3} =$ $4\frac{1}{2} \div 3 =$ $5\frac{1}{7} \div 1\frac{1}{5} =$ $7\frac{1}{3} \div 2\frac{2}{3} =$

(2) **Divide and simplify.**

$7\frac{1}{5} \div \frac{4}{5} =$ $12 \div 5\frac{1}{3} =$ $8 \div 9\frac{3}{5} =$ $4\frac{1}{2} \div 5\frac{1}{4} =$

(3) **Divide. Simplify in the problem, if possible. Simplify answers.**

a. $22 \div 2\frac{1}{5} =$ $2\frac{1}{4} \div 15 =$ $7\frac{1}{2} \div 5\frac{5}{8} =$ $8\frac{1}{10} \div 9 =$ $12\frac{1}{2} \div \frac{15}{16} =$

b. $11\frac{2}{3} \div 4\frac{2}{3} =$ $\frac{3}{8} \div 12 =$ $24 \div \frac{15}{16} =$ $7\frac{1}{9} \div 1\frac{1}{7} =$ $4\frac{7}{8} \div 5\frac{1}{4} =$

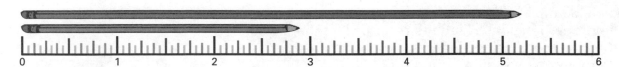

Most of the standard rulers that we use are divided into sixteenths of an inch.
The closer that we measure, the more precise the measurement.
As we increase our knowledge, we need to be more exact in our figures.

(1) **Use the illustration to answer the questions.**

a. Draw a line from the word to a correct marking on the ruler.

whole inches   half inches   quarter inches   eighth inches   sixteenth inches

b. The length of the ...

short pencil measured to the eighth of an inch is _____ inches.

long pencil measure to the sixteenth of an inch is _____ inches.

(2) **Use your ruler to measure each line.**

(3) **Use your ruler to measure each line. Write the measurement as a fraction (mixed number) and as a decimal.**

(4) **Write the measurement in standard measure.**

(5) **Write the measurement as a fraction or mixed number and as a decimal.**

(6) **Measure.**

(7) **Write the measurement as a fraction and as a decimal.**

Measurements can be simplified by subtraction.

5 ft. 19 in.	19 in. is more than 1 ft. (12 in. = 1 ft.)
− 12 in.	Subtract 12 in. (1 ft.)
7 in.	Now there are 7 in.
1 ft.	Add the 1 ft. (12 in.) that was subtracted to 5 ft.
6 ft. 7 in.	Bring down the 7 in. 5 ft. 19 in. = 6 ft. 7 in.

(1) **Simplify.**

a.　　18 yd. 5 ft. = _____　　　　pounds in a ton? _____

b.　　9 ft. 17 in. = _____　　　　tons in 5,000 lb? _____

Measurements can be simplified by division.

```
      7 ft. 8 in.
12) 92          92 in. is more than 1 ft.   (12 in. = 1 ft.)
    84          Divide 92 by 12 in.  There is a remainder of 8 in.
    ―
     8          92 in. = 7 ft. 8 in.
```

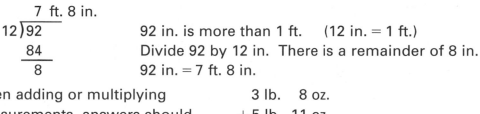

When adding or multiplying　　　　　3 lb.　8 oz.
measurements, answers should　　　+ 5 lb.　11 oz.
be stated in simplest terms.　　　　8 lb.　19 oz.
　　　　　　　　　　　　　　　　　+ 1 lb.(−16 oz.)
　　　　　　　　　　　　　　　　　9 lb.　3 oz.

(2) **Add or multiply. Simplify by subtraction or division.**

12 ft. 7 in.	3 mi. 1475 ft.	4 yd. 18 in.
+ 18 ft. 9 in.	× 5	× 4

To complete problems in subtraction of measurements,
we may need to borrow. Borrow 1 yd. Convert to 36 in.
Add 36 in. to 5 in. and subtract.

```
   12    41
  ̷1̷3 yd.  ̷5 in.
− 4 yd.  14 in.
  9 yd.  27 in.
```

To complete problems in division of measurements,
we may need to convert. 4 does not divide evenly into 9.
Change 1 lb. to 16 oz. and add to 7 oz. Divide.
There is a remainder of $\frac{3}{4}$ of an ounce.

```
        2 lb.  5 3/4 oz.
4) 9 lb.  7 oz.
   8      23
```

(3) **Subtract or divide. Borrow or convert in problems.**

5 ft. 7 in.	3) 5 yd. 2 ft.	2) 5 yd. 4 in.
− 2 ft. 8 in.		

(4) **Solve problems in standard measurements.**

12 lb. 7 oz.	2 T. 500 lb.	2) 6 T. 318 lb.
+ 8 lb. 14 oz.	× 5	

(1) **Simplify.**

    a. 7 gal. 6 qt. = _____

    b. 3 pt. 21 oz. = _____

(2) **Simplify.**

35 qt. = _____ gal. _____ qt.

(3) **Add. Simplify by subtraction.**

$$
\begin{array}{r}
2 \text{ pt.} \quad 7 \text{ oz.} \\
+ 7 \text{ pt.} \quad 13 \text{ oz.} \\
\hline
\end{array}
\qquad
\begin{array}{r}
5 \text{ gal.} \quad 2 \text{ qt.} \\
+ 8 \text{ gal.} \quad 3 \text{ qt.} \\
\hline
\end{array}
$$

(4) **Subtract or divide. Borrow or convert in problems.**

$$
\begin{array}{r}
9 \text{ lb.} \quad 3 \text{ oz.} \\
- 4 \text{ lb.} \quad 7 \text{ oz.} \\
\hline
\end{array}
\qquad
4\overline{)7 \text{ qt. 1pt.}}
\qquad
\begin{array}{r}
3 \text{ pt} \quad 1 \text{ cup} \\
\times \quad\quad 8 \\
\hline
\end{array}
$$

(5) **Complete the problems in measurements. Show answers in simplest terms.**

Sarah has a large cookie recipe that she wants to
cut in half. The recipe calls for 3 pints plus 1 cup
of milk. How much milk will Sarah need for her
cookies?   _____

Sam has 3 quarts plus 8 ounces of paint that he needs
to divide between 2 projects. How much paint can he
plan for each project?   _____

Using a 12 oz. glass, how many glasses of water
would be needed to fill a 6 qt. pitcher?   _____

(6) **Write the answer. How many ...**

cups in a pint? _____   cups in 3 pt.? _____

(7) **Solve problems in standard measurements. Simplify answers.**

$$
\begin{array}{r}
4 \text{ gal.} \quad 3 \text{ qt.} \\
+ 2 \text{ gal.} \quad 3 \text{ qt.} \\
\hline
\end{array}
\qquad
\begin{array}{r}
2 \text{ qt.} \quad 12 \text{ oz.} \\
\times \quad\quad 4 \\
\hline
\end{array}
\qquad
5\overline{)6 \text{ qt. 3 oz.}}
$$

The metric system ...

is based on ten: each unit is ten times greater or less than the next unit.
has three *basic units*: meter, liter, gram.
has six standard prefixes: milli, centi, deci, deca, hecto, kilo.

Chart of Prefixes

smallest	milli	- a unit contains 1,000
	centi	- a unit contains 100
	deci	- a unit contains 10
	unit	- meter, liter, gram
	deca	contains 10 units
	hecto	contains 100 units
largest	kilo	contains 1,000 units

(1)   Answer questions about the metric system.

a.   What number is the metric system based on?   _____

b.   Write the three basic units. Can you name the standard measurements they are similar to?

   _____ _____ ,   _____ _____ ,   _____ _____

c.   Write the prefixes in order from smallest to largest.

   _____ _____ _____ _____ _____ _____

d.   Write the abbreviation after each unit.

   millimeter _____   centimeter _____   decimeter _____   meter _____   kilometer_____

   milliliter _____   centiliter _____   deciliter _____   liter _____   kiloliter _____

   milligram _____   centigram _____   decigram _____   gram _____   kilogram_____

e.   To change meters to kilometers,   (multiply, divide).
     To change meters to centimeters,   (multiply, divide).

(2)   Express each number in terms of the units. *If the number is expressed in centimeters, then the number in ones' place is centimeters.* Identify the other units by working to the right or left of ones' place. Write how many ...

   kilometer   hectometer   decameter   meter   decimeter   centimeter   millimeter

a. 5.47 meters   _____

b. 38.6 centimeters   _____

c. 8.05 decimeters   _____

d. 5.476 kilometers   _____

e. 8.37 decameters   _____

The metric system is a base ten system.
Each unit is either ten times greater or ten times less than the next unit.

Chart of Prefixes

smallest	milli	- a unit contains 1,000
	centi	- a unit contains 100
	deci	- a unit contains 10
	unit	- meter, liter, gram
	deca	contains 10 units
	hecto	contains 100 units
largest	kilo	contains 1,000 units

(1) **Write the standard measure that is closest to the metric unit.**

meter _____   liter _____   gram _____

There are abbreviations for the most commonly used metric units.
Note: Abbreviations for deca and hecto are not on this chart.

mm - millimeter	cm - centimeter	dm - decimeter	m - meter	km - kilometer
ml - milliliter	cl- centiliter	dl - deciliter	L - liter	kl - kiloliter
mg - milligram	cg - centigram	dg - decigram	g - gram	kg - kilogram

multiply to change to smaller units
←

divide to change to larger units
→

We use the same steps to change metrics units, that we use to change standard units.
To change to *smaller* units, *multiply*; to change to *larger* units, *divide*.

(2) **Write M (multiply) or D (divide) to change units.**

a.   m to mm _____   dg to cg _____   L to kl _____

b.   dm to m _____   cl to ml _____   kg to g _____

c.   g to mg _____   dm to mm _____   dl to L _____

Each time we move ...
←   →
one unit,   we multiply or divide by 10.   m to cm = 2 units   m to km = 3 units
two units,   we multiply or divide by 100.   multiply by 100   divide by 1,000
three units,   we multiply or divide by 1,000.

(3) **Write the multiplier or divisor (10, 100, 1,000).**
Remember! There are 3 units from meter, liter, gram to kilometer, kiloliter, or kilogram.

a.   m to dm _____   L to kl _____   dg to g _____

b.   dl to ml _____   cm to mm _____   cg to g _____

c.   mg to g _____   dl to cl _____   m to km _____

To multiply or divide by 10, 100, 1,000, count zeros and move the decimal ...
to the right to multiply, to the left to divide.

(4) **Multiply or divide.**

a. $10 \times 8 =$ _____ $43 \div 100 =$ _____ $1,000 \times 5 =$ _____ $438 \div 10 =$ _____

b. $100 \times 72 =$ _____ $9 \div 1,000 =$ _____ $100 \times 63 =$ _____ $7.5 \div 10 =$ _____

c. $10 \times 2.30 =$ _____ $.3 \div 100 =$ _____ $1,000 \times .007 =$ _____ $4.59 \div 1,000 =$ _____

In the metric system, we can change
from one unit of measure to another by multiplying or dividing by 10, 100, 1,000, …

How many milligrams equal 6 decigrams?   6 dg = _____ mg

To change to a lower unit - multiply.   ? × 6 dg = _____ mg

To move two units multiply by 100.   100 × 6 dg = 600 mg

(1) Write the value.

a.   3 cm = _____ mm   18 km = _____ m   73 m = _____ dm

b.   5,000 L = _____ kl   23 cl = _____ dl   14 L = _____ ml

c.   2 kg = _____ g   1,346 mg = _____ g   90 cg = _____ dg

```
0    1    2    3    4    5    6    7    8    9    10
|iiii|iiii|iiii|iiii|iiii|iiii|iiii|iiii|iiii|iiii|
```

1 decimeter
10 centimeters
100 millimeters

(2) Use the illustration of the decimeter to answer the questions.

a.   How many centimeters are there in a decimeter? _____

Write a fraction that compares 1 centimeter to a decimeter. _____

Write a decimal that compares 1 centimeter to a decimeter. _____

Write the equivalent.   .1 dm = _____ cm

b.   How many millimeters are there in a decimeter? _____

Write a fraction that compares 1 millimeter to a decimeter. _____

Write a decimal that compares 1 millimeter to a decimeter. _____

Write the equivalent.   .01 dm = _____ mm

c.   How many millimeters are there in a centimeter? _____

Write a fraction that compares 1 millimeter to a centimeter. _____

Write a decimal that compares 1 millimeter to a centimeter. _____

Write the equivalent.   .1 cm = _____ mm

d.   Write a fraction that compares 5 millimeters to a centimeter. _____

Write a decimal that compares 5 millimeters to a centimeter. _____

Write the equivalent.   .5 cm = _____ mm

In standard measure,
smaller units are expressed in words.   The board is 7 yd. 9 in. long.

In metric measure,
smaller units are expressed with a decimal point.   The board is 7.8 m long. 7 m 8 dm

(3) Each measure is expressed with a decimal point.
Write the value as shown in the shaded part of the example.
Remember! There are 3 units from meter, liter, gram to kilometer, kiloliter, or kilogram.

a.   3.5 L = _____   4.3 cm = _____   2.7 dm = _____

b.   9.45 m = _____   6.23 dl = _____   3.4 g = _____

c.   8.006 km = _____   2.005 kg = _____   7.009 kl = _____

d.   2.07 dm = _____   2.1 L = _____   3.006 kg = _____

1 Find the perimeter and area. One unit of measurement is shown for each figure.

1 square foot →

perimeter _____

area _____

1 square yard →

perimeter _____

area _____

2 Find the perimeter and area of each polygon. Label answers in proper units.

				Perimeter	Area
A square	side	=	2 yards	_____	_____
A rectangle	length	=	8 yards		
	width	=	4 yards	_____	_____
A rectangle	length	=	23 inches		
	width	=	9 inches	_____	_____
A rectangle	length	=	14 feet		
	width	=	5 feet	_____	_____
A square	side	=	6 feet	_____	_____
A square	side	=	9 meters	_____	_____
A rectangle	length	=	21 centimeters		
	width	=	8 centimeters	_____	_____
A rectangle	length	=	12 meters		
	width	=	8 meters	_____	_____
A rectangle	length	=	16 feet		
	width	=	6 feet	_____	_____
A square	side	=	10 miles	_____	_____
A square	side	=	4 centimeters	_____	_____
A square	side	=	8 kilometers	_____	_____
A rectangle	length	=	50 kilometers		
	width	=	8 kilometers	_____	_____
A rectangle	length	=	28 inches		
	width	=	6 inches	_____	_____

We can find the area of a parallelogram by using a formula.
Any side of the parallelogram may be its base.
The height is the length of a straight line perpendicular
   to the base drawn to the opposite side.
The formula for the area of a parallelogram is $A = bh$.

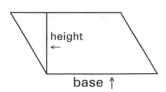

height

base ↑

(1)   Find the missing measurements of a parallelogram that measures...

a. $b = 7$ in. $h = 3$ in.

b. $b = 9$ m $h = 8$ m

c. $b = 12$ ft. $h = 11$ ft.

$A =$ _____

$A =$ _____

$A =$ _____

(2)   Find the area of the plane shape by using the formula.

parallelogram $b = 7$ in. $h = 3$ in.

(3)   Write the formula for the area of each plane shape. Solve. Label answers.

parallelogram $b = 3$ yd. $h = 2$ yd. $A =$ _____   _____

parallelogram $b = 5$ yd. $h = 6$ yd. $A =$ _____   _____

The perimeter and area of a regular polygon (triangle) can be measured with a formula.

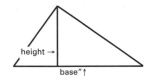

The perimeter of a triangle is equal to the sum of its sides.

The illustration shows the right triangle as one-half of a rectangle. The area of the triangle is one-half the area of the rectangle, or one-half the base times the height.

$$P = S + S + S$$
$$P = 12 + 18 + 21$$
$$P = 51"$$

$$A = \frac{1}{2}BH$$
$$A = \frac{1}{2}(18 \cdot 12)$$
$$A = \frac{1}{2} \cdot 216$$
$$A = 108 \text{ sq. in.}$$

The height of any triangle is measured by a perpendicular line drawn from the highest point of the triangle to its base.

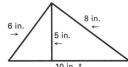

(1) **Use the formulas to solve the problems.**

a. Find the perimeter and area measurement of the triangle.

perimeter = _____

area = _____

b. What is the perimeter of an equilateral triangle with sides measuring 7 in.? _____

c. What is the perimeter of an isosceles triangle with one side that measures 5 ft. and two sides that measure 11 ft. each? _____

d. What is the area of a triangle with a base of 3 ft. and height of 6 ft.? _____

e. What is the area of a triangle with a base of 14 ft. and height of 7 ft.? _____

f. Two sides of a triangle measure 9 in. and 7 in.
The perimeter of the triangle measures 23 in.
What is the measure of the third side of the triangle? _____

g. The height of a triangle measures 4 in.
The area of the triangle measures 18 sq. in.
What is the measure of the base of the triangle? _____

h. The area of the triangle is 42 sq. in.
The base is 12 in.
What is the height? _____

i. The area of the triangle is 18 sq. ft.
The height is 9 in.
What is the base? _____

(2) **Write the word that the variable represents in the formula.**
Write what the formula is for.

c. $A = \frac{1}{2}bh$ A _____ b _____ h _____ _____

A circle is a plane shape. It can be measured for its circumference and its area.
The special ratio between the diameter of a circle and its circumference is 3.14:1.
The mathematics symbol pi(π) represents the value 3.14.
The formula for the circumference of a circle is 3.14 *times* the diameter or $C = \pi d$.
Because the diameter is twice the size of the radius,
   the formula is sometimes shown as 2 *times* 3.14 *times* the radius or $C = 2\pi r$.

(1) **Solve for C** using the formula $C = \pi d$.   **Solve for C** using the formula $C = 2\pi r$.
The diameter is 9 in.   The radius is 7 in.

The special ratio between the radius $A = \pi r^2$ (radius = 7 in.)
of a circle and its area is $3.14:1^2$. $A = 3.14 \cdot 7^2$
The formula for the area of a circle is $A = 3.14 \cdot 49$
3.14 times the radius squared or $A = \pi r^2$. $A = 153.86$ *rounded to* 154 sq. in.

(2) **Solve for A** using the formula $A = \pi r^2$. The radius is ...

a. 8 in.   b. 4 ft.   c. 3 yd.   d. 6 mi.

(3) **The formula for the ...**

circumference of a circle is $C = $ _____ or $C = $ _____.

area of a circle is $A = $ _____.

(4) **Find the circumference and area of a circle with a ...**

a. diameter of 6 in.   b. radius of 5 in.

C _____ A _____ C _____ A _____

(5) What is the measure of
the radius of the circle? _____ the diameter? _____

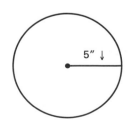

5" ↓

(6) What is the circumference
            of the circle? _____   area? _____

(1) Each face of the cube in the illustration is lettered.
Suppose the pattern shown were folded into the shape of the cube.
How would each face of the pattern be lettered?
Side ABCD is started for you.

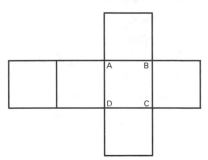

Volume is the amount a solid shape will hold or the space it displaces.
Volume may be measured in cubic inches, feet, yards, miles.

(2) **The illustration shows a rectangular prism. Answer the questions.**

a. The base of the rectangular prism is covered with cubic inches.
How many cubic inches are there? _____

b. Measure the number of cubic inches along the length of the base _____ and the width of the base _____.
Multiply. What is your answer? _____

c. Suppose you decide to fill the prism with cubic inches. How many layers would you need? _____

d. How many cubic inches would you have altogether in the prism? _____

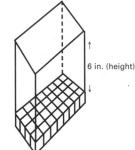

6 in. (height)

The formula for the volume of a rectangular prism is V = L × W × H.
Measurements are always in cubic units.

(3) **Find the volume of the rectangular prisms. Label answers correctly.**

a.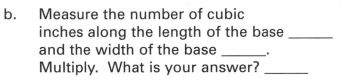
6 ft. →   ← 3 ft.
↑ 8 ft.

b.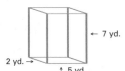
← 7 yd.
2 yd. →
↑ 5 yd.

c.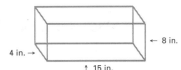
← 8 in.
4 in. →
↑ 15 in.

_____   _____   _____

The formula for the volume of a square prism is V = S × S × S or V = S³

(4) **Find the volume of the square prisms. Label answers correctly.**

a.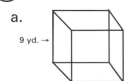
9 yd. →

b.
← 10 in.

c.
↑ 14 ft.

_____   _____   _____

Surface area.
Look carefully at the 3-dimensional figure.

Write the answers below.

Width = 12 in.
Length = 15 in.
Height = 18 in.

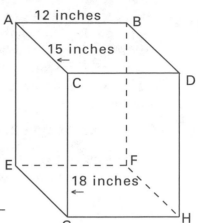

(1) Find the area of
rectangle ABCD. _____

(2) Find the area of rectangle ACGE.
(Label correctly.) _____

(3) Find the area of rectangle CDHG. _____

(4) Rectangle ABCD is congruent to rectangle _____.

Rectangle ACGE is congruent to rectangle _____.

Rectangle CDHG is congruent to rectangle _____.

(5) Two times the area of rectangle ABDC.   _____ x 2 = _____

Two times the area of rectangle ACGE.   _____ x 2 = _____

Two times the area of rectangle CDHG.   _____ x 2 = _____

(6) Add the surface area of the six sides
to find the total surface area.   _____

(7) Find the surface area of the two boxes.

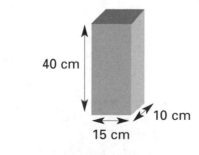

40 cm
15 cm
10 cm

Front	40 cm x 15 cm = _____	x 2 = _____
Top	15 cm x 10 cm = _____	x 2 = _____
Side	40 cm x 10 cm = _____	x 2 = _____
	Total	_____

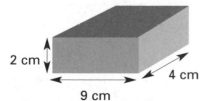

2 cm
9 cm
4 cm

Front	2 cm x 9 cm = _____	x 2 = _____
Top	9 cm x 4 cm = _____	x 2 = _____
Side	2 cm x 4 cm = _____	x 2 = _____
	Total	_____

Because the earth rotates once every twenty-four hours, various parts of the world experience day and night at different times. If clocks were set at the same time in all parts of the world, some people would be working when their clocks were set at midnight and some people would be sleeping at noon. To solve this problem, the earth was divided into 24 **time zones** to correspond to the 24 hours in the day. These international time zones are shown on maps and globes.

Refer to a world atlas or map on International Time Zones.

Each one of the 24 lines that begin at the North Pole comes together at the South Pole. These are lines of **longitude**.

A **meridian** is an imaginary circle or half-circle that passes around the earth through the North and South Poles. Lines of longitude are examples of meridians. There are two special meridians.

The **prime meridian** is the longitude line at 0°. It passes through Greenwich, England and is called the starting point. The **International Date Line** is the longitude line at 180°. This is the line where the date changes.

When the International Date Line is crossed going west ←, the date is one day later.
When it is crossed going east →, the date becomes one day earlier.

(1) **Follow the map to answer the questions. A plane prepares to leave …**

a. Sydney, Australia at 10:00 A.M. on November 8 and fly east to Los Angeles, CA. What is the time and date in Los Angeles? _____

b. Chicago, IL at 6:00 A.M. on May 3 and fly west to Tokyo, Japan. What is the time and date in Tokyo? _____

c. New York, NY at 7:00 P.M. on April 1 and fly east to Berlin, Germany. What is the time and date in Berlin? _____

(2) **How many time zones are there in …**

a. Australia? _____ b. Africa? _____ c. India? _____

d. South America? _____ e. Mexico? _____ f. Canada? _____

The time zones in the U.S. are Eastern, Central, Mountain, Pacific, Alaskan, Hawaiian.

(3) **Answer questions about time zones. If it is …**

a. 5:00 P.M. CST, it is _____ EST. b. 7:15 A.M. AST, it is _____ MST

c. 4:00 P.M. HST, it is _____ PST. d. 1:30 P.M. EST, it is _____ AST

e. 11:45 A.M. EST, it is _____ AST. f. 3:00 A.M. HST, it is _____ EST

g. 1:00 A.M. PST, it is _____ MST. h. 8:45 P.M. PST, it is _____ CST

i. 3:00 P.M. on July 8 in the Eastern Time Zone,
what is the time and date in Alaska? _____ Hawaii? _____

j. 1:00 A.M. on March 15 in the Eastern Time Zone,
what is the time and date in California? _____ Hawaii? _____

① **The drawing below illustrates three circles: A, B, and C.**

a. Are the circles congruent? _____ Are they similar? _____

b. How many degrees in ... circle A _____, B, _____, C, _____?

c. Using point E as a vertex, draw a 90° angle inside circle A that extends to the perimeter of the circle. Label the points that intersect circle A as M and N.

d. Using a pencil, trace the shortest path along the perimeter (circumference) of circle A from point M to point N. An **arc** is a curved section (line segment) of the perimeter of a circle. You have traced arc MN.

e. Draw a straight line connecting points M and N on circle A. A **chord** is a straight line (line segment) drawn between two points on a circle.

f. Extend lines EM and EN so that they intersect circle B.
Mark the points of intersection as R and S.
        How many degrees are there in angle RES? _____
Extend lines ER and ES so that they intersect circle C.
Mark the points of intersection as X and Y.
        How many degrees are there in angle XEY? _____

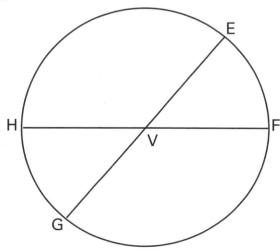

g. Draw chords RS and XY.
Write the symbol >, <, or = to describe the relationship between ...

Arc MN _____ Arc RS _____ Arc XY

    Chord MN _____ Chord RS _____ Chord XY

        Angle MEN _____ Angle RES _____ Angle XEY

h. The number of degrees in the angles in the circles remained _____ but

the distance between the sides _____ as the size of the circle increased.

② **Use a protractor to measure the angles in the circle.**

∠EVF = _____

∠EVH = _____

∠GVH = _____

∠GVF = _____

∠EVF + ∠EVH + ∠GVH + ∠GVF =

_____ + _____ + _____ + _____ = _____

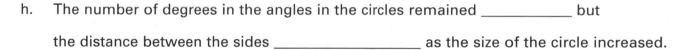

Construct an Angle Bisector

Given an angle, construct a ray that bisects the angle.

To construct: $\overrightarrow{BD}$ that bisects $\angle ABC$

Steps: Using a convenient radius and the vertex of the angle
B as center, construct an arc that intersects both sides
of the angle. Call these points X and Y. Using points
X and Y as centers and a radius greater than half of
XY, construct two arcs that intersect in the interior
of $\angle ABC$. Call this point D. Draw $\overrightarrow{BD}$. $\overrightarrow{BD}$ is the
ray that bisects $\angle ABC$.

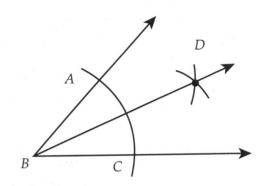

(1) **Construct the bisector of the following angles.**

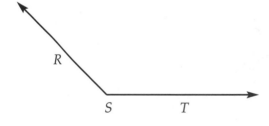

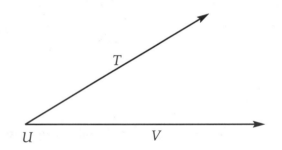

(2) **Divide angle ABC into four equal angles.**

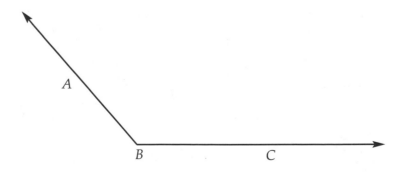

To construct a regular hexagon where the length of a side is known, follow these steps.

1. Construct a circle with a radius the same length as the side of the hexagon.

2. Using the same radius, place the compass point on the circle and mark off all the way around the circle. Name these points *A, B, C, D, E,* and *F.*

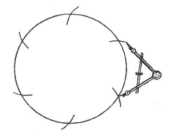

3. Now connect these points in order and you have a regular hexagon.

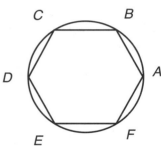

(1) **Construct regular hexagons with sides of the given length. Use another sheet of paper.**

   a. side = 1 in.   b. side = 2 cm   c. side = $\frac{3}{4}$ "

   d. side = 2.5 cm   e. side = $\frac{1}{2}$ "

To draw an equilateral line with length AB, follow these steps.

1. Draw a work line and put a point *A* on it.

    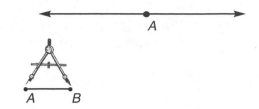

2. Measure $\overline{AB}$ with your compass by putting the point at *A* and the pencil at *B*.

    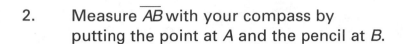

3. Without changing the legs of the compass for the next three steps, put the point of the compass down at point *A* of your work line. Make a mark across the work line where the pencil touches. This step will give you point *B*.

    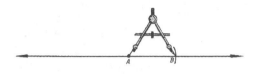

4. Put the compass point at B. Make an arc. Vertex *C* will be someplace on this arc. The next step will locate point *C*.

    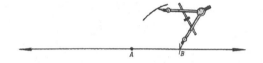

5. Place the point of the compass at *A* and make an arc that crosses the arc from B. *C* is located where the two arcs cross each other.

6. Finally, connect *A* to *C* and *B* to *C* to finish the triangle.

    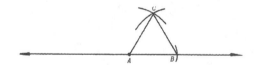

(1) **Construct equilateral triangles with sides of the following lengths. Use another sheet of paper.**

a. 1"

b. $1\frac{1}{2}$"

c. $\frac{3}{4}$"

d. 4 cm

e. 3 cm

f. 5 cm

g. 3"

h. $2\frac{1}{2}$"

i. $1\frac{3}{4}$"

To construct a square, the length of one side must be known.

With a ruler and compass, follow these steps.

1.   Draw a work line and label a point *A* on it.

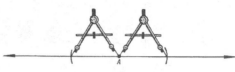

2.   Place the point of the compass at point *A* and make an arc on each side of *A*.

3.   Spread the points of the compass a little more than they were spread for Step 2. Place the point of the compass at the new points on either side of *A* and make crossing arcs above the line.

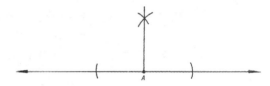

4.   Connect this point to *A*, and you have made your right angle.

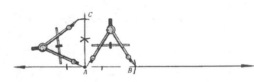

5.   Measure the side of your square with the compass and mark off the sides from point *A* on the work line and on the right angle ray.

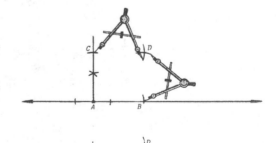

6.   Using the marks on the work line and the right angle ray, make arcs that cross. Keep the compass points spread to the length of the side.

7.   Then connect the points.

(1)   **Construct squares with sides of the given length, using a compass. Use another sheet of paper.**

a. ⌐————⌐

b. ⌐—————————⌐

c. ⌐————————⌐

d. ⌐————————————⌐

Ratio expresses a relationship between two numbers.
  The numbers can be written as fractions.
  Equivalent fractions have the same ratio.
  The fractions are in **proportion** to each other.

$$4:5 \qquad\qquad 10:20$$
$$\frac{4}{5} \qquad\qquad \frac{10}{20}$$
$$\frac{4}{5} \qquad\qquad \frac{10}{20}$$

4 is to 5   as   10 is to 20.

There are 15 birds sitting on the first fence.   6 are robins.   9 are wrens.
We can write ratios comparing each kind of $\frac{6}{15}$ are robins. $\frac{9}{15}$ are wrens.
bird to the total number of birds on the fence.

Ratios may be simplified. $\frac{6}{15}$ robins $= \frac{2}{5}$ robins $\frac{9}{15}$ wrens $= \frac{3}{5}$ wrens

There are 20 birds sitting on the second fence.
If the ratios stay the same ($\frac{2}{3}$ robins, $\frac{3}{5}$ wrens), $\frac{2}{5} = \frac{8}{20}$ $\frac{3}{5} = \frac{12}{20}$
how many are robins and how many are wrens?
Write the new denominator of 20 (20 birds).
Solve for equivalent fractions.   8 are robins.   12 are wrens.

1 **Using the ratio 2:3, how many chocolate chip cookies would there be on a plate of ...**

9 cookies _____   15 cookies _____   21 cookies _____   27 cookies _____

2 **There are 24 crayons on the table. 4 are blue, 12 are green, and 8 are orange.**

a. Write each color as a ratio simplified.   blue _____ green _____ orange _____

b. The next table has 36 crayons in the same ratio.
Write the number of crayons for each color.   blue _____ green _____ orange _____

3 **There are 18 crayons on the table. 3 are red, 6 are purple, and 9 are yellow.**

a. Write each color as a ratio simplified.   red _____ purple _____ yellow _____

b. The next table has 36 crayons in the same ratio.
Write the number of crayons for each color.   red _____ purple _____ yellow _____

4 **Solve for missing numbers. Be sure to write the missing number (N) in the correct place in the ratio.**

a. The ratio of peanuts to candy is 4:5. If there are 40 pieces
of candy in the bag, how many peanuts are there?   _____

b. The ratio of boys to girls in the class is 7:8. If there are
32 girls in the class, how many boys are there in the class?   _____

c. The ratio dogs to cats at the pet show was 2:3. If there
were 12 dogs at the pet show, how many cats were there?   _____

d. The ratio of rainy days to sunny days is 1:3. If it rained
6 days in the month, how many days were sunny?   _____

We can use cross multiplication to solve for a missing numerator (N). Multiply opposite numerators and denominators. Divide both sides of the equation by the same number. Substitute 8 for N in the equation. Both fractions simplify to $\frac{2}{3}$.

$$\frac{6}{9} = \frac{N}{12}$$
$$6 \times 12 = N \times 9$$
$$72 = N \times 9$$
$$72 \div 9 = N \times 9 \;(\div 9)$$
$$8 = N$$
$$\frac{6}{9} = \frac{8}{12} = \boxed{\frac{2}{3}}$$

(1) Use cross multiplication to find the missing number. Substitute. Prove your answer. Show the fractions are equivalent by simplifying.

a. $\frac{2}{4} = \frac{N}{10}$ _____ $\frac{2}{6} = \frac{N}{9}$ _____ $\frac{6}{8} = \frac{N}{16}$ _____ $\frac{2}{10} = \frac{N}{15}$ _____

_____ = N   _____ = N   _____ = N   _____ = N

b. $\frac{4}{6} = \frac{N}{9}$ _____ $\frac{2}{8} = \frac{N}{12}$ _____ $\frac{9}{15} = \frac{N}{10}$ _____ $\frac{2}{12} = \frac{N}{18}$ _____

_____ = N   _____ = N   _____ = N   _____ = N

c. $\frac{8}{12} = \frac{N}{18}$ _____ $\frac{15}{25} = \frac{N}{10}$ _____ $\frac{3}{24} = \frac{N}{16}$ _____ $\frac{5}{20} = \frac{N}{24}$ _____

_____ = N   _____ = N   _____ = N   _____ = N

There are 5 bananas on the counter. 2 are ripe and 3 are green.

(2) Write four possible ways to show the relationship of ripe and green bananas as ratios.

a. ripe to all bananas _____   b. green to all bananas _____

c. ripe to green bananas _____   d. green to ripe bananas _____

Suppose there are 20 bananas in a bag. The ratios are the same as above.
We can tell the number of ripe and green bananas in the bag using a proportion.

Write the ratio for ripe to total bananas as a fraction.
Write an equivalent fraction.
Write "2 is to 5 (total) as x is to 20 (total)."
Solve using cross multiplication.
There are 8 ripe bananas. There are 12 green bananas.

$$\frac{2}{5}$$
$$\frac{2}{5} = \frac{x}{20} \quad \begin{matrix}\text{(ripe)}\\ \text{(total)}\end{matrix}$$
$$40 = 5x$$
$$40 \div 5 = 5(\div 5) \cdot x$$
$$8 = x \qquad 20 - 8 = 12$$

(3) Use the ratios from ex. 2 to find the missing numbers (x).

a. Find the number of green and ripe bananas using the ratio of green to all bananas. There are 25 bananas in the bag.

green _____ ripe _____

b. Find the number of ripe bananas and total bananas using the ratio of ripe to green bananas. There are 9 green bananas in the bag.

ripe _____ total _____

Problem solving requires us to ...
define and state a problem clearly,
gather data to solve a problem,
draw conclusions based on the results of data collection.

Probability tells us the possibility that something will or will not happen.
The patterns of probability are an aid in problem solving.
We can study the probability of any one object being selected from a group of objects.

The group of objects for this lesson is the word: M A T H E M A T I C

(1) Establish ratios.

a. How many letters are there in the word? _____

b. Write the number of times each letter appears in the word.

A _____   C _____   E _____   H _____   I _____   M _____   T _____

c. Write ratios. Compare each letter to the total letters in the word.

A _____   C _____   E _____   H _____   I _____   M _____   T _____

d. Write the ratios in percent.

A _____   C _____   E _____   H _____   I _____   M _____   T _____

Prediction means to tell in advance the probability of an event or occurrence.
A **random selection** is an item that has been selected at random or without deliberate choice.

e. Based on the ratios, predict which letter(s) in a random selection has the ...

greatest probability of being chosen. _____

least probability of being chosen. _____

f. Arrange the letters in order of
greatest to least probability. ____ ____ ____ ____ ____ ____ ____

We can try to verify the probability.
Draw 10 one-inch squares on cardboard. Write one of the letters in
each square. Cut out and place the squares in a paper bag. Mix well.

To verify the probability, we will make random selections from the bag.

(2) Answer the questions.

Suppose the letter M is drawn out of the bag and not put back in.

a. Would that change the ratio for the next drawing? _____

b. What would be the ratio of M to the total? _____

c. Would that also change the ratios of the other letters? _____

The word "of" tells us to multiply.
  To find the percent of a number,
  change the percent to a decimal
  and multiply.
35% of 20 is 7. 18% of 35 is 6.3.

35% of 20 =	20	18% of 35 =	35
	.35		.18
	100		280
	600		350
	7.00 *or* 7		6.30 *or* 6.3

Percent means part of a whole.
If we are solving for a percent of a number, the answer will be less than the number.

(1) **Find the amount. Change percent to a decimal and multiply.**

a.   20% of 54 = _____   45% of 32 = _____   90% of 46 = _____

b.   52% of 16 = _____   16% of 81 = _____   27% of 65 = _____

c.   73% of 29 = _____   40% of 60 = _____   75% of 36 = _____

We have learned fraction equivalents for decimals and percent.
Finding the percent of a number may be
simplified by using equivalent fractions.
We may solve for 25% of 60 using decimals,
or we may solve for 25% of 60 using fractions.

60 *or* 15
.25
300
1200
15.00

$$\frac{1}{\underset{1}{4}} \times \frac{\overset{15}{\cancel{60}}}{1} = 15$$

(2) **Find the amount. Change percent to a common fraction and multiply.**

a.   20% of 45 = _____   75% of 32 = _____   87.5% of 64 = _____

b.   60% of 55 = _____   25% of 16 = _____ $33\frac{1}{3}$% of 18 = _____

c.   50% of 92 – _____   40% of 75 = _____ $66\frac{2}{3}$% of 36 = _____

Percent is a special ratio.
Percent always compares a number to 100.
The symbol for percent is %.

There are a 100 books on the shelf. 40 of the books are science books.
The ratio is 40:100. 40% of the books are science books.

(1) Write the percent for each of the ratios.

32:100 _____   7:100 _____   94:100 _____   52:100 _____   5:100 _____   11:100 _____

The ratio 40:100 can be written
as a fraction, a decimal, or a percent. $40:100 = \frac{40}{100} = .40 = 40\%$

(2) Write the ratios as a fraction, a decimal, and a percent.

a.   68:100 _____ _____ _____   4:100 _____ _____ _____

b.   15:100 _____ _____ _____   70:100 _____ _____ _____

Any ratio, fraction, or decimal with a denominator
of 100, can be written as a percent. $8:100 = 8\%$ $\frac{15}{100} = 15\%$ $.74 = 74\%$

(3) Write the values as percent.

a.   .46 _____   3:100 _____ $\frac{51}{100}$ _____   82:100 _____   .27 _____

b.   2:100 _____ $\frac{61}{100}$ _____   14:100 _____ $\frac{91}{100}$ _____   .03 _____

(4) Write each percent as a ratio, fraction, and decimal.

a.   53% _____ _____ _____   16% _____ _____ _____

b.   9% _____ _____ _____   74% _____ _____ _____

(5) Write each fraction as a decimal with a denominator of 100. Write as a percent.

a. $\frac{1}{2} =$ _____ _____ $\frac{1}{4} =$ _____ _____ $\frac{3}{4} =$ _____ _____

b. $\frac{1}{5} =$ _____ _____ $\frac{2}{5} =$ _____ _____ $\frac{3}{5} =$ _____ _____ $\frac{4}{5} =$ _____ _____

c. $\frac{1}{8} =$ _____ _____ $\frac{3}{8} =$ _____ _____ $\frac{5}{8} =$ _____ _____ $\frac{7}{8} =$ _____ _____

d. $\frac{1}{3} =$ _____ _____ $\frac{2}{3} =$ _____ _____ $\frac{1}{6} =$ _____ _____ $\frac{5}{6} =$ _____ _____

© MCMXCIX, Alpha Omega Publications, Inc.

Fractions, ratios, decimals, and percent are interchangeable.
Each one can be written as or converted to the other.

$5:8 = \frac{5}{8}$

    Ratios can be written as *fractions*. The first number is
the numerator, the second number is the denominator.
Fractions can be converted to *decimals*.
Divide the denominator into the numerator.
Decimals can be converted to *percent*.
Round the denominator to hundredths.

$\frac{5}{8} = 8\overline{)5.000}\;^{.625}$

.625 = .63 = 63%

(1) **Rewrite or convert each number.**

	ratio	fraction	decimal	percent
a.	7:8	_____	_____	_____
b.	3:5	_____	_____	_____
c.	1:4	_____	_____	_____
d.	3:10	_____	_____	_____

Some common fractions should be committed to memory.
You should be able to write each fraction as a ratio, decimal, or percent.

Remember! Percent has a denominator of hundredths.
   Write an equivalent decimal by adding a zero,
         or rounding to hundredths' place.

.5 = .50 = 50%
.625 = .63 = 63%

(2) **Rewrite or convert each fraction.**
If you have not committed the answer to memory, find it through division.

		ratio	decimal	percent			ratio	decimal	percent
a.	$\frac{1}{2}=$	_____	_____	_____		$\frac{1}{4}=$	_____	_____	_____
b.	$\frac{3}{4}=$	_____	_____	_____		$\frac{1}{5}=$	_____	_____	_____
c.	$\frac{2}{5}=$	_____	_____	_____		$\frac{3}{5}=$	_____	_____	_____
d.	$\frac{4}{5}=$	_____	_____	_____		$\frac{1}{8}=$	_____	_____	_____
e.	$\frac{3}{8}=$	_____	_____	_____		$\frac{5}{8}=$	_____	_____	_____
f.	$\frac{7}{8}=$	_____	_____	_____		$\frac{1}{3}=$	_____	_____	_____
g.	$\frac{2}{3}=$	_____	_____	_____		$\frac{1}{6}=$	_____	_____	_____
h.	$\frac{5}{6}=$	_____	_____	_____					

What is 5% of $62.25?

Change the percent to a decimal and then multiply.

$$0.05 \times \$62.25 =$$

(1) **Find 1%. Round to the nearest hundredth.**

$102.10 $1,234.60 $56.32 $0.95

(2) **Find 10%. Round to the nearest hundredth.**

$201.01 $6,412.30 $63.52 $0.73

(3) **Find the percentages.**

5% of 85.6   63% of 2.74   73% of .548

2.8% of 6.731   40.5% of 237   28% of 3,654

6% of $9.37   49% of 0.0832   4% of $659.00

(1) Answer questions about percent.

a. Jason has completed 75% of the 120-page project.
How many pages has Jason completed? _____

b. 20% of the 25 pencils in the box need to be sharpened.
How many pencils need to be sharpened? _____

c. 18% of the 400 pieces of the puzzle were missing.
How many pieces of the puzzle were missing? _____

d. Jason drank 50% of a quart of milk.
How many ounces of milk did Jason drink? _____

e. There were 24 cookies in the jar on Thursday.
On Friday, 25% of the cookies were missing.
How many cookies were in the jar on Friday? _____

f. There were 40 people at a meeting on Monday.
15% more people attended the meeting on Tuesday.
How many more people were at the meeting on Tuesday? _____

(2) Answer questions about percent.

a. Jeff has reached 75% of his goal of selling 36 magazine subscriptions.
How many subscriptions has Jason sold? _____

b. There were 60 cars in the used car lot on Monday.
There were 25% more cars on the lot on Tuesday.
How many more cars were on the lot on Tuesday? _____

(3) Solve the multi-operation problem.

James went to the mall. He bought a T-shirt for $8.32,
a pair of gloves for $5.16, and notebook paper for $3.29.
If the sales tax was 7.5%, how much money did James
spend? _____

(4) Write the answer.

a. The house buyer paid a commission of 10% of the value of the house.
The house sold for $123,000. What was the amount of the commission? _____

b. Jason charged each person for 25% of the cost of the sub sandwich.
If the sandwich cost $6.24, what was the charge per person? _____

Model: Josephine works for a clothing store that offers its employees a 5% discount. Josephine buys a dress with a selling price of $47.00. The discount is $47.00 x 0.05 = $2.35. Josephine pays $47.00 − $2.35 = $44.65 for the dress.

(1) **Solve the following problems.**

a. Sam's Discount Store offers a 2% discount for paying cash. How much would Joan pay if she pays cash for a set of skillets priced at $38.95?

_____

b. Fairhaven Church buys four tires for its van. Each tire is priced at $43.95. The tire store offers churches a 3.5% discount. How much does Fairhaven Church pay in all?

_____

c. Ink, Inc., offers pencils at $1.10 per dozen, with a 1.5% discount for purchases of more than 12 dozen. If Jerry buys 19 dozen for his club, how much does he pay?

_____

d. Quality Merchandising offers a 2% discount on all purchases if payment is made within 10 days of delivery. Rosemarie orders a couch from Quality. The couch is marked $104.89. It is delivered on May 12, and Rosemarie mails a check to Quality on May 15. How much does Rosemarie pay for the couch?

_____

The numbers that you have learned about have been divided into two categories, whole numbers and fractions. Decimals belong in the category of fractions. The special name for a whole number is **integer**. Integer means *whole*. Integers may be described as **positive integers** or **negative integers**. The addition symbol (+) is used to describe a positive integer. The subtraction symbol (-) is used to describe a negative integer.

The number line illustrates positive and negative integers. Zero (0) is an integer. It is neither positive or negative. The integers to the right of zero (0) are positive, to the left of zero (0) are negative. A move to the right is positive, to the left is negative.

(1) Follow the number line. Write the location (the integer) on the number line.

a. Start at 0. Move right 4 places. _____ Move left 7 places. _____

b. Start at -1. Move left 3 places. _____ Move right 6 places. _____

c. Start at 0. Move +5 places. _____ Move -7 places. _____

d. Start at 0. Move -6 places. _____ Move +3 places. _____

There are two ways to express an equation. We can say …

$5 - 3 = 2$ *or* $5 + (-3) = 2$

"five minus three equals two" "five plus negative three equals two"

$4 - 7 = -3$ *or* $4 + (-7) = -3$

"four minus seven equals negative three" "four plus negative seven equals negative three"

If we do not say positive or negative, we assume the integer is positive.

(2) Write the answers to the equations.

a. $3 + 2 =$ _____ $(-1) + (-4) =$ _____ $(-3) + 5 =$ _____

b. $4 + 1 =$ _____ $(-2) + (-3) =$ _____ $5 + (-6) =$ _____

c. $2 + 5 =$ _____ $(-2) + (-2) =$ _____ $(-4) + 1 =$ _____

d. $1 + 6 =$ _____ $(-5) + (-4) =$ _____ $3 + (-2) =$ _____

There are patterns in adding positive and negative integers.

(3) Review the answers to ex. 2. Write *positive* or *negative*.

a. When adding two positive integers, the answer is always _____.

b. When adding two negative integers, the answer is always _____.

c. When adding a positive integer and a negative integer, the answer may be _____ or _____.

Two numbers are *opposites* when they are the same number of units from zero, but one is to the left of zero and the other is to the right of zero.

(1) Write the opposite of each number.

5 _____   -1_____

18 _____   173_____

-3 _____   -325_____

40 _____   9_____

-22 _____   -15_____

To *subtract* two numbers, add the first number and the opposite of the second number.

$$10 - 8 = 10 + (-8) = 2 \qquad 20 - (-6) = 20 + (6) = 26$$

(2) Find each difference.

5 – 3   -4 – (-5)

3 – 5   7 – 0

7 – (-4)   0 – 7

-2 – (-6)   0 – (-5)

-4 – 5   6 – (-6)

6 – (-1)   -3 – (-3)

-1 – 6   1 – 8

(3) Find each difference.

12 – 4 _____   -73 – 48 _____

9 – (-3) _____   0 – (-500) _____

-7 – 2 _____   234 – 240 _____

-15 – (-9) _____   6 – (-11) _____

14 – 0 _____   -15 – (-29) _____

0 – 38 _____   225 – 225 _____

-64 – (-64) _____   -50 – 75 _____

50 – (-20) _____   -75 – 50 _____

Positive and negative integers can be illustrated on perpendicular lines.
The horizontal line is the **x-axis**. The vertical line is the **y-axis**.
The point that the lines intersect is the **point of origin** (0).

On the *x*-axis, integers to the right of 0
    are positive, to the left of 0 are negative.
A move to the right is positive, to the left is negative.

On the *y*-axis, integers above 0
    are positive, below 0 are negative.
A move up is positive, down is negative.

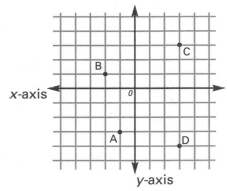

Points are located on the graph using coordinate numbers or ordered pairs.

The *first* number describes the *horizontal* movement (positive or negative) on the *x*-axis. The *second* number describes the *vertical* movement (positive or negative) on the *y*-axis. Always begin at zero (*0*), the point of origin, to locate points.

(1) **Write (P) positive or (N) negative on the first line. Write the number of places on the second line. Name points (letters) on the coordinate graph. The coordinate points are …**

a. (4, 3) Begin at zero (*0*).
    4 is the first number.   It is _____.   Move on the *x*-axis, to the right, _____ places.

    3 is the second number.   It is _____.   Move on the *y*-axis, up _____ places.

    What is the point (letter) at (4, 3)?   _____

b. (-2, 1) Begin at zero (*0*).
    -2 is the first number.   It is _____.   Move on the *x*-axis, to the left, _____ places.

    1 is the second number.   It is _____.   Move on the *y*-axis, up _____ places.

    What is the point (letter) at (-2, 1)?   _____

c. (3, -4) Begin at zero (*0*).
    3 is the first number.   It is _____.   Move on the *x*-axis, to the right, _____ places.

    -4 is the second number.   It is _____.   Move on the *y*-axis, down _____ places.

    What is the point (letter) at (3, -4)?   _____

d. (-1, -3) Begin at zero (*0*).
    -1 is the first number.   It is _____.   Move on the *x*-axis, to the left, _____ places.

    -3 is the second number.   It is _____.   Move on the *y*-axis, down _____ places.

    What is the point (letter) at (-1, -3)?   _____

RULES FOR MULTIPLICATION

1. The product of two positive numbers is positive.

2. The product of two negative numbers is also positive.

3. The product of one positive number and one negative number is negative.

(1) **Find each product.**

12 • (-4) _____   -7 • (-15) _____

-8 • (-5) _____   0 • (-11) _____

-1 • 17 _____   -47 • 1 _____

50 • 30 _____   -8 • 7 _____

-9 • 12 _____   -14 • (-14) _____

When multiplying more than two integers, multiply the first two, multiply the third by the product of the first two, multiply the fourth by that product, and so on.

Model: 5 • (-3) • (-2) • 8

=   -15 • (-2) • 8

=   30 • 8

=   240

(2) **Find each product.**

6 • (-2) • (-1) • 3   _____

11 • 80 • (-74) • (-235) • 0   _____

-1 • (-1) • (-1) • (-1) • (-1)   _____

-5 • 4 • (-3) • 2 • (-1)   _____

5 • (-4) • 3 • (-2) • 1   _____

RULES FOR DIVISION

1. The quotient of two positive numbers is positive.

2. The quotient of two negative numbers is also positive.

3. The quotient of one positive number and one negative number is negative.

(1) **Find each quotient.**

$16 \div 2$ _____

$-24 \div 6$ _____

$100 \div (-50)$ _____

$-34 \div (-2)$ _____

$0 \div 41$ _____

$-54 \div 6$ _____

$12 \div (-12)$ _____

$-62 \div 0$ _____

$0 \div -62$ _____

$(-100) \div (-100)$ _____

$45 \div (-15)$ _____

$-276 \div 1$ _____

$-78 \div (-6)$ _____

$-60 \div 12$ _____

$37 \div 0$ _____

$59 \div (-1)$ _____

$44 \div 11$ _____

$-25 \div 5$ _____

$-240 \div (-3)$ _____

$-19 \div 19$ _____

1 Given the following transactions, fill in the check register and answer the summary questions in the spaces provided.

Date	Check No.	Description	Amount
3/15	101	Check: Ace Pool Co.	$48.38
3/16	102	Check: XYZ Market	58.58
3/18	103	Check: Jones Auto	205.38
3/20	---	Deposit	412.56
3/22	104	Check: Best Beauty Supply	210.88
3/24	105	Check: 1st Ave. Church	58.28
3/28	106	Check: USA Plumbing	149.39
3/30	107	Check: Tickets America	175.38
3/30	---	Bank Charges	5.00
4/1	---	Deposit	155.00
4/4	108	Check: New Sound Audio	20.88
4/10	109	Check: Builders Supply	83.50
4/14	---	Deposit	258.38

Date	Check Number	To	Credit	Debit	Balance
3/14		beginning balance			576.94

2

Number of checks   _____

Number of deposits   _____

Previous balance   _____

Total deposits   _____

Total withdrawals   _____

Service charge   _____

Ending balance   _____

Horizons Mathematics 6

Worksheet

Answer
Key

Worksheet 1

1. 700 + 20 + 6

2. 27,529

3. a. 800,000,000
   b. eight hundred million

4. a. 5,000,000,000
   b. five billion

5. 6,000,000,000

6. 4,000,000,000,000

Worksheet 2

1. 0.145

2. 0.0456

3. 5.45

4. 127.009

5. 56.14

6. 0.035

7. b

8. a

9. a

10. d

Worksheet 3

1. 40   50   60   100   50   10

2. a. 1,600   778,400   16,400
   b. 6,000   49,000   313,000
   c. 100,000   4,850,000   60,000

3. a. 550,000   20,000   1,329,000
   b. 30,000,000   9,000,000   550,000,000
   c. 50,000,000   990,000,000   30,000,000
   d. 570,000,000,000   30,000,000,000

Worksheet 4

1. a. >   <   <
   b. >   <   <
   c. <   >   >

2. a. 3,685,942
      3,856,924
      3,865,924
      6,685,942
      6,835,492
   b. 1,397,102
      1,973,102
      2,379,103
      2,397,102
      2,973,102

3. a. $4 < 5$ $10 > 9$
   b. $6 > 2$ $7 < 11$
   c. $35 \div 7 = 15 \div 3$
   d. $14 - 2 \neq 8 + 5$

4. a. $3,957 < 4,558 < 6,492$
   b. $6,492 > 4,558 > 3,957$

Worksheet 5

1. 203,578;   224,005;   383,207

   281,200;   400,432;   432,991

   513,158;   596,954;   640,519

   1,106;   49,555;   48,496

   11,260;   58,034;   29,610

   144,885;   33,497;   44,697

Worksheet 6

1. a. $\neq$ N   = Y   = Y
   b.   = Y $\neq$ N $\neq$ N
   c.   = Y $\neq$ N $\neq$ N
   d. $\neq$ N $\neq$ N   = Y

2. 9   4   8
   6   14   11

Horizons Math 6 Worksheet Key

3. a.

$$236 + N = 529$$
$$236(-236) + N = 529 - 236$$
$$N = 293$$
$$236 + 293 = 529$$
$$N + 417 = 631$$
$$N + 417(-417) = 631 - 417$$
$$N = 214$$
$$214 + 417 = 631$$

$$518 + N = 874$$
$$518(-518) + N = 874 - 518$$
$$N = 356$$
$$518 + 356 = 874$$

$$N + 316 = 522$$
$$N + 316(-316) = 522 - 316$$
$$N = 206$$
$$206 + 316 = 522$$

4. a.

$$N - 439 = 518$$
$$N - 439(+439) = 518 + 439$$
$$N = 957$$
$$957 - 439 = 518$$

$$N - 347 = 625$$
$$N - 347(+347) = 625 + 347$$
$$N = 972$$
$$972 - 347 = 625$$

$$N - 238 = 671$$
$$N - 238(+238) = 671 + 238$$
$$N = 909$$
$$909 - 238 = 671$$

$$N - 312 = 526$$
$$N - 312(+312) = 526 + 312$$
$$N = 838$$
$$838 - 312 = 526$$

Worksheet 7

1. a.

$$(3 + 4) \times (15 \div 3) = N$$
$$7 \times 5 = N$$
$$35 = N$$

$$8 + (2 \times 3) + 9 = N$$
$$8 + 6 + 9 = N$$
$$23 = N$$

$$(9 - 2) \times (5 + 5) = N$$
$$7 \times 10 = N$$
$$70 = N$$

   b.

$$14 + 16 + (4 \times 2) = N$$
$$14 + 16 + 8 = N$$
$$38 = N$$

$$(37 - 9) \div (2 + 2) = N$$
$$28 \div 4 = N$$
$$7 = N$$

$$(52 + 8) + (46 - 6) = N$$
$$60 + 40 = N$$
$$100 = N$$

   c.

$$7 + (2 \times 6) + (2 \times 8) = N$$
$$7 + 12 + 16 = N$$
$$35 \text{ hits} = N$$

2. a. $8 + (27 \div 3) - (5 \times 3) = 8 + 9 - 15 = 2$
   $(6 \times 7) - (4 \times 5) + 9 = 42 - 20 + 9 = 31$

   b. $14 + (3 \times 2) - 10 = 14 + 6 - 10 = 10$
   $17 - (5 \times 3) + (4 \times 4) = 17 - 15 + 16 = 18$

   c. $(7 \times 6) + (32 \div 4) - 16 = 42 + 8 - 16 = 34$
   $(2 \times 0) \times (5 \times 7) = 0 \times 35 = 0$

3. a. $3 \times [(2 \times 6) - 5] = 3 \times (12 - 5) =$
   $$3 \times 7 = 21$$
   $[7 + (3 \times 6)] \div 5 = (7 + 18) \div 5 =$
   $$25 \div 5 = 5$$

   $8 + [5 \times (4 + 3)] = 8 + (5 \times 7) =$
   $$8 + 35 = 43$$

   b. $[2 \times (9 - 5)] - 6 = (2 \times 4) - 6 =$
   $$8 - 6 = 2$$

   $36 \div [13 - (2 \times 2)] = 36 \div (13 - 4) =$
   $$36 \div 9 = 4$$

   $[3 + (4 \times 6)] \div 9 = (3 + 24) \div 9 =$
   $$27 \div 9 = 3$$

c. $[(54 - 12) \div 6] \times 3 = (42 \div 6) \times 3 =$
$7 \times 3 = 21$

$4 \times [9 + (3 \times 4)] = 4 \times (9 + 12) =$
$4 \times 21 = 84$

$64 \div [4 + (28 \div 7)] = 64 \div (4 + 4) =$
$64 \div 8 = 8$

Worksheet 8

1. 64,400;   50,160;   37,297
   171,536;   433,758;   281,428
   249,508;   231,770;   240,648
   135,044;   288,960;   109,664

Worksheet 9

1. 315;   35 R7;   61;   31 R12;   36
   204 R4;   156;   410 R11;   169 R2;   51
   432;   805;   403;   702;   460
   900;   747;   688;   741;   532
   764;   513;   431;   840;   333
   623;   289;   821;   917;   726

Worksheet 10

1. a. 17 3/4 = 18;   47 1/2 = 48;   31

   b. 21 4/5 = 22;   48 1/5 = 48;   27 2/5 = 27

   c. 465 2/3 = 466; 261 2/3 = 262; 420 2/3 = 421

   d. 17 1/2 = 18;   23 4/7 = 24

   e. 4 2/3 = 5;   10 3/4 = 11;   10 4/5 = 11

   f. 16 2/3 = 17;   23 1/2 = 24;   27 4/5 = 28

   g. 76 1/4 = 76;   78 3/4 = 79;   636

   h. 503 1/2 = 504; 197 1/5 = 197

   i. 4450 1/5 = 4450

Worksheet 11

1. 1,209,618;   2,197,500;   1,933,140
   2,148,750;   1,609,875;   2,325,400
   5,422,192;   4,800,950;   5,208,000
   7,405,926;   12,144,550;   5,578,185

Worksheet 12

1. 122,061,000;   216,087,550;   370,382,736
   538,914,012;   799,157,632;   753,000,000
   1,015,251,237;   1,355,674,793   1,474,864,750

Worksheet 13

1. a. 5 1589/7252;   112 28/281;   126 1560/2604
   b. 59 590/4813;   43 1508/1789;   88 2187/8973
   c. 94 3007/3591;   33 293/671;   248 2464/4521
   d. 361 355/1369;   751 4725/4792;   224 2032/3761

Worksheet 14

1. a. 2   6
   b. 3   9
   c. 5   8
   d. 1   10
   e. 4   7

2. a. 4   8
   b. 5   7
   c. 2   6
   d. 1   9
   e. 3   10

3. a. 4   6
   b. 3   5
   c. 2   7
   d. 1   8

4. A   10°   acute
   B   55°   acute
   C   90°   right
   D   105°   obtuse
   E   140°   obtuse
   F   180°   straight

Worksheet 15

1. oval, circle

2. a. 3   b. 2   c. 1   d. 4

3. 3   4   5   6   8

4. pentagon

5. hexagon   octagon

Worksheet 16

1.

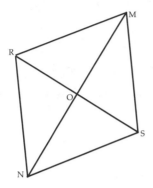

$\overline{RM} = 1\frac{1}{4}''$ $\overline{MS} = 1\frac{1}{4}''$

$\overline{SN} = 1\frac{1}{4}''$ $\overline{NR} = 1\frac{1}{4}''$

2. a. 4, 6
    b. 1, 8
    c. 2, 7
    d. 3, 5

3. a. 5   9
    b. 4   11
    c. 2   7
    d. 3   10
    e. 6   12
    f. 1   8

Worksheet 17

1.   congruent
    congruent   congruent
    not congruent   not congruent
    similar   similar
    congruent   congruent
                       congruent

Worksheet 18

1. a. O   A   R   R   A   O
    b. S   I   E   S   I   E

2. 3 , 60° + 80° + 40° , 180°

3. no   no
    The sum of the angles would be more
    than 180°

4. a. 180° ÷ 3 = 60°
    b. (180° − 30°) ÷ 2 = 150° ÷ 2 = 75°
    c. 180° − (53° + 69°) = 180° − 122° = 58°

Worksheet 19

1. center – b   diameter   – e
    radius – a   circumference – f
    arc   – c   chord   – d

2. a. 8
    b. 7
    c. 6
    d. 2
    e. 4
    f. 1
    g. 5
    h. 3

Worksheet 20

1. a. rectangle
    b. square
    c. triangle
    d. pentagon

2. a. 4
    b. 6
    c. 3
    d. 5
    e. 2
    f. 1

3. a. 1   b. 8   c. 3   d. 7
    e. 4   f. 2   g. 6   h. 5

4. a. 2   b. 5
    c. 6   d. 3
    e. 1   f. 4

Worksheet 21

1. a.

20		42		15		27
2 | 10		2 | 21		3 | 5		3 | 9
2 | 5		3 | 7		5 | 1		3 | 3
5 | 1		7 | 1				3 | 1

   2, 2, 5   2, 3, 7   3, 5   3, 3, 3

   b.

25		36		56		40
5 | 5		2 | 18		2 | 28		2 | 20
5 | 1		2 | 9		2 | 14		2 | 10
		3 | 3		2 | 7		2 | 5
		3 | 1		7 | 1		5 | 1

   5, 5   2, 2, 3, 3   2, 2, 2, 7   2, 2, 2, 5

2. a.

84		225		156
2 | 42		3 | 75		2 | 78
2 | 21		3 | 25		2 | 39
3 | 7		5 | 5		3 | 13
7 | 1		5 | 1		13 | 1

   2, 2, 3, 7   3, 3, 5, 5   2, 2, 3, 13

   b.

126		72		420
2 | 63		2 | 36		2 | 210
3 | 21		2 | 18		2 | 105
3 | 7		2 | 9		3 | 35
7 | 1		3 | 3		5 | 7
		3 | 1		7 | 1

   2, 3, 3, 7   2, 2, 2, 3, 3   2, 2, 3, 5, 7

Worksheet 22

1. a. 1, 3 - P 1, 2, 4 - C   1, 3, 5, 15 - C
   b. 1, 2, 3, 6, 9, 18, - C
       1, 23 - P
       1, 3, 9, 27 - C
   c. 1, 7 - P
       1, 2, 3, 4, 6, 8, 12, 24 - C
       1, 2, 4, 8, 16 - C
   d. 1, 3, 9 - C
       1, 5 - P
       1, 2, 4, 8, 16, 32 - C

2. a. 20, 24, 28, 32, 36, 40, 44, 48
   b. 45, 54, 63, 72, 81, 90 ,99, 108
   c. 15, 30, 45, 60, 75, 90, 105, 120

3.

18	1	9	2	6	3
$\times 1$	$\times 18$	$\times 2$	$\times 9$	$\times 3$	$\times 6$

4. 1, 2, 3, 6, 9, 18

5. a. 1, 5 - P   1, 2, 4, 5, 10, 20 - C
    b. 1, 2, 7, 14 - C   1, 23 - P
    c. 1, 2, 3, 5, 6, 10, 15, 30 - C   1, 3, 5, 15 - C
    d. 1, 3, 9, 27 - C   1, 29 - P

Worksheet 23

1. a. 2   4 2^4 16
    b. 5   3 5^3 125
    c. 3   4 3^4 81
    d. 7   3 7^3 343
    e. 2   5 2^5 32

2. 64,   81,   64,   625,   243

3. 81   49   125   32   0

Worksheet 24

1. 9, 16, 25, 36, 49, 64, 81, 100, 121, 144

2. 12, 11, 10, 9, 8, 7, 6, 5, 4, 3

3. a. 4, 9, 25, 36, 49, 64, 81, 100, 121, 144
    b. 12, 11, 10, 9, 8, 7, 6, 5, 3, 2

4. $\sqrt{49}$ $\sqrt{81}$ $\sqrt{25}$ $\sqrt{36}$ $\sqrt{121}$

Worksheet 25

1. a. $4.37295086191 \times 10^{11}$
    b. 2.76049568×10^{8}
    c. $7.239567446 \times 10^{9}$
    d. 5.1468332×10^{7}
    e. 9.367×10^{3}
    f. 2.73854×10^{5}
    g. 3.6×10^{9}
    h. 4.8×10^{8}
    i. 6.7×10^{7}
    j. Venus, Jupiter, Pluto

2. a. 7,000,000,000,000
    b. 420,000,000
    c. 350

Horizons Math 6 Worksheet Key

3. a. $4.86237154008 \times 10^{11}$ 3.2158994×10^{7}
   b. $9.116482305 \times 10^{9}$ 8.54231647×10^{8}
   c. $3.67254938152 \times 10^{11}$ 2.8946157×10^{7}
   d. $9.3857116038 \times 10^{10}$ 5.382194×10^{6}

Worksheet 26

1. a. $6 = 110_2$ f. $31 = 11111_2$
   b. $12 = 1100_2$ g. $45 = 101101_2$
   c. $15 = 1111_2$ h. $50 = 110010_2$
   d. $17 = 10001_2$ i. $100 = 1100100_2$
   e. $24 = 11000_2$ j. $128 = 10000000_2$

2. a. 3   f. 38
   b. 8   g. 64
   c. 28   h. 7
   d. 63   i. 85
   e. 19   j 204

Worksheet 27

1. a. 28.258   66.804   68.65
   b. 86.631   .669   24.44
   c. 36.72   53.63   .746
   d. 5.85   7.52   6.44   2.51
   e. 3.04   6.684   3.96   3.37
   f. 7.4   14.1   .539   1.75

2. a. 28.854   11.832   7.985
   b. 44.808   1.3863   51.982
   c. 3.8532   15.306   16.23
   d. 21.037   17.75   41.002

3. a. 20.705   34.535   65.109
   b. .015   3.479   33.878
   c. 3.093   17.459   .0313
   d. 1.48   .0171   4.8091

Worksheet 28

1. a. 16   47   30
   b. 22   48   27
   c. 465   261   422
   d. 17   23

2. a. 14   14   14
   b. 78   77   70
   c. 35   33   33
   d. 6   6.5, 6 .7   2
   e. 20   22   22

3. Suggested Answers:
   a. mode
   b. mean
   c. median
   d. mode - Because he reached that number (23) the greatest number of times it is probably the most accurate of what he is able to do

4. a. 9   8   15
   b. 13   14   11
   c. 14   13   13
   d. 50   51   68

Worksheet 29

1. a. $1\frac{1}{4}$ 1 $\frac{1}{2}$ $\frac{9}{10}$ $1\frac{3}{16}$ $\frac{2}{3}$
   b. $\frac{1}{3}$ $\frac{5}{8}$ $\frac{7}{10}$ $\frac{4}{9}$ $\frac{2}{3}$ $\frac{1}{3}$

2. a. $\frac{8}{8} = 1$ $1\frac{8}{15}$ $\frac{16}{10} = 1\frac{6}{10} = 1\frac{3}{5}$ $\frac{7}{9}$ $\frac{16}{24} = \frac{2}{3}$
   b. $\frac{6}{12} = \frac{1}{2}$ $\frac{8}{14} = \frac{4}{7}$ $\frac{2}{8} = \frac{1}{4}$ $\frac{4}{16} = \frac{1}{4}$ $\frac{4}{6} = \frac{2}{3}$

3. a. $\frac{8}{10} = \frac{4}{5}$ $\frac{15}{15} = 1$ $\frac{9}{12} = \frac{3}{4}$ $\frac{20}{16} = 1\frac{4}{16} = 1\frac{1}{4}$ $\frac{6}{9} = \frac{2}{3}$
   b. $\frac{4}{20} = \frac{1}{5}$ 0 $\frac{6}{8} = \frac{3}{4}$ $\frac{9}{15} = \frac{3}{5}$ $\frac{5}{10} = \frac{1}{2}$

Worksheet 30

1. a. 12, 6, 16, 9, 21, 25
   b. 10, 9, 8, 21, 4, 8
   c. 4, 9, 14, 4, 7, 10

2. a. $\frac{7}{16}$ $\frac{10}{16}$ $\frac{8}{16}$ $\frac{12}{16}$ $\frac{7}{16}$ $\frac{1}{2}$ $\frac{5}{8}$ $\frac{3}{4}$
   b. $\frac{21}{24}$ $\frac{18}{24}$ $\frac{20}{24}$ $\frac{16}{24}$ $\frac{19}{24}$ $\frac{2}{3}$ $\frac{3}{4}$ $\frac{19}{24}$ $\frac{5}{6}$ $\frac{7}{8}$
   c. $\frac{13}{18}$ $\frac{9}{18}$ $\frac{14}{18}$ $\frac{12}{18}$ $\frac{15}{18}$ $\frac{1}{2}$ $\frac{2}{3}$ $\frac{13}{18}$ $\frac{7}{9}$ $\frac{5}{6}$
   d. $\frac{16}{36}$ $\frac{24}{36}$ $\frac{21}{36}$ $\frac{30}{36}$ $\frac{25}{36}$ $\frac{4}{9}$ $\frac{7}{12}$ $\frac{2}{3}$ $\frac{25}{36}$ $\frac{5}{6}$
   e. $\frac{2}{3} = \frac{8}{12}$ $\frac{3}{4} = \frac{9}{12}$ $\frac{5}{6} = \frac{10}{12}$ $\frac{7}{12}$

Mark, Jess, James, Karen

Worksheet 31

1. a. $\frac{5}{18}$ $\frac{1}{3}=\frac{6}{18}$ $\frac{5}{9}=\frac{10}{18}$ $\frac{1}{2}=\frac{9}{18}$ $\frac{5}{6}=\frac{15}{18}$ $\frac{7}{9}=\frac{14}{18}$

   $\frac{5}{18}, \frac{1}{3}, \frac{1}{2}, \frac{5}{9}, \frac{7}{9}, \frac{5}{6}$

   b. $\frac{3}{4}=\frac{18}{24}$ $\frac{1}{6}=\frac{4}{24}$ $\frac{2}{3}=\frac{16}{24}$ $\frac{7}{12}=\frac{14}{24}$ $\frac{11}{24}$ $\frac{5}{8}=\frac{15}{24}$

   $\frac{1}{6}, \frac{11}{24}, \frac{7}{12}, \frac{5}{8}, \frac{2}{3}, \frac{3}{4}$

2. a. ≠ $6\times3=18$ $2\times8=16$
      ≠ $7\times5=35$ $4\times8=32$
   b. = $2\times21=42$ $6\times7=42$
      = $3\times12=36$ $4\times9=36$
   c. ≠ $4\times15=60$ $8\times9=72$
      ≠ $2\times16=32$ $5\times8=40$
   d. = $5\times30=150$ $10\times15=150$
      = $4\times15=60$ $6\times10=60$

3. a. >   =   <   >
   b. =   <   >   =
   c. <   =   =   <
   d. <   =   >   >

Worksheet 32

1. a. 5, 10, 15, 20, 25
      4, 8, 12, 16, 20
      20
      20

   b. $\frac{3}{5}=\frac{12}{20}$
      $+\frac{1}{4}=\frac{5}{20}$
      $\frac{17}{20}$

2. $\frac{3}{6}=\frac{12}{24}$
   $-\frac{3}{8}=\frac{9}{24}$
   $\frac{3}{24}=\frac{1}{8}$

3. a. $1\frac{1}{9}$, $1\frac{1}{16}$, $\frac{19}{24}$, $\frac{13}{15}$, $1\frac{5}{24}$, $\frac{5}{6}$

   b. $\frac{1}{3}$, $\frac{7}{15}$, $\frac{7}{16}$, $\frac{1}{12}$, $\frac{3}{10}$, $\frac{3}{10}$

   c. $\frac{31}{36}$, $\frac{23}{24}$, $\frac{13}{14}$, $\frac{1}{4}$, $\frac{13}{30}$, $\frac{13}{18}$

Worksheet 33

1. a.   a   c   a   b   b   c   c   a
   b.   a   c   b   c   b   a   b   c

2. a.   2   4 $4\frac{1}{5}$
   b. $1\frac{8}{9}$ 5 $8\frac{1}{2}$
   c.   3 $2\frac{3}{4}$ $1\frac{1}{7}$

3. a.   2 $1\frac{4}{5}$ 2 $2\frac{2}{5}$
   b. $3\frac{1}{2}$ $1\frac{2}{4}(1\frac{1}{2})3\frac{1}{3}$ 1

Worksheet 34

1. a. $13\frac{1}{10}$ $14\frac{11}{12}$ $9\frac{1}{8}$ $18\frac{1}{4}$ $14\frac{3}{10}$ $30\frac{4}{45}$
   b. $5\frac{3}{8}$ $5\frac{2}{9}$ $3\frac{5}{16}$ $9\frac{7}{15}$ $7\frac{5}{14}$ $7\frac{11}{36}$
   c. $6\frac{3}{8}$ $14\frac{4}{15}$ $15\frac{1}{2}$ $12\frac{1}{4}$ $31\frac{5}{6}$ $39\frac{19}{24}$
   d. $4\frac{4}{15}$ $6\frac{1}{30}$ $8\frac{1}{24}$ $4\frac{11}{21}$ $7\frac{7}{20}$ $19\frac{4}{45}$
   e. 36 $24\frac{1}{2}$ $25\frac{13}{15}$ $3\frac{1}{5}$ $6\frac{1}{3}$ $11\frac{1}{4}$
   f. $11\frac{23}{24}$ $12\frac{1}{2}$ $31\frac{5}{18}$ 14 $7\frac{1}{6}$ $12\frac{1}{6}$

Worksheet 35

1. $11\frac{1}{8}$ $9\frac{5}{6}$ $7\frac{1}{3}$ $9\frac{1}{2}$ $3\frac{3}{4}$ $5\frac{1}{9}$ $3\frac{5}{6}$

2. $6\frac{1}{3}$ $15\frac{5}{12}$ $13\frac{1}{5}$ $4\frac{7}{9}$ $5\frac{7}{10}$ $1\frac{2}{5}$ $10\frac{3}{8}$

3. a. $3\frac{7}{8}$ $13\frac{2}{3}$ $5\frac{3}{4}$ $20\frac{1}{2}$ $13\frac{3}{5}$ $19\frac{5}{7}$
   b. $14\frac{5}{9}$ $9\frac{4}{11}$ $17\frac{5}{12}$ $7\frac{3}{10}$ $6\frac{1}{4}$ $3\frac{7}{12}$
   c. $5\frac{2}{5}$ $4\frac{1}{2}$ $5\frac{1}{4}$ $4\frac{1}{3}$ $\frac{5}{6}$ $2\frac{3}{8}$

Worksheet 36

1. a. .2072   5.888   2.1252   1.0368   .038394
   b. .3448   43.424   26.88   .8192   2.34

Horizons Math 6 Worksheet Key

2. a. 1.44   27.06   .5272   20.51   .01872   .368
   b. 114.66   .04648   .1862   46.177   .37582   69.496

3. .63114   .368   .06076   2553.6   387.66

4. 2.456   .02232   .23042

3. a. 129   125   24   35
   b. 1.6   3.8   .46   .62

4. a. $3.50 = 3.5$ $9.70 = 9.7$ $.700 = .7$
   b. $7.070 = 7.07$ $.4300 = .43$ $58.210 = 58.21$

Worksheet 37

1. a. .34   .09   .002   4.3   4.02
   b. 21.8   .0688   69.4   .053   .391

2. a. $.81\frac{3}{4} = .82$ $7.9\frac{5}{8} = 8.0$ $.007\frac{1}{6} = .007$
        $.70\frac{2}{9} = .70$ $.315\frac{1}{3} = .315$
   b. $.033\frac{2}{5} = .033$ $.070\frac{3}{7} = .070$ $.125\frac{4}{6} = .126$
        $7.0\frac{3}{4} = 7.1$ $6.5\frac{5}{8} = 6.6$
   c. $.91\frac{2}{5} = .91$ $.082\frac{2}{3} = .083$ $.020\frac{1}{2} = .021$
        $1.02\frac{1}{3} = 1.02$ $8.1\frac{7}{9} = 8.2$

3. $1.16 = 1.2$ $.37 = .4$ $1.28 = 1.3$ $.66 = .7$ $.83 = .8$

Worksheet 38

1. a. .60   .625(.63)   .75 $.\overline{3}$ $.8\overline{3}$
   b. .50 $.\overline{2}$ .166(.17)   .583(.58)   .375(.38)

2. .2   .25   .5   .75   .8

3. 19.2   23.25   15.5   67.75   58.8

4. a. .625 $.\overline{33}$ .125   .4 $.8\overline{33}$
   b. $.\overline{2}$ .375 $.\overline{7}$ .6   .875

Worksheet 39

1. a. $2.70 = 2.7$ $36.10 = 36.1$ $.800 = .8$
        $7.500 = 7.5$ $.3000 = .3$
   b. $3.480 = 3.48$ $.3200 = .32$ $41.070 = 41.07$
        $.470 = .47$ $6.040 = 6.04$

2. a. 9.4; $35.83 = 35.8$; $190.66 = 190.7$
        $10.55 = 10.6$ $47.37 = 47.4$
   b. $2.866 = 2.87$; $0.074 = 0.07$; $1.175 = 1.18$
        $5.142 = 5.140$; $0.195 = 0.2$

Worksheet 40

1. a. 1.3   16.   490   820   9
   b. 3   5   .4   .06   3
   c. .06   8   200   1.4   18.6

Worksheet 41

1. a. $142.6\frac{2}{3} = 142.7$ $.31\frac{5}{8} = .32$
        $23.6\frac{1}{2} = 23.7$ $8.7\frac{1}{3} = 8.7$
   b. $91.\frac{1}{5} = 91.0$ $54.0\frac{1}{14} = 54.0$
        $2.7\frac{29}{32} = 2.8$ $1.1\frac{46}{47} = 1.2$
   c. $18.0\frac{2}{3} = 18.1$ $.26\frac{5}{84} = .26$
        $1.2\frac{1}{53} = 1.2$ $3.8\frac{2}{62} = 3.8$

2. a. 20.9   12   3240 $2.1\frac{5}{9} = 2.2$
   b. .2 $2.5\frac{19}{29} = 2.6$ .02   30

3. $6.1\frac{2}{6} = 6.1$ $215\frac{3}{4} = 2.16$ $31.4\frac{1}{3} = 31.4$ $3.65\frac{1}{2} = 3.66$

4. $.54\frac{7}{8} = .55$ $.090\frac{1}{5} = .090$ $9.7\frac{1}{6} = 9.7$ $20.4\frac{1}{9} = 20.4$

Worksheet 42

1.

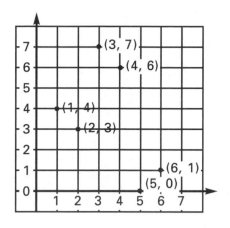

2. A (1, 2) D (6, 6)
    B (3, 1) E (8, 4)
    C (4, 4)

Worksheet 43

1. a. 6 cans   9 boxes
    b. 4 jars   4 pails
    c. 5 boxes $18 \times 5 = 90$ b-day cards

2. a. $\frac{1}{3}, \frac{8}{9}, \frac{3}{4}, \frac{3}{4}, \frac{5}{8}, \frac{7}{8}$

    b. $\frac{1}{2}, \frac{2}{3}, \frac{1}{2}, \frac{4}{5}, \frac{4}{5}, \frac{3}{7}$

3. a. $\frac{1}{6}$ $\frac{2}{3}$ $\frac{2}{3}$ $\frac{1}{4}$ $\frac{22}{27}$

    b. $\frac{7}{20}$ $\frac{27}{32}$ $\frac{1}{10}$ $\frac{10}{21}$ $\frac{28}{39}$

    c. $\frac{5}{9}$ $\frac{7}{10}$ $\frac{5}{21}$ $\frac{1}{4}$ $\frac{1}{4}$

    d. $\frac{5}{8}$ $\frac{1}{4}$ $\frac{2}{3}$ $\frac{3}{5}$ $\frac{3}{7}$

Worksheet 44

1. $\frac{7}{2}$ $\frac{23}{4}$ $\frac{49}{5}$ $\frac{20}{3}$ $\frac{77}{6}$ $\frac{59}{7}$ $\frac{37}{8}$

2. a. 4   3   40

    b. 7 $5\frac{1}{4}$ 21

    c. $2\frac{4}{7}$ $1\frac{1}{5}$ $58\frac{1}{2}$

    d. 3 $3\frac{1}{4}$ 36

    e. 4 $8\frac{3}{4}$ 90

    f. 3 $1\frac{1}{3}$ 10

3. a. $2\frac{3}{4}$ $2\frac{2}{3}$ $\frac{3}{10}$ 18

    b. $\frac{7}{18}$ 4 $1\frac{3}{7}$ 14

    c.   4 $5\frac{1}{2}$ 12 $\frac{2}{3}$

    d.   56   22 $6\frac{2}{3}$ 5

Worksheet 45

1.

    $\frac{1}{6}$ $\frac{2}{12}$ $\frac{2}{15}$

2. $\frac{1}{3}$ $\frac{7}{10}$ $\frac{1}{4}$ $\frac{1}{3}$ $\frac{3}{4}$ $\frac{2}{3}$

3. $1\frac{1}{2}$ $3\frac{3}{4}$ 6   18 $14\frac{2}{3}$ $11\frac{2}{3}$

4. a. 2   56 $2\frac{2}{3}$ 22   3

    b. 5   3   20   5   24

Worksheet 46

1. a. $1\frac{1}{5}$ $\frac{1}{2}$ $\frac{1}{2}$ $3\frac{1}{2}$ $1\frac{1}{3}$
    b. $2\frac{1}{4}$ $1\frac{1}{4}$ $\frac{7}{8}$ $\frac{2}{5}$ $1\frac{1}{5}$

2. a. 12 $\frac{1}{15}$ 16 $\frac{1}{14}$

    b. $\frac{2}{5}$ $\frac{16}{21}$ $1\frac{3}{4}$ $\frac{27}{32}$

3. a. $\frac{5}{6}$ $\frac{1}{21}$ 30   1   63 $\frac{2}{3}$

4. a. $\frac{1}{16}$ 28 $1\frac{1}{2}$ $\frac{4}{5}$ $1\frac{1}{20}$

Worksheet 47

1. a. $\frac{2}{3}$ $1\frac{1}{4}$ $\frac{3}{8}$ $1\frac{1}{3}$

    b. $7\frac{1}{2}$ $\frac{6}{25}$ 12 $\frac{7}{32}$

    c. $\frac{6}{7}$ $1\frac{3}{5}$ $1\frac{2}{11}$ $1\frac{9}{11}$

    d. $2\frac{2}{5}$ $1\frac{1}{2}$ $4\frac{2}{7}$ $2\frac{3}{4}$

Horizons Math 6 Worksheet Key

2.   9 $2\frac{1}{4}$ $\frac{5}{6}$ $\frac{6}{7}$

3.   a.   10 $\frac{3}{20}$ $1\frac{1}{3}$ $\frac{9}{10}$ $13\frac{1}{3}$

   b. $2\frac{1}{2}$ $\frac{1}{32}$ $25\frac{3}{5}$ $6\frac{2}{9}$ $\frac{13}{14}$

Worksheet 48

1.   a.   teacher check

   b. $2\frac{7}{8}$ in. , $5\frac{3}{16}$ in.

2. $1\frac{1}{16}$ in. $1\frac{9}{16}$ in. $\frac{7}{16}$ in.
    $2\frac{3}{16}$ in. $1\frac{15}{16}$ in.

3. $1\frac{1}{4}$ in., 1.25 in. $1\frac{3}{4}$ in., 1.75 in.
    $1\frac{3}{8}$ in., 1.375 in. $1\frac{7}{8}$ in., 1.875 in.

4. $\frac{15}{16}$ in., $1\frac{3}{16}$ in.

5. $\frac{7}{8}$ in., .875 in. $1\frac{1}{4}$ in., 1.25 in.

6. $\frac{9}{16}$ $1\frac{3}{16}$

7. $\frac{7}{8}$, .875

Worksheet 49

1.   a.   19 yd. 2 ft.   2,000 pounds
    b.   10 ft. 5 in. $2\frac{1}{2}$ tons

2.   30 ft. 16 in. = 31 ft. 4 in.
    15 mi. 7,375 ft. = 16 mi. 2,095 ft.
    16 yd. 72 in. = 18 yd.

3.   2 ft. 11 in.   1 yd $2\frac{2}{3}$ ft.   2 yd. 20 in.

4.   20 lb. 21 oz. = 21 lb. 5 oz.
    10 T. 2,500 lb. = 11 T. 500lb.
    3 T. 159 lb.

Worksheet 50

1.   a.   8 gal. 2 qt.   b.   4 pt 5 oz.

2.   8 gal. 3 qt.

3.   9 pt. 20 oz. = 10 pt. 4 oz.
    13 gal. 5 qt. = 14 gal. 1 qt.

4.   4 lb. 12 oz.   1 qt. $1\frac{3}{4}$ pt.
    24 pt. 8 cups = 28 qt.

5.   1 pt. $1\frac{1}{2}$ cup
    1 qt. 20 oz. *or* 1 qt. 1 pt. 20 oz.
    16 glasses

6.   2;   6

7.   6 gal. 6 qt. = 7 gal. 2 qt.
    8 qt. 48 oz. = 9 qt 16 oz. = 9 qt. 1 pt.
    1 qt. 7oz.

Worksheet 51

1.   a.   10
    b.   meter - yard, liter - quart, gram - ounce
    c.   milli, centi, deci, deca, hecto, Kilo
    d.   mm   cm   dm   m   Km
        ml   cl   dl   l   Kl
        mg   cg   dg   g   Kg
    e.   divide
        multiply

2.	kilo	hecto	deca	meter	deci	centi	milli
a.				5	4	7	
b.					3	8	6
c.					8	0	5
d.	5	4	7	6			
e.				8	3	7	

Worksheet 52

1.   yard   quart   ounce

2.   a.   m   m   d
    b.   d   m   m
    c.   m   m   d

3.   a.   10   1,000   10
    b.   100   10   100
    c.   1,000   10   1,000

4. a. 80   .43   5,000   43.8
    b. 7,200   .009   6,300   .75
    c. 23.0   .003   7   .00459

Worksheet 53

1. a. $3 \times 10 = 30$
        $18 \times 1,000 = 18,000$
        $73 \times 10 = 730$
    b. $5,000 \div 1,000 = 5$
        $23 \div 10 = 2.3$
        $14 \times 1,000 = 14,000$
    c. $2 \times 1,000 = 2,000$
        $1,346 \div 1,000 = 1.346$
        $90 \div 10 = 9$

2. a. $10 , \frac{1}{10} , .1 , 1$
    b. $100 , \frac{1}{100} , .01 , 1$
    c. $10 , \frac{1}{10} , .1 , 1$
    d. $\frac{5}{10} , .5 , 5$

3. a. 3 L 5 dl   4 cm 3mm   2 dm 7 cm
    b. 9 m 45 cm   6 dl 23 ml   3 g 4 dg
    c. 8 Km 6 m   2Kg 5 g   7 Kl 9 L
    d. 2 dm 7mm   2 L 1 dl   3 Kg 6 g

Worksheet 54

1. 12 feet   18 yards
    8 square feet   10 square yards

2. 4 yards   4 square yards
    24 yards   32 square yards
    64 inches   207 square inches
    38 feet   70 square feet
    24 feet   36 square feet
    36 meters   81 square meters
    58 centimeters   168 square centimeters
    40 meters   96 square meters
    44 feet   96 square feet
    40 miles   100 square miles
    16 centimeters   16 square centimeters
    32 kilometers   64 square kilometers
    116 kilometers   400 square kilometers
    68 inches   168 square inches

Worksheet 55

1. a. $A = bh$
        $A = 7 \cdot 3$
        $A = 21$ in.^{2}
    b. $A = bh$
        $A = 9 \cdot 8$
        $A = 72$ m^2
    c. $A = bh$
        $A = 12 \cdot 11$
        $A = 132$ ft^2

2. $A = 21$ in.^{2}

3. bh 6 yd.^{2}
    bh 30 yd.^{2}

Worksheet 56

1. a. $P = S + S + S$ $A = \frac{1}{2} B \times H$
        $P = 6 + 10 + 8$ $A = \frac{1}{2} (10 \times 5)$
        $P = 24$ in. $A = \frac{1}{2} \times 50$
                              $A = 25$ sq. in.
    b. $P = S + S + S$
        $P = 7 + 7 + 7$
        $P = 21$ in.
    c. $P = S + S + S$
        $P = 5 + 11 + 11$
        $P = 27$ ft.
    d. $A = \frac{1}{2} B \times H$
        $A = \frac{1}{2} (3 \times 6)$
        $A = \frac{1}{2} \times 18$
        $A = 9$ sq. ft.
    e. $A = \frac{1}{2} B \times H$
        $A = \frac{1}{2} (14 \times 7)$
        $A = \frac{1}{2} \times 98$
        $A = 49$ sq. ft.

f. $P = S + S + S$
$23 = (9 + 7) + N$
$23 = 16 + N$
$23 - 16 = (16 - 16) + N$
$7 \text{ in.} = N \text{ (side)}$

g. $A = \frac{1}{2} B \times H$
$18 = \frac{1}{2}(N \times 4)$
$18 \times 2 = \frac{1}{2} \times 2(N \times 4)$
$36 = N \times 4$
$36 \div 4 = N \times (4 \div 4)$
$9 \text{ in.} = N \text{ (height)}$

h. $A = \frac{1}{2} bh$
$42 = \frac{1}{2}(12 \cdot h)$
$42 = \dfrac{(12 \cdot h)}{\frac{1}{2}}$
$42 \cdot 2 = \dfrac{\overset{1}{\cancel{2}}(12 \cdot h)}{\underset{1}{\cancel{2}}}$
$84 = 12 \cdot h$
$84 \div 12 = 12 \cdot h (\div 12)$
$7 \text{ in.} = h$

i. $A = \frac{1}{2} bh$
$18 = \frac{1}{2}(bh)$
$18 = \dfrac{(b \cdot 9)}{\frac{1}{2}}$
$18 \cdot 2 = \dfrac{\overset{1}{\cancel{2}}(b \cdot 9)}{\underset{1}{\cancel{2}}}$
$36 = b \cdot 9$
$36 \div 9 = b \cdot 9 (\div 9)$
$4 \text{ ft.} = b$

2. area - base - height - area of triangle

Worksheet 57

1. $C = \pi d$ $C = 2\pi r$
$C = 3.14 \cdot 9$ $C = 2 \cdot (3.14 \cdot 7)$
$C = 28.26 \text{ in.}$ $C = 2 \cdot 21.98$
$C = 43.96 \text{ in.}$

2. a. $A = \pi r^2$
$A = 3.14 \cdot 8^2$
$A = 3.14 \cdot 64$
$A = 200.96 \text{ sq. in. or } 201 \text{ sq. in.}$

b. $A = \pi r^2$
$A = 3.14 \cdot 4^2$
$A = 3.14 \cdot 16$
$A = 50.24 \text{ sq. ft. or } 50 \text{ sq. ft.}$

c. $A = \pi r^2$
$A = 3.14 \cdot 3^2$
$A = 3.14 \cdot 9$
$A = 28.26 \text{ sq. yd. or } 28 \text{ sq. yd.}$

d. $A = \pi r^2$
$A = 3.14 \cdot 6^2$
$A = 3.14 \cdot 36$
$A = 113.04 \text{ sq. mi. or } 113 \text{ sq. mi.}$

3. $C = \pi d$ or $C = 2\pi r$
$A = \pi r^2$

4. a. $C = \pi d$
$C = 3.14 \cdot 6$
$C = 18.84 \text{ in.}$

radius = 3 in.
$A = \pi r^2$
$A = 3.14 \cdot 3^2$
$A = 3.14 \cdot 9$
$A = 28.26 \text{ sq. in.}$

b. diameter = 10 in.
$C = \pi d$
$C = 3.14 \cdot 10$
$C = 31.4 \text{ in.}$

$A = \pi r^2$
$A = 3.14 \cdot 5^2$
$A = 3.14 \cdot 25$
$A = 78.5 \text{ sq. in.}$

5. 5″   10″

6. $C = \pi d$ $A = \pi r^2$
$C = 3.14 \cdot 10$ $A = 3.14 \cdot 5^2$
$C = 31.4 \text{ in.}$ $A = 3.14 \cdot 25$
$A = 78.5 \text{ sq. in.}$

Worksheet 58

1.

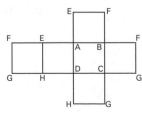

© MCMXCIX, Alpha Omega Publications, Inc.

2. a. 32 cu. in.
    b. L = 8   W = 4   L × W = 32 cu. in.
    c. 6
    d. 6 × 32 = 192 cu. in.

3. a. V = LWH
        V = 8 · 6 · 3
        V = 144 cu. ft.
    b. V = LWH
        V = 5 · 2 · 7
        V = 70 cu. yd.
    c. V = LWH
        V = 15 · 4 · 8
        V = 480 cu. in.

4. a. V = S³
        V = 9³
        V = 729 cu. yd.
    b. V = S³
        V = 10³
        V = 1,000 cu. in.
    c. V = S³
        V = 14³
        V = 2,744 cu. ft.

Worksheet 59

1. 180 square in.

2. 270 square in.

3. 216 square in.

4. EFHG
    BDHF
    ABFE

5. 180 x 2 = 360
    270 x 2 = 540
    216 x 2 = 432

6. 1,332 inches

7. 600 cm² x 2 = 1,200 cm²
    150 cm² x 2 =   300 cm²
    400 cm² x 2 =   800 cm²
        Total   2,300 cm²

    18 cm² x 2 = 36 cm²
    36 cm² x 2 = 72 cm²
    08 cm² x 2 = 16 cm²
        Total   124 cm²

Worksheet 60

1. a. 4:00 A.M., November 7
    b. 9:00 P.M., May 4
    c. 1:00 P.M., April 1

2. a. 3   b. 5   c. 2
    d. 4   e. 3   f. 6

3. a. 6:00 P.M.   b. 9:15 A.M.
    c. 6:00 P.M.   d. 9:30 A.M.
    e. 7:45 A.M.   f. 8:00 A.M.
    g. 2:00 A.M.   h. 10:45 P.M.
    i. 11:00 A.M., July 8   10:00 A.M., July 8
    j. 10:00 P.M., March 14   8:00 P.M., March 14

Worksheet 61

1. a. no   yes
    b. 360°   360°   360°
    c. - g.

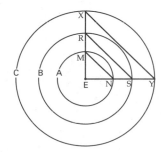

    f. 90°, 90°
    g. Arc MN < Arc RS < Arc XY
        Chord MN < Chord RS < Chord XY
        Angle MEN = Angle RES = Angle XEY
    h. the same, increased

2. ∠EVF = 50°
    ∠EVH = 130°
    ∠GVH = 50°
    ∠GVF = 130°
    50° + 130° + 50° + 130° = 360°

Horizons Math 6 Worksheet Key

Worksheet 62

1.

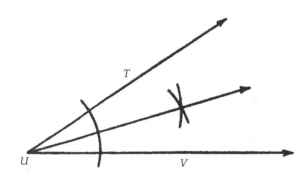

2.

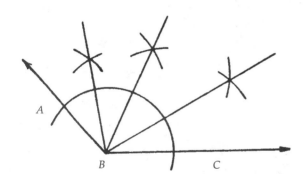

Worksheet 63

1. a.–e.: Check student work for procedures and measurements.

Worksheet 64

1. a.–i.: Check student work for procedures and measurements.

Worksheet 65

1. a.–d.: Check student work for procedures and measurements.

Worksheet 66

1.   6   10   14   18

2.   a. $\frac{4}{24} = \frac{1}{6}$ $\frac{12}{24} = \frac{1}{2}$ $\frac{8}{24} = \frac{1}{3}$
     b. 6   18   12

3.   a. $\frac{1}{6}$ $\frac{1}{3}$ $\frac{1}{2}$
     b. 6   12   18

4.   a. $\frac{4}{5} = \frac{32}{40}$ 32 peanuts
     b. $\frac{7}{8} = \frac{28}{32}$ 28 boys
     c. $\frac{2}{3} = \frac{12}{18}$ 18 cats
     d. $\frac{1}{3} = \frac{6}{18}$ 18 days

Worksheet 67

1.   a.

$$\frac{2}{4} = \frac{N}{10}$$
$$20 = N \cdot 4$$
$$20 \div 4 = N \cdot (4 \div 4)$$
$$5 = N$$
$$\frac{2}{4} = \frac{1}{2} = \frac{5}{10} = \frac{1}{2}$$

$$\frac{2}{6} = \frac{N}{9}$$
$$18 = N \cdot 6$$
$$18 \div 6 = N \cdot (6 \div 6)$$
$$3 = N$$
$$\frac{2}{6} = \frac{1}{3} = \frac{3}{9} = \frac{1}{3}$$

$$\frac{6}{8} = \frac{N}{16}$$
$$96 = N \cdot 8$$
$$96 \div 8 = N \cdot (8 \div 8)$$
$$12 = N$$
$$\frac{6}{8} = \frac{3}{4} = \frac{12}{16} = \frac{3}{4}$$

$$\frac{2}{10} = \frac{N}{15}$$
$$30 = N \cdot 10$$
$$30 \div 10 = N \cdot (10 \div 10)$$
$$3 = N$$
$$\frac{2}{10} = \frac{1}{5} = \frac{3}{15} = \frac{1}{5}$$

b.

$$\frac{4}{6} = \frac{N}{9}$$
$$36 = N \cdot 6$$
$$36 \div 6 = N \cdot (6 \div 6)$$
$$6 = N$$
$$\frac{4}{6} = \frac{2}{3} = \qquad \frac{6}{9} = \frac{2}{3}$$

$$\frac{2}{8} = \frac{N}{12}$$
$$24 = N \cdot 8$$
$$24 \div 8 = N \cdot (8 \div 8)$$
$$3 = N$$
$$\frac{2}{8} = \frac{1}{4} = \qquad \frac{3}{12} = \frac{1}{4}$$

$$\frac{9}{15} = \frac{N}{10}$$
$$90 = N \cdot 15$$
$$90 \div 15 = N \cdot (15 \div 15)$$
$$6 = N$$
$$\frac{9}{15} = \frac{3}{5} = \qquad \frac{6}{10} = \frac{3}{5}$$

$$\frac{2}{12} = \frac{N}{18}$$
$$36 = N \cdot 12$$
$$36 \div 12 = N \cdot (12 \div 12)$$
$$3 = N$$
$$\frac{2}{12} = \frac{1}{6} = \qquad \frac{3}{18} = \frac{1}{6}$$

c.

$$\frac{8}{12} = \frac{N}{18}$$
$$144 = N \cdot 12$$
$$144 \div 12 = N \cdot (12 \div 12)$$
$$12 = N$$
$$\frac{8}{12} = \frac{2}{3} = \qquad \frac{12}{18} = \frac{2}{3}$$

$$\frac{15}{25} = \frac{N}{10}$$
$$150 = N \cdot 25$$
$$150 \div 25 = N \cdot (25 \div 25)$$
$$6 = N$$
$$\frac{15}{25} = \frac{3}{5} = \qquad \frac{6}{10} = \frac{3}{5}$$

$$\frac{3}{24} = \frac{N}{16}$$
$$48 = N \cdot 24$$
$$48 \div 24 = N \cdot (24 \div 24)$$
$$2 = N$$
$$\frac{3}{24} = \frac{1}{8} = \qquad \frac{2}{16} = \frac{1}{8}$$

$$\frac{5}{20} = \frac{N}{24}$$
$$120 = N \cdot 20$$
$$120 \div 20 = N \cdot (20 \div 20)$$
$$6 = N$$
$$\frac{5}{20} = \frac{1}{4} = \qquad \frac{6}{24} = \frac{1}{4}$$

2. a. 2:5   b. 3:5
   c. 2:3   d. 3:2

3. a. $\frac{3}{5} = \frac{x}{25} \; \frac{\text{(green)}}{\text{(total)}}$

   $$75 = 5x$$
   $$75 \div 5 = 5x \; (\div 5)$$
   $$15 = x$$
   $$15 = \text{green} \qquad 25 - 15 = 10 \text{ ripe}$$

   b. $\frac{2}{3} = \frac{x}{9} \; \frac{\text{(ripe)}}{\text{(green)}}$

   $$18 = 3x$$
   $$18 \div 3 = 3x \; (\div 3)$$
   $$6 = x$$
   $$6 = \text{ripe} \qquad 6 + 9 = 15 \text{ bananas}$$

Worksheet 68

1. a. 10
   b. A-2, C-1, E-1, H-1, I-1, M-2, T-2
   c. A-2:10, C-1:10, E-1:10, H-1:10, I-1:10, M-2:10, T-2:10
   d. A-20%, C-10%, E-10%, H-10%, I-10% M-20%, T-20%
   e. A, M, T
      C, E, H, I
   f. A, M, T, C, E, H, I

2. a. yes
   b. 1:9
   c. yes

Worksheet 69

1. a. 10.8   14.4   41.4
   b. 8.32   12.96   17.55
   c. 21.17   24.00   27.00

2. a. $\frac{1}{5} \times \frac{\overset{9}{\cancel{45}}}{1} = 9 \qquad \frac{3}{4} \times \frac{\overset{8}{\cancel{32}}}{1} = 24 \qquad \frac{7}{8} \times \frac{\overset{8}{\cancel{64}}}{1} = 56$

   b. $\frac{3}{5} \times \frac{\overset{11}{\cancel{55}}}{1} = 33 \qquad \frac{1}{4} \times \frac{\overset{4}{\cancel{16}}}{1} = 4 \qquad \frac{1}{3} \times \frac{\overset{6}{\cancel{18}}}{1} = 6$

   c. $\frac{1}{2} \times \frac{\overset{46}{\cancel{92}}}{1} = 46 \qquad \frac{2}{5} \times \frac{\overset{15}{\cancel{75}}}{1} = 30 \qquad \frac{2}{3} \times \frac{\overset{12}{\cancel{36}}}{1} = 24$

Horizons Math 6 Worksheet Key

Worksheet 70

1. 32%   7%   94%   52%   5%   11%

2. a. $\frac{68}{100}$ .68   68% $\frac{4}{100}$ .04   4%

   b. $\frac{15}{100}$ .15   15% $\frac{70}{100}$ .70   70%

3. a. 46%   3%   51%   82%   27%

   b. 2%   61%   14%   91%   3%

4. a. 53:100 $\frac{53}{100}$ .53   16:100 $\frac{16}{100}$ .16

   b. 9:100 $\frac{9}{100}$ .09   74:100 $\frac{74}{100}$ .74

5. a. .50   50%, .25   25%, .75   75%
   b. .20   20%, .40   40%, .60   60%, .80   80%
   c. .125, 12.5%, .375, 37.5%,
      .625, 62.5%, .875, 87.5%
   d. .33   33%, .67   67%, .17   17%, .83   83%

Worksheet 71

1. a. $\frac{7}{8}$ .875   88%
   b. $\frac{3}{5}$ .6   60%
   c. $\frac{1}{4}$ .25   25%
   d. $\frac{3}{10}$ .3   30%

2. a. 1:2   .5   50%   1:4 .25   25%
   b. 3:4   .75   75%   1:5 .2   20%
   c. 2:5   .4   40%   3:5 .6   60%
   d. 4:5   .8   80%   1:8 .125   13%
   e. 3:8   .375   38%   5:8 .625   63%
   f. 7:8   .875   88%   1:3 $.\overline{333}$ 33%
   g. 2:3 $.\overline{666}$ 67%   1:6 $.1\overline{66}$ 17%
   h. 5:6 $.8\overline{33}$ 83%

Worksheet 72

1. $1.02 $12.35 $0.56 $0.01

2. 20.10   641.23   6.35   .07

3. 4.28   1.7262   0.40004
   0.188468   95.985   1,023.12
   $0.5622   .040768 $26.36

Worksheet 73

1. a. 90 pages
   b. 5 pencils
   c. 72 pieces
   d. 16 oz.
   e. 18 cookies
   f. 6 people

2. a. 27 subscriptions
   b. 15 cars

3. $16.77 × 7.5% = $1.26
   $16.77 + $1.26 = $18.03

4. a.   10% of $123,000 $= x$
            $.10 × 123,000$ $= x$
            $12,300 $= x$ (commission paid)
   b. $\frac{1}{4}$ of $6.24 $= x$
         $\frac{1}{\overset{4}{1}} × 6.24$ $= x$
         $1.56 $= x$ charge for sub

Worksheet 74

1. a. $38.17
   b. $169.65
   c. $20.59
   d. $102.79

Worksheet 75

1. a. + 4   − 3
   b. − 4   + 2
   c. + 5   − 2
   d. − 6   − 3

2. a. 5   − 5   2
   b. 5   − 5   − 1
   c. 7   − 4   − 3
   d. 7   − 9   1

3. a. positive
   b. negative
   c. positive, negative

Worksheet 76

1. -5
   -18
   3
   -40
   22
   1
   -173
   325
   -9
   15

2. 2
   -2
   11
   4
   -9
   7
   -7
   1
   7
   -7
   5
   12
   0
   -7

3. 8
   12
   -9
   -6
   14
   -38
   0
   70
   -121
   500
   -6
   17
   14
   0
   -125
   -125

Worksheet 77

1. a. P 4
      P 3
      C
   b. N 2
      P 1
      B
   c. P 3
      N 4
      D
   d. N 1
      N 3
      A

Worksheet 78

1. -48
   40
   -17
   1,500
   -108
   105
   0
   -47
   -56
   196

2. $$6 \cdot (-2) \cdot (-1) \cdot 3$$
   $$= -12 \cdot (-1) \cdot 3$$
   $$= 12 \cdot 3$$
   $$= 36$$

   $$11 \cdot 80 \cdot (-74) \cdot (-235) \cdot 0 = 0$$

   $$-1 \cdot (-1) \cdot (-1) \cdot (-1) \cdot (-1)$$
   $$= 1 \cdot (-1) \cdot (-1) \cdot (-1)$$
   $$= -1 \cdot (-1) \cdot (-1)$$
   $$= 1 \cdot (-1)$$
   $$= -1$$

Horizons Math 6 Worksheet Key

$-5 \cdot 4 \cdot (-3) \cdot 2 \cdot (-1)$

$= \quad \underbrace{-20 \cdot (-3)} \cdot 2 \cdot (-1)$

$= \quad \underbrace{60 \quad \cdot 2} \cdot (-1)$

$= \quad \underbrace{120 \quad \cdot (-1)}$

$= \quad\quad\quad -120$

$5 \cdot (-4) \cdot 3 \cdot (-2) \cdot 1$

$= \quad -20 \quad \cdot 3 \cdot (-2) \cdot 1$

$= \quad\quad -60 \quad \cdot (-2) \cdot 1$

$= \quad\quad\quad 120 \quad \cdot 1$

$= \quad\quad\quad\quad 120$

Worksheet 79

1. 8
   -4
   -2
   17
   0
   -9
   -1
   undefined
   0
   1
   -3
   -276
   13
   -5
   undefined
   -59
   4
   -5
   80
   -1

Worksheet 80

1. teacher check

2. 9
   3
   $576.94
   $825.94
   $1,010.65
   $5.00
   $387.23

Unit Tests

1 Write the value of each digit.

100,005,000,800,900.23674

1 _____

5 _____

8 _____

9 _____

2 _____

3 _____

6 _____

7 _____

4 _____

2 Solve using the correct order of operations.

$(8 + 8) \times (15 - 3) =$ _____

$7 \times (13 - 5) + 12 =$ _____

$34 - 6 + (6 \times 7) - 15 =$ _____

$46 + 6 - 5 \times 2 =$ _____

3 Add or subtract.

82,332	94,561	88,959	98,641
+ 80,016	+ 90,224	+ 2,211	+ 70,342

99,080	54,872	72,443	391,889
− 24,799	− 9,187	− 9,199	− 62,422

(4) Find the product.

781	213	197	252
x 59	x 39	x 322	x 403

(5) Find the quotient.

$113\overline{)1,921}$ $204\overline{)5,712}$ $1,202\overline{)34,858}$ $1,809\overline{)37,989}$

(6) Find the average of these numbers; if there is a remainder, round it to the nearest whole number.

14, 15, 22, 12   88, 99, 77   88, 105, 127, 76

(7) Match.

1. _____   line *m* intersects line *n*

2. _____ $n \parallel m$

3. _____ $m \perp n$

4. _____   Point Y

5. _____   Line Segment NM

6. _____   Line *t*

7. _____   Ray NM

8. _____   Acute angle

9. _____   Obtuse angle

10. _____   Right angle

A.

B.

C. ←——*t*——→

D.

E. • Y

F.

G. N———————M

H. N———————M→

I.

J.

© MCMXCIX, Alpha Omega Publications, Inc.

8) Place the following names above the correct figure; triangle, rectangle, hexagon, trapezoid, parallelogram, octagon, square, pentagon, rhombus, and dodecagon.

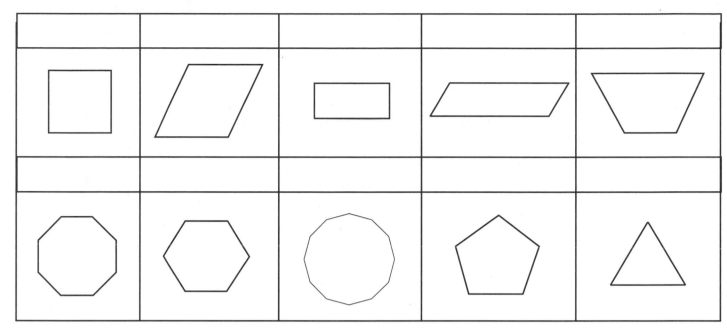

9) Beside each picture write scalene, equilateral, or isosceles.

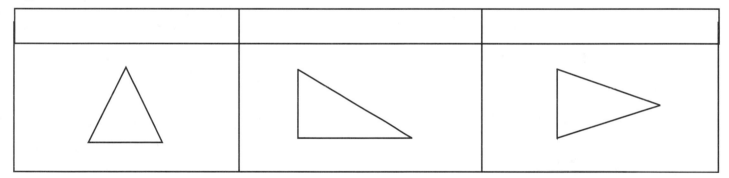

10) Find the missing angles.

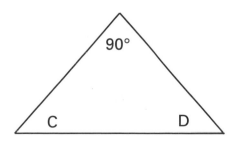

C = _____   D = _____

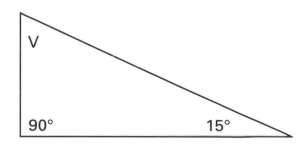

V = _____

405

11   Use the figure to answer the question.

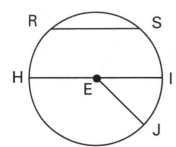

1. If the diameter of Circle E is 50 mm, what is the radius?

2. If another circle is twice as big as Circle C, what is the diameter?

3. Name the acute central angle in Circle C. Name the obtuse angle.

4. Name the chord in Circle C.

12   Match.

1. _____ cube

2. _____ sphere

3. _____ rectangular pyramid

4. _____ rectangular prism

5. _____ triangular pyramid

6. _____ triangular prism

7. _____ cone

8. _____ cylinder

a.

b.

c. This figure has one polygon base. All faces are triangles and meet at a point.

d.

e.

f.

g. All points are the same distance from the center.

h.

1 The following information was found in a Junior High School newsletter. Use the data to draw a circle graph.

Kids at Mesa Junior High Love Sports–Especially Soccer

The sports reporters at Mesa Junior High School took a poll last week to find out what sports the students liked the best. The results may surprise you!

Soccer   30%
Baseball   25%
Basketball   20%
Football   15%
Other   10%

2 Shade the prime numbers. The shaded blocks will form a letter.

73	83	11
29	25	2
89	27	5
59	67	43
7	12	16
71	24	6
13	9	14
17	15	10

3 Find the square root of each number.

4 _____   49 _____   36 _____

9 _____   121 _____   144 _____

169 _____   81 _____   25 _____

④ Write in standard form. The first one has been done for you.

$6.14 \times 10^3 = 6{,}140$

$7.12 \times 10^5 =$ _____

$1.02 \times 10^5 =$ _____

$4.4 \times 10^2 =$ _____

$5.9 \times 10^3 =$ _____

$6.51 \times 10^7 =$ _____

$8.10 \times 10^6 =$ _____

⑤ Write these base 10 numerals in base 2.

20 = _____

34 = _____

2 = _____

14 = _____

62 = _____

57 = _____

⑥ Add or subtract. Order the answers from greatest to least. The corresponding letters will spell a word.

```
    6.988          55.13          802.32          91.741
 + 4.091         + 6.18         +  9.92         + 9.756
         E               C               A               N
```

```
  129.013        354.251        851.59        1,459.28
 -  8.654       - 13.032       - 86.112       -  633.00
         E               I               T               P
```

Through patience a ruler can be persuaded, and a gentle tongue can break a bone.
Proverbs 25:15

408

(7) Find the range, mean, mode, and median.

8, 2, 3, 9, 2, 6, 2, 4   32, 57, 19, 34, 88, 44, 34

Range: _____   Range: _____
Mean: _____   Mean: _____
Mode: _____   Mode: _____
Median: _____   Median: _____

112, 131, 118, 135, 163, 151, 135

Range: _____
Mean: _____
Mode: _____
Median: _____

(8) Write each fraction in simplest form.

$\dfrac{25}{35}$ $\dfrac{15}{90}$ $\dfrac{27}{36}$ $\dfrac{70}{350}$ $\dfrac{81}{135}$ $\dfrac{18}{54}$

(9) Compare with the correct sign. (>, <, =)

$\dfrac{1}{9}$ ____ $\dfrac{2}{6}$ $\dfrac{8}{43}$ ____ $\dfrac{9}{43}$ $\dfrac{3}{21}$ ____ $\dfrac{1}{7}$ $\dfrac{3}{4}$ ____ $\dfrac{7}{12}$

(10) Add and subtract the fractions. Rename in lowest terms.

$\dfrac{2}{12} + \dfrac{1}{2}$ $\dfrac{4}{10} + \dfrac{1}{7}$ $\dfrac{1}{3} + \dfrac{1}{6}$ $\dfrac{3}{12} + \dfrac{2}{4}$

$\dfrac{10}{14} - \dfrac{1}{6}$ $\dfrac{9}{10} - \dfrac{1}{3}$ $\dfrac{8}{9} - \dfrac{1}{3}$ $\dfrac{14}{15} - \dfrac{3}{5}$

(11) Change each improper fraction to a whole number or mixed fraction. Write the answers in simplest form.

$\frac{19}{5}$ = _____ $\frac{24}{4}$ = _____ $\frac{28}{3}$ = _____ $\frac{19}{3}$ = _____

Change each mixed fraction to an improper fraction.

$2\frac{2}{5}$ = _____ $3\frac{4}{7}$ = _____ $4\frac{3}{4}$ = _____ $1\frac{2}{6}$ = _____

(12) Find the difference. You will need to borrow from the whole number and rename the fraction.

$$7\frac{1}{6}$$
$$-\ 4\frac{5}{12}$$

$$11\frac{1}{4}$$
$$-\ 8\frac{7}{12}$$

$$8\frac{1}{6}$$
$$-\ 7\frac{13}{18}$$

$$22\frac{1}{5}$$
$$-\ 12\frac{1}{2}$$

(13) Multiply.

9.2	4.9	17.3	0.87	6.53
x 7.3	x 1.8	x 0.9	x 8	x 0.89

(14) Divide. Move the decimal points when necessary.

$2.4\overline{)20.424}$ $3.11\overline{)18.349}$ $4.7\overline{)41.36}$

(15) Change the fractions to decimals and round to the nearest tenth.

$\dfrac{1}{5}$ $\dfrac{7}{9}$ $\dfrac{6}{7}$ $\dfrac{3}{4}$

① Find these points on the grid below and connect them in the order given.

1. (5, 10)   5. (8, 0)   9. (0, 6)

2. (6, 6)   6. (5, 3)   10. (4, 6)

3. (10, 6)   7. (2, 0)   11. (5, 10) STOP

4. (7, 4)   8. (3, 4)

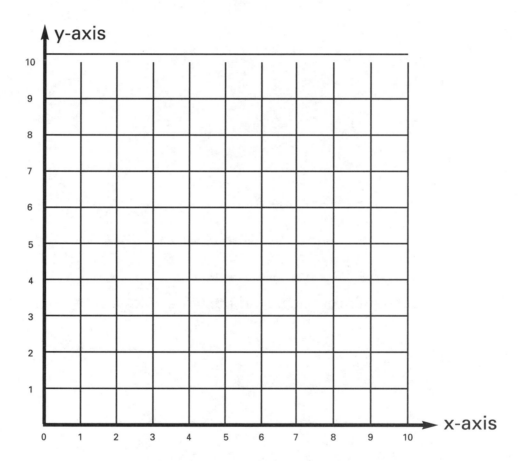

② Multiply. Reduce to lowest terms.

$\frac{7}{11} \times \frac{1}{4}$ $\frac{2}{9} \times \frac{1}{3}$ $\frac{3}{5} \times \frac{1}{8}$ $\frac{5}{8} \times \frac{8}{9}$

$\frac{7}{12} \times \frac{3}{4}$ $\frac{4}{5} \times \frac{3}{9}$ $\frac{7}{9} \times \frac{5}{6}$ $\frac{1}{8} \times \frac{1}{6}$

③ Solve.

$\frac{3}{4}$ of 12 $\qquad$ $\frac{4}{5}$ of 5 $\qquad$ $\frac{3}{4}$ of 8 $\qquad$ $\frac{3}{6}$ of 10

④ Multiply. Reduce to lowest terms.

$3\frac{1}{8} \times 2\frac{1}{4} =$ $\qquad$ $6\frac{1}{7} \times 3\frac{1}{2} =$ $\qquad$ $3\frac{1}{4} \times 3\frac{2}{5} =$

$4 \times 2\frac{7}{12} =$ $\qquad$ $2\frac{2}{3} \times 9\frac{1}{8} =$ $\qquad$ $5\frac{1}{6} \times 1\frac{2}{7} =$

⑤ Divide. Rename the answers as mixed fractions in lowest terms.

$\frac{8}{9} \div 2 =$ $\qquad$ $\frac{3}{11} \div 2 =$ $\qquad$ $2\frac{5}{6} \div 7 =$ $\qquad$ $3\frac{4}{7} \div 5 =$

⑥ Find the quotient. Write the answer in lowest terms.

$3\frac{1}{2} \div 2\frac{4}{5} =$ $\qquad$ $3\frac{1}{3} \div 2\frac{7}{8} =$ $\qquad$ $2\frac{1}{9} \div 2\frac{3}{4} =$ $\qquad$ $5\frac{2}{7} \div 4\frac{5}{6} =$

⑦ Solve.

$\frac{1}{8}$ gal = _____ pt   10 c = _____ qt   3 pt = _____ qt

19 cups = _____ pt   36 c = _____ gal   16 pt = _____ gal

⑧ Complete.

9,000 millimeter = _____ meter   7 meters = _____ millimeters

9 meter = _____ centimeters   30 millimeters = _____ centimeters

2 centimeters = _____ millimeters   5 Kilometers = _____ meters

⑨ Find the perimeter and area of the figure below.

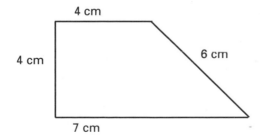

Perimeter = _____

Area = _____

(10) Find the volume of each figure.

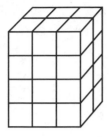

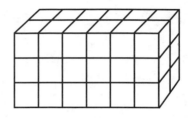

Volume = _____ cm³

Volume = _____ cm³

(11) Given line JK, draw another line that bisects line JK and forms four congruent right angles. Label the new line, the perpendicular bisector, FG.

J   K

(12) Find the volume of the cylinder. Round the answer to the tenths.

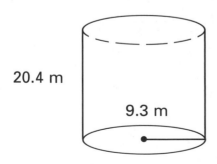

20.4 m

9.3 m

Volume = _____ m³

416

(1) Construct an equilateral triangle using a compass and straight edge. Use Line CD as one side of the triangle. Label the triangle △BCD.

C   D

(2) Construct a square using Line AB as one side. Label the square ABCD.

A   B

(3) Use the cross-product method to see if the ratios are equal. Circle the ratios that are equal.

$\frac{6}{8} \stackrel{?}{=} \frac{42}{56}$ $\frac{3}{11} \stackrel{?}{=} \frac{6}{33}$ $\frac{21}{45} \stackrel{?}{=} \frac{63}{135}$ $\frac{7}{66} \stackrel{?}{=} \frac{21}{198}$

$\frac{40}{45} \stackrel{?}{=} \frac{120}{135}$ $\frac{19}{20} \stackrel{?}{=} \frac{361}{380}$ $\frac{12}{15} \stackrel{?}{=} \frac{46}{60}$ $\frac{17}{55} \stackrel{?}{=} \frac{85}{285}$

$\begin{array}{c}\textbf{4}\end{array}$ Use cross products to solve each equation.

$\dfrac{15}{17} = \dfrac{N}{85}$ $\qquad$ $\dfrac{34}{41} = \dfrac{204}{N}$ $\qquad$ $\dfrac{11}{72} = \dfrac{N}{432}$ $\qquad$ $\dfrac{90}{N} = \dfrac{45}{25}$

$\begin{array}{c}\textbf{5}\end{array}$ Write each ratio as a percent.

$\dfrac{9}{10} =$ _____ $\qquad$ $\dfrac{17}{50} =$ _____ $\qquad$ $\dfrac{7}{20} =$ _____ $\qquad$ $\dfrac{2}{5} =$ _____

$\dfrac{1}{2} =$ _____ $\qquad$ $\dfrac{3}{4} =$ _____ $\qquad$ $\dfrac{9}{25} =$ _____ $\qquad$ $\dfrac{2}{10} =$ _____

$\begin{array}{c}\textbf{6}\end{array}$ Complete the table.

Fraction	Decimal	Percent
$\dfrac{98}{100}$	0.98	98%
$\dfrac{5}{100}$		
	0.78	
		2%
$\dfrac{9}{100}$		
$\dfrac{34}{100}$	0.34	
$\dfrac{12}{100}$		

© MCMXCIX, Alpha Omega Publications, Inc.

$\begin{array}{c}\textbf{7}\end{array}$ Find 1% and 10% of each number. (Round to the nearest hundredth.)

$917.08 _____ _____ $\qquad$ $80,100.75 _____ _____

3,211 _____ _____ $\qquad$ 105 _____ _____

$7,921.00 _____ _____ $\qquad$ $5.10 _____ _____

9 _____ _____ $\qquad$ 95 _____ _____

$\left(8\right)$ Find the sum.

0 + (-9) _____   (+12) + (+9) _____   (-85) + (-9) _____

(-41) + (-19) _____   (-24) + (-30) _____   (+56) + (-18) _____

(-9) + (+70) _____   (+27) + (+19) _____   (-31) + (+5) _____

$\left(9\right)$ Find the difference.

15 − 11 = _____   19 − (-34) = _____

71 − (-9) = _____   41 − 4 = _____

(-81) − 13 = _____   (-82) − (-75) = _____

(-26) − (-10) = _____   (-90) − 8 = _____

$\left(10\right)$ Find the product.

(+3) x (-8) = _____

(-9) x (-7) = _____

(+9) x (+9) = _____

(+4) x (-9) = _____

(-7) x (-8) = _____

$\left(11\right)$ Find the quotient.

(+63) ÷ (-9) = _____

(-64) ÷ (+8) = _____

(-32) ÷ (+8) = _____

(-45) ÷ (-5) = _____

(+49) ÷ (+7) = _____

12 Complete the table.

Interest	Principal	Rate	Time
	$8,000	5%	1 year
	$23,000	12%	3 months (1/4)
	$2,000	9 1/2% (0.095)	1 year
	$19,000	10%	6 months (1/2)
	$6,000	8%	9 months (3/4)

13 Find these points on the grid below and connect them in the order given.

1. (0, 5)

2. (1, 1)

3. (5, 1)

4. (2, -1)

5. (3, -5)

6. (0, -2)

7. (-3, -5)

8. (-2, -1)

9. (-5, 1)

10. (-1, 1)

11. (0, 5) STOP

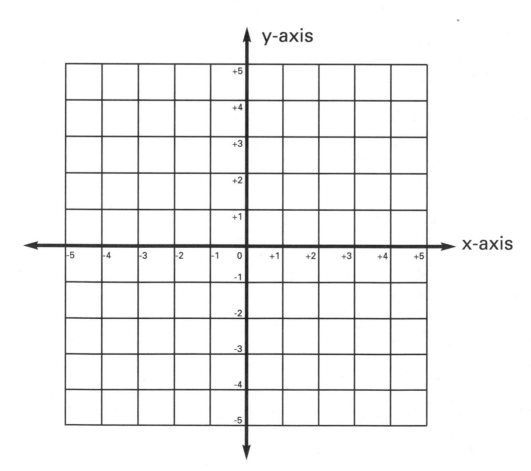

1   Match.

1. _____   Thirty-five and nine ten thousandths   a. 5,000,000,000.004

2. _____   Five million and four hundredths   b. 7.005

3. _____   Five trillion and four thousandths   c. 5,000,000,000,000.004

4. _____   Seven and five hundred thousandths   d. 35.00009

5. _____   Seven and five thousandths   e. 5,000,000.04

6. _____   Thirty-five and nine hundred thousandths   f. 7.00005

7. _____   Five billion and four thousandths   g. 35.0009

© MCMXCIX, Alpha Omega Publications, Inc.

2   Compare using <, >, or =.

143,000,560,000   ◯   143,001,560,000

one million   ◯   1,000,000,000,000

three trillion   ◯   3,000,000,000,000

891,000,000   ◯   791,000,000

3   Solve the equations.

$3b = 21$ $9c = 81$ $9d = 36$ $7k = 77$

$\dfrac{x}{5} = 6$ $\dfrac{x}{7} = 7$ $\dfrac{x}{7} = 8$ $\dfrac{x}{4} = 4$

4   Solve using the correct order of operations.

$9 + 8 \times 7 =$ _____ $(39 - 14) \times 8 - 7 =$ _____ $39 \div 3 - 3 \times 3 =$ _____

5 Find the average of these numbers; if there is a remainder, round it to the nearest tenth.

38, 90, 54, 88, 14   12, 14, 20, 19   154, 188, 170, 138

6 Place the names above the correct figure: parallelogram, rhombus, trapezoid, equilateral triangle, scalene triangle, and isosceles triangle.

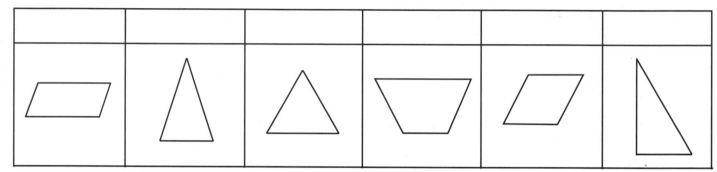

7 Find the measure of the angle not given.

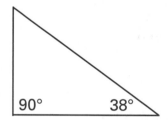

_____   _____   _____

8 Name these shapes.

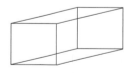   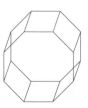

_____   _____   _____   _____

_____   _____   _____   _____

⑨ Complete the table.

	Factors	Product	Exponent	Number of Zeros
10^2				
10^3				
		10,000		
	10 x 10 x 10 x 10 x 10			
10^6				

⑩ Complete the table. The first one has been done for you.

Number	Square Root	Multiplication Problem
16	4	4 x 4 = 16 or 4^2
121		
36		
25		
169		

⑪ Complete the table with the help of a calculator. The first one has been done for you.

	Factors	Product	Exponent	Number of Zeros
7^2	7 x 7	49	2	N/A
10^5				
7^4				
10^6				
5^6				

⑫ Write these base 10 numerals in base 2.

2 = _____   39 = _____   7 = _____

14 = _____   64 = _____   59 = _____

13 Find the range, mean, mode, and median.

8, 2, 10, 9, 2, 14

Range: _____

Mean: _____

Mode: _____

Median: _____

99, 101, 118, 115, 112, 151, 116

Range: _____

Mean: _____

Mode: _____

Median: _____

14 Find the sum or the difference. Make sure the answer is in simplest form.

$$\begin{array}{r} \frac{5}{9} \\ + \ \frac{5}{9} \\ \hline \end{array}$$

$$\begin{array}{r} \frac{1}{17} \\ + \ \frac{16}{17} \\ \hline \end{array}$$

$$\begin{array}{r} \frac{9}{9} \\ + \ \frac{7}{9} \\ \hline \end{array}$$

$$\begin{array}{r} \frac{19}{20} \\ - \ \frac{7}{20} \\ \hline \end{array}$$

$$\begin{array}{r} \frac{23}{24} \\ - \ \frac{2}{24} \\ \hline \end{array}$$

$$\begin{array}{r} \frac{9}{12} \\ - \ \frac{2}{12} \\ \hline \end{array}$$

15 Solve.

$$\begin{array}{r} 10\frac{1}{14} \\ + \ 18\frac{1}{7} \\ \hline \end{array}$$

$$\begin{array}{r} 12\frac{1}{3} \\ + \ 65\frac{1}{13} \\ \hline \end{array}$$

$$\begin{array}{r} 108\frac{1}{9} \\ - \ 44\frac{3}{4} \\ \hline \end{array}$$

$$\begin{array}{r} 48\frac{2}{11} \\ - \ 17\frac{1}{2} \\ \hline \end{array}$$

$$\begin{array}{r} 14\frac{1}{9} \\ - \ 12\frac{4}{5} \\ \hline \end{array}$$

(16) Multiply.

91.1	88.1	72.9	4.11	8.09
x 8.3	x 1.2	x 0.8	x 0.75	x 0.49

(17) Divide.

$1.9\overline{)5.32}$
$12.1\overline{)22.99}$
$0.11\overline{)0.418}$

(18) Multiply. Write the answer in lowest terms.

$6\frac{1}{6} \times 2\frac{1}{3} =$ $3\frac{1}{8} \times 4\frac{1}{4} =$ $7\frac{2}{5} \times 2\frac{1}{3} =$

$9 \times 1\frac{5}{9} =$ $2\frac{1}{7} \times 12 =$ $5\frac{3}{5} \times 2\frac{1}{3} =$

(19) Find the quotient. Write the answer in lowest terms.

$2\frac{1}{7} \div 1\frac{4}{5} =$ $4\frac{1}{4} \div 2\frac{3}{7} =$ $2\frac{2}{3} \div 1\frac{1}{5} =$ $4\frac{5}{9} \div 1\frac{1}{2} =$

$5\frac{1}{2} \div 2\frac{2}{9} =$ $3\frac{1}{11} \div 1\frac{2}{3} =$ $4\frac{7}{8} \div 3\frac{1}{4} =$ $3\frac{2}{9} \div 1\frac{3}{5} =$

(20) Complete.

10 c = _____ qt   88 c = _____ gal $4\frac{3}{4}$ qt = _____ c

$\frac{3}{4}$ gal = _____ qt   84 pt = _____ gal   41 pt _____ qt

(21) Complete. Use the chart as a reference.

Kilometer 1 Km	Hectometer 1 Hm	Dekameter 1 Dam	Meter 1 m	Decimeter 1 dm	Centimeter 1 cm	Millimeter 1 mm
1,000 m	100 m	10 m	1 m	0.1 m	0.01 m	0.001 m

30 mm   = _____ cm   7.9 m   = _____ cm

1,829 mm = _____ m   1.9 Km   = _____ m

1.93 m   = _____ mm   3.60 dm = _____ mm

2,000 m   = _____ Km   7.9 Km   = _____ m

80 mm   = _____ cm   400 cm   = _____ m

8.9 Km   = _____ mm   4 m   = _____ mm

(22) Find the area of each triangle and write it on the line provided.

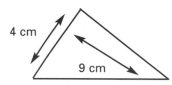

4 cm

9 cm

$A = \frac{bh}{2}$

$A = $ _____ cm²

7.2 cm

15.3 cm

$A = \frac{bh}{2}$

$A = $ _____ cm²

(23) Find the surface area.

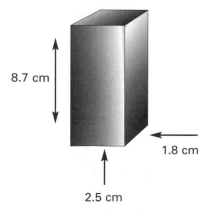

8.7 cm

1.8 cm

2.5 cm

Front _____ × 2 = _____

Top _____ × 2 = _____

Side _____ × 2 = _____

Total _____

24 Find the volume of the cylinder. Round the answer to the tenths.

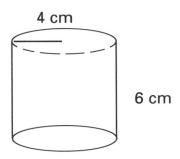

4 cm

6 cm

Volume = _____

25 Use the protractor to measure the angles in the circle. Write the measurement on the lines provided.

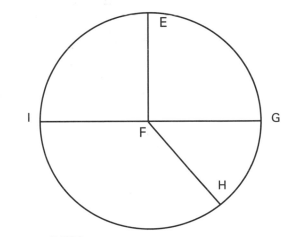

∠EFG = _____

∠GFH = _____

∠HFI = _____

∠IFE = _____

∠EFG + ∠GFH + ∠HFI + ∠IFE = 360°

_____ + _____ + _____ + _____ + = 360°

26 Bisect the angle using a compass and straight edge. Label the bisector DB.

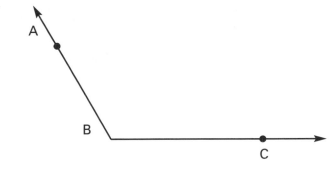

∠ABD measures _____ degrees

∠CBD measures _____ degrees

27 Find the sum.

(-9) + (-14) = _____   45 + (-19) = _____

71 + 34 = _____   (-34) + (-54) = _____

(-65) + 28 = _____   82 + (-18) = _____

（28） Find these points on the grid below and connect them in the order given.

1. (3, 2)

2. (1, 4)

3. (-1, 4)

4. (-3, 2)

5. (-3, -2)

6. (-1, -4)

7. (1, -4)

8. (3, -2)

9. (3, 2) STOP

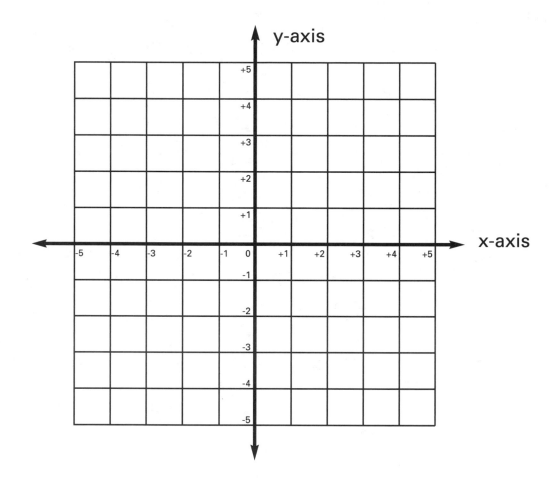

（29） Find the difference.

(-23) − (-44)   = _____

131 − 92   = _____

(-99) − 51   = _____

(-85) − (-60)   = _____

(-87) − 39   = _____

73 − (-29)   = _____

30 Find the product.

$(+9) \times (-9) =$ _____

$(-5) \times (-9) =$ _____

$(+7) \times (+3) =$ _____

$(+5) \times (-8) =$ _____

$(-9) \times (-8) =$ _____

31 Find the quotient.

$180 \div (-12) =$ _____

$(-153) \div (+9) =$ _____

$(-90) \div (+15) =$ _____

$(-200) \div (-25) =$ _____

$(406) \div (+29) =$ _____

32 Complete the table.

Interest	Principal	Rate	Time
	$5,000	9%	1 year
	$900	10%	6 months (1/2)
	$3,500	8 1/2% (0.085)	1 year
	$8,000	12%	3 months (1/4)
	$10,000	7%	6 months (1/2)

33 Complete the checkbook ledger.

Date	Check #	Transaction	Amount of Check	Deposit	Balance
					$1,535.19
5-4-99	512	Action Sports	$34.89		
5-5-99	513	Orville Shoes	$29.75		
5-5-99		Payroll Check		1,789.00	
5-5-99	514	Parson's Drugstore	$18.12		
5-7-99	515	Kroger's	$127.99		

Horizons Mathematics 6

Unit Tests

Answer Key

Quarter Test 1

1. one hundred trillion
   five billion
   eight hundred thousand
   nine hundred
   two tenths
   three hundredths
   six thousandths
   seven ten thousandths
   four hundred thousandths

2. 192;   68
   55;   42

3. 162,348;   184,785;   91,170;   168,983
   74,281;   45,685;   63,244;   329,467

4. 46,079;   8,307;   63,434;   101,556

5. 17;   28;   29;   21

6. 16;   88;   99

7. 1. – B
   2. – I
   3. – J
   4. – E
   5. – G
   6. – C
   7. – H
   8. – D
   9. – F
   10. – A

8. square   rhombus   rectangle
   parallelogram   trapezoid

   octagon   hexagon   dodecagon
   pentagon   triangle

9. Equilateral   Scalene   Isosceles

10. C = 45°   D = 45°;   V = 75°

11. 1. 25 mm
    2. 100 mm

3. ∠ IEJ,   ∠ HEJ
4. $\overline{RS}$

12. 1. – h
    2. – g
    3. – e
    4. – b
    5. – c
    6. – f
    7. – d
    8. – a

Quarter Test 2

1. Example:

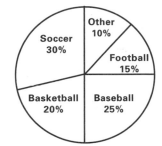

2.

73	83	11
29	25	2
89	27	5
59	67	43
7	12	16
71	24	6
13	9	14
17	15	10

3. 2;   7;   6
   3;   11;   12
   13;   9;   5

4. 712,000;   102,000
   440;   5,900
   65,100,000;   8,100,000

5. 10100_{two} 100010_{two} 10_{two}
   1110_{two} 111110_{two} 111001_{two}

6. 11.079;   61.31;   812.24;   101.497
   120.359;   341.219;   765.478;   826.28
   PATIENCE

7. Range: 7   Range: 69
   Mean: 4.5   Mean: 44
   Mode: 2   Mode: 34
   Median: 3.5   Median: 34

   Range: 51
   Mean: 135
   Mode: 135
   Median: 135

8. $\frac{5}{7}$; $\frac{1}{6}$; $\frac{3}{4}$; $\frac{1}{5}$; $\frac{3}{5}$; $\frac{1}{3}$

9. $\frac{1}{9} \leq \frac{2}{6}$; $\frac{8}{43} \leq \frac{9}{43}$
   $\frac{3}{21} = \frac{1}{7}$; $\frac{3}{4} > \frac{7}{12}$

10. $\frac{8}{12} = \frac{2}{3}$; $\frac{38}{70} = \frac{19}{35}$; $\frac{3}{6} = \frac{1}{2}$
    $\frac{9}{12} = \frac{3}{4}$; $\frac{23}{42}$; $\frac{17}{30}$
    $\frac{5}{9}$; $\frac{5}{15} = \frac{1}{3}$

11. $3\frac{4}{5}$;   6; $9\frac{1}{3}$; $6\frac{1}{3}$
    $\frac{12}{5}$; $\frac{25}{7}$; $\frac{19}{4}$; $\frac{8}{6}$

12. $2\frac{9}{12} = 2\frac{3}{4}$; $2\frac{8}{12} = 2\frac{2}{3}$
    $\frac{8}{18} = \frac{4}{9}$; $9\frac{7}{10}$

13. 67.16; 8.82;   15.57; 6.96;   5.8117

14. 8.51;   5.9;   8.8

15. 0.2;   0.8;   0.9;   0.8

Quarter Test 3

1.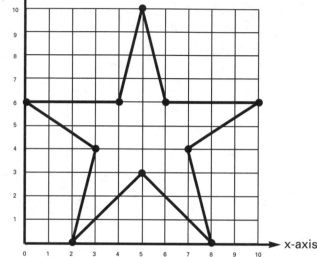

2. $\frac{7}{44}$; $\frac{2}{27}$; $\frac{3}{40}$; $\frac{40}{72} = \frac{5}{9}$
   $\frac{21}{48} = \frac{7}{16}$; $\frac{12}{45} = \frac{4}{15}$; $\frac{35}{54}$; $\frac{1}{48}$

3. 9;   4;   6;   5

4. $7\frac{1}{32}$; $21\frac{7}{14} = 21\frac{1}{2}$; $11\frac{1}{20}$
   $10\frac{4}{12} = 10\frac{1}{3}$; $24\frac{8}{24} = 24\frac{1}{3}$; $6\frac{27}{42} = 6\frac{9}{14}$

5. $\frac{8}{18} = \frac{4}{9}$; $\frac{3}{22}$; $\frac{17}{42}$; $\frac{25}{35} = \frac{5}{7}$

6. $1\frac{7}{28} = 1\frac{1}{4}$; $1\frac{11}{69}$; $\frac{76}{99}$; $1\frac{19}{203}$

7. 1; $2\frac{1}{2}$; $1\frac{1}{2}$
   $9\frac{1}{2}$; $2\frac{1}{4}$;   2

8. 9;   7,000
   900;   3
   20;   5,000

© MCMXCIX, Alpha Omega Publications, Inc.

9. 21 cm

    22 cm²

10. 24 cm³

    36 cm³

11.
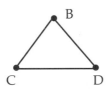

12. 5,540.2 cm³

Quarter Test 4

1.
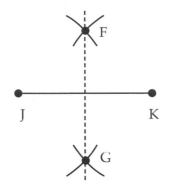

2.

3.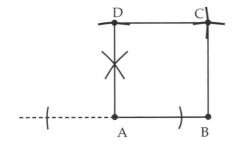

4. 75;   246;   66;   50

5. 90%;   34%;   35%;   40%
    50%;   75%;   36%;   20%

6. $\frac{98}{100}$ 0.98   98%

    $\frac{5}{100}$ 0.05   5%

    $\frac{78}{100}$ 0.78   78%

    $\frac{2}{100}$ 0.02   2%

    $\frac{9}{100}$ 0.09   9%

    $\frac{34}{100}$ 0.34   34%

    $\frac{12}{100}$ 0.12   12%

7. $9.17; $91.71; $801.00; $8,010.08
    32.11; 321.10;   1.05;   10.50
    $79.21; $792.10; $0.05; $0.51
    0.09;   0.90;   0.95;   9.50

8. (-9);   (+21);   (-94)
    (-60);   (-54);   (+38)
    (+61);   (+46);   (-26)

9. 4;   53   10. (-24)
    80;   37   (+63)
    (-94);   (-7)   (+81)
    (-16);   (-98)   (-36)
                            (+56)

11. (-7)   12. $400.00
    (-8) $690.00
    (-4) $190.00
    (+9) $950.00
    (+7) $360.00

13.
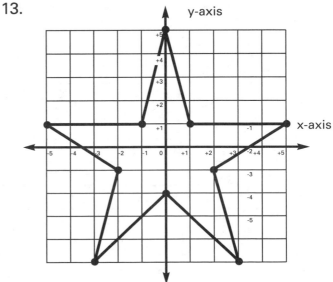

Horizons Math 6 Final Exam Test Key

Final Exam

1. 1. g
    2. e
    3. c
    4. f
    5. b
    6. d
    7. a

2. 143,000,560,000 < 143,001,560,000
    one million < 1,000,000,000,000
    three trillion = 3,000,000,000,000
    891,000,000 > 791,000,000

3. $b = 7$; $c = 9$; $d = 4$; $k = 11$
    $x = 30$; $x = 49$; $x = 56$; $x = 16$

4. 65;   193;   4

5. 56.8;   16.3;   162.5

6. parallelogram;   isosceles triangle
    equilateral triangle;   trapezoid
    rhombus;   scalene triangle

7. 60°   52°   45°

8. rectangular prism;   hexagonal prism
    cylinder;   octagonal prism
    cone;   cube;   rectangular pyramid
    triangular pyramid

9.
10^2	10 x 10	100	2	2
10^3	10 x 10 x 10	1,000	3	3
10^4	10 x 10 x 10 x 10	10,000	4	4
10^5	10 x 10 x 10 x 10 x 10	100,000	5	5
10^6	10 x 10 x 10 x 10 x 10 x 10	1,000,000	6	6

10.
16	4	4 x 4 = 16 or 4^2
121	11	11 x 11 = 121 or 11^2
36	6	6 x 6 = 36 or 6^2
25	5	5 x 5 = 25 or 5^2
169	13	13 x 13 = 169 or 13^2

11.
7^2	7 x 7		49	2	N/A
10^5	10 x 10 x 10 x 10 x 10		100,000	5	5
7^4	7 x 7 x 7 x 7		2,401	4	N/A
10^4	10 x 10 x 10 x 10		10,000	4	4
5^6	5 x 5 x 5 x 5 x 5 x 5		15,625	6	N/A

12. 10_{two} 100111_{two} 111_{two}
     1110_{two} 1000000_{two} 111011_{two}

13. Range: 12   Range: 52
     Mean: 7.5   Mean: 116
     Mode: 2   Mode: NONE
     Median: 8.5   Median: 115

14. $\frac{10}{9} = 1\frac{1}{9}$; $\frac{17}{17} = 1$; $\frac{16}{9} = 1\frac{7}{9}$

     $\frac{12}{20} = \frac{3}{5}$; $\frac{21}{24} = \frac{7}{8}$; $\frac{7}{12}$

15. $28\frac{3}{14}$; $77\frac{16}{39}$; $63\frac{13}{36}$

     $30\frac{15}{22}$; $1\frac{14}{45}$

16. 756.13;   105.72;   58.32
     3.0825;   3.9641

17. 2.8;   1.9;   3.8

18. $14\frac{7}{18}$; $13\frac{9}{32}$; $17\frac{4}{15}$
     14; $25\frac{5}{7}$; $13\frac{1}{15}$

19. $1\frac{12}{63} = 1\frac{4}{21}$; $1\frac{51}{68} = 1\frac{3}{4}$; $2\frac{4}{18} = 2\frac{2}{9}$; $3\frac{1}{27}$

     $2\frac{19}{40}$; $1\frac{47}{55}$ $1\frac{52}{104} = 1\frac{1}{2}$; $2\frac{1}{72}$

20. $2\frac{1}{2}$; $5\frac{1}{2}$;   19

     3; $10\frac{1}{2}$; $20\frac{1}{2}$

21. 3;   790
     1.829;   1,900
     1,930;   360
     2;   7,900
     8;   4
     8,900,000; 4,000

22. 18;   55.08

23. 21.75 cm²,   43.5 cm²
    4.5 cm²,   9 cm²
    15.66 cm²,   31.32 cm²
    83.82 cm²

24. 301.4 cm³

25. ∠EFG = 90°
    ∠GFH = 50°
    ∠HFI = 130°
    ∠IFE = 90°

    90° + 50° + 130° + 90° = 360°

26.

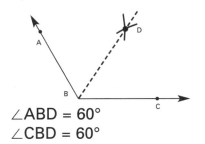

    ∠ABD = 60°
    ∠CBD = 60°

27. (-23);   26
    105;   (-88)
    (-37);   64

28.

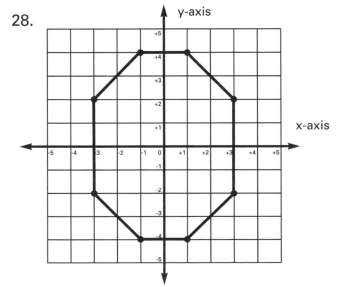

29. 21;   (-25)
    39;   (-126)
    (-150);   102

30. (-81)
    (+45)
    (+21)
    (-40)
    (+72)

31. (-15)
    (-17)
    (-6)
    (+8)
    14

32. $450.00
    $45.00
    $297.50
    $240.00
    $350.00

33. $1,500.30
    $1,470.55
    $3,259.55
    $3,241.43
    $3,113.44